The Library of the Earls of Macclesfield removed from Shirburn Castle

Part Five: Science I-O

London | Thursday 14 April 2005

Hipparchus

Prolemeus

R. Alfonsus

Nic. Copernicus.

Consiliorum

Participes.

Tycho Brahe.

naturæ

TABVLÆ
FRISICÆ
Lunæ-Solares
quadruplices;

è fontibus
Cl. Ptolemæi,
Regis Alfonsi,
Nic. Copernici, &
Tychonis Brahe,
recens constructæ
Operâ et studio NICOLAI
MVLERI Doct. Medici et
Gymnasiarchæ Leowardiani.

Quibus accessêre Solis tabulæ totidem; hypotheses Tychonis illustratæ: Kalendarium Rom.
vetus, cum methodo Paschali emendatâ.

ALCMARIÆ
Excudebat Iacobus Meesterus
Typographus ordinarius.
Veneunt Amstelrodami
apud Wilhelmum Ianssonium. año 1611.
Cum privilegio ad decennium.

The Library of the Earls of Macclesfield removed from Shirburn Castle

Part Five: Science I-O

AUCTION

34-35 New Bond Street
London W1A 2AA

Thursday 14 April
at 10 am and 2.30 pm

sold by instruction of
Radford Fine Art Limited

Session One at 10 am
Lots 1091-1362

Session Two at 2.30 pm
Lots 1363-1571

EXHIBITION

Friday 8 April
9 am to 4.30 pm

Sunday 10 April
12 noon to 4 pm

Monday 11 April
9 am to 4.30 pm

Tuesday 12 April
9 am to 4.30 pm

Wednesday 13 April
9 am to 4.30 pm

AUCTION ENQUIRIES AND INFORMATION

SPECIALISTS IN CHARGE
Paul Quarrie
020 7293 5300
paul.quarrie@sothebys.com
Charlotte Miller
020 7293 5893
charlotte.miller@sothebys.com
Fax 020 7293 5904

SALE ADMINISTRATOR
Samantha Todd
020 7293 5463
samantha.todd@sothebys.com
Fax 020 7293 5904

ABSENTEE BIDS
David Stanley
020 7293 5283
Fax 020 7293 6255
This catalogue may
be referred to as
L05402 "KEPLER"
Fax for bids only:
020 7293 6255

TELEPHONE BIDDING
Meghan Watson Donald
020 7293 5002
Fax 020 7293 5924
Telephone bid requests should
be received 24 hours prior to
the sale. This service is offered
for lots with a minimum low
estimate of £1,000.

PRIVATE CLIENT SERVICES
Anthea Roberts
020 7293 5184
Alexandra Brenninkmeyer
020 7293 5720
James Murray
020 7293 5847
Fax 020 7293 6949

PAYMENT
Client Account Manager
Phil Barnard
020 7293 5761
Fax 020 7293 5926

SHIPPING
Exports
Helen Roo
020 7293 6418
Fax 020 7293 5952
Imports
Olivier Rostan
020 7293 6070
Fax 020 7293 5952
Kings Warehouse
Paul Dennis
020 8232 5600

CATALOGUE
£30 at the gallery
£35 by mail
£40 overseas

**CATALOGUE
SUBSCRIPTIONS AND
SINGLE ORDERS**
020 7293 6444
Fax 020 7293 5909

**24 HOUR RECORDED
INFORMATION**
Current Auctions
and Exhibitions
020 7293 5868
Spoken Auction Results
020 7293 5855
*Auction Results are
available on our website*

SOTHEBY'S WEB SITE
www.sothebys.com

**SOTHEBY'S
INSTITUTE OF ART**
Course Information
020 7462 3232
Fax 020 7580 8160
education@sothebys.com

GENERAL ENQUIRIES

SWITCHBOARD
020 7293 5000

**AUCTION AND EXHIBITION
INFORMATION**
020 7293 5868

IMPORTANT NOTICE

Please note that all lots are sold
subject to our Conditions of
Business for Buyers and
Authenticity Guarantee, which
are set forth at the back of this
catalogue and Conditions of
Business for Sellers, which are
available from Sotheby's offices
on request. Prospective bidders
should review the Conditions
of Business, Authenticity
Guarantee and the Guide for
Prospective Buyers.

For all lots marked with a #, †,
‡, α or Ω please refer to the
VAT information pages at the
back of the catalogue. For all
lots marked with a ○ or △ or □
please refer to the Guide for
Prospective Buyers.

For information concerning
post sale storage and charges,
please see the Warehouse,
Storage and Collection
Information at the back of this
catalogue.

SAFETY AT SOTHEBY'S
Sotheby's is concerned for your
safety while you are on our
premises. For further
information, refer to the
Important Notices page at the
back of this catalogue.

FRONT COVER
ILLUSTRATION
Lot 1522
Isaac Newton

PRINTED BOOK, MANUSCRIPT AND PHOTOGRAPH DEPARTMENTS

EUROPE
LONDON
Head of Division
Dr. Stephen Roe
020 7293 5286

Senior Book Expert
Paul Quarrie F.S.A.
020 7293 5300

Continental Books,
Manuscripts, Science,
Medicine & Bindings
Dr. Susan Wharton
020 7293 5299
Paul Quarrie F.S.A.
020 7293 5300
Charlotte Miller
020 7293 5893
Charlotte Brown ‡

Printed and
Manuscript Music
Dr. Stephen Roe
020 7293 5286
Dr. Simon Maguire
020 7293 5016

English Literature
and History
Dr. Peter Beal F.B.A.
020 7293 5298
Peter Selley
020 7293 5295
Tessa Milne
020 7293 5293

Natural History, Travel, Atlases
and Maps
Roger Griffiths
020 7293 5292
Catherine Slowther
020 7293 5291
Dr. David Goldthorpe
020 7293 5303
Richard Fattorini
020 7293 5301

Children's Books, Illustrated
Books
and Drawings
Dr. Philip W. Errington
020 7293 5302
Catherine Porter ‡

General Books, Libraries
and House Sales
Roger Griffiths
020 7293 5292
Richard Fattorini
020 7293 5301

Western Manuscripts
Camilla Previté
020 7293 5334
Dr. Christopher de Hamel ‡

Photographs
Dr. Juliet Hacking
020 7293 5818

Administrator
Samantha Todd
020 7293 5463
Anna Ramell
020 7293 5288

Secretarial
Joanne Wainwright
020 7293 5287
Sophia Mooney
020 7293 5297

Auction Operations
Russell Campbell
Rafe Mullarkey
Norman Wyllie

General Enquiries
020 7293 5287

MILAN

Books and Manuscripts
Filippo Lotti
Roberta dell'Acqua
Esmeralda Benvenuti
39 02 295 001

PARIS

Books and Manuscripts
Thomas Bompard
Sylvie Delaume-Garcia
Anne Heilbronn
331 53 05 53 19

UNITED STATES
NEW YORK
David N. Redden
Head of Division

Selby Kiffer
Marsha Malinowski
Justin Caldwell
Elizabeth Muller
Jean Griffin Borho
Sandra Sider
Paul Needham ‡
Bart Auerbach ‡
212 606 7385

BOSTON
Rodney Armstrong
617 367 6323

CHICAGO
Jason Preston
312 396 9569

LOS ANGELES
Fred Backler
310 786 1856

SÃO PAULO
Pedro Corrêa do Lago
55 11 3168 1559

‡ Consultant

CONTENTS

INTRODUCTION

With this, the third part of the Macclesfield Scientific Library, we move into the middle of the alphabet and encounter the great names of Kepler and Newton, and it is in a sense towards this nexus that the earlier catalogues have been leading, with Copernicus in the first and Galileo in the second. It was, as Newton memorably wrote to Hooke in February 1675/6, by standing on the shoulders of giants that he had been able to see further, and whilst the combination of alphabet and chronology is hardly exact, and Oughtred, whom Newton read at Cambridge (and two of whose annotated books are here described for the first time), must perforce come after Newton, it plays here a happy role. With Newton too we come to a personal contact with the creator of this great library. The first Earl of Macclesfield was one of the great noblemen, all fellows of the Royal Society, who supported Newton's pall at his funeral in Westminster Abbey. The fine portrait of Newton still in the possession of the Earl of Macclesfield, which used to hang in the library, and which we are privileged to reproduce here, is another testimony to the link.

The Macclesfield Scientific Archive, sold to Cambridge University Library some four years ago, included a substantial mass of Newton material and of other items brought together initially by John Collins, and then by William Jones, the latter of whom commissioned copies of certain texts. The careers of both of these figures have been briefly dealt with in the preface to Macclesfield Science A-C, but we must now turn to them again and try to show how much not only the generality of the scientific library owes to them, but more particularly how their role in Newton's life and publications is also represented in the library.

NEWTON: THE COLLINS-JONES NEXUS

The seventeenth century was a great time for letters, and it was through the epistolary medium, generally in Latin, that scholarship was discussed and augmented, new ideas and discoveries announced, the publication of books and their printing and ordering rehearsed, and all manner of literary and scientific knowledge and gossip, even the setting and solution of mathematical problems, as well as other more domestic matters disseminated the length and breadth of Europe and beyond. In the sixteenth century the importance of the transfer of news for political and financial reasons, whether from ambassadors or bankers, had early been realised, and the archives of the European powers continue to yield up their treasures to historians. The Jesuits too had realised the utility of communication and their *Litterae annuae* are full of important information.

The correspondence of scholars is likewise a rich mine. Kepler was a tireless correspondent, and his letters tell us a great deal about him and his books. Mersenne was at the centre of an international scientific community. Peiresc, whose correspondence is vast, affords us an unparalleled entry into the scholarly world of his time, where everything from the Portland Vase to oriental manuscripts and typography, from antiquities to sun-spots, is discussed. Christiaan Huygens also had a huge correspondence from which one learns a great deal about new books and ideas. The Oldenburg Correspondence is of great importance for the history of science, as is that of John Locke, Leibnitz and others. There is some overlap, and sometimes the same letters are printed in several places, but the context is different. Most recently the publication of the first two volumes of the letters of the Oxford mathematician John Wallis has joined the ranks, marvellously edited by Philip Beeley and C.J. Scriba.

LEFT: Portrait of Sir Isaac Newton as Master of the Mint, dated 1719, by Sir Godfrey Kneller.

(Photographed by David Smith, reproduced by courtesy of the Earl of Macclesfield)

Social networks are also very important, whether it be the provision of a meeting place, as Mersenne in Paris provided for the likes of Descartes and Hobbes, and as Wilkins provided in Oxford at Wadham College, or whether it be patronage or the paying of pensions or salaries, the provision of sinecures and tutorships. Had it not been for the wealth and interest of men of power (popes, emperors, kings, princes and noblemen), the work of such men as Galileo, Kepler and Hobbes, not to mention a good many musicians, might not have seen the light of day. Institutional support from church or university obviously co-existed, but tended to be rather circumscribing. On a much lower level both John Collins and William Jones fit very well into this, both of them, as it were, picking up crumbs from the tables of much greater men, but often telling us much about these men which they themselves disregarded. The collection of laundry lists is not, as Cyril Connolly knew, without its merits.

When the great orientalist William (later Sir William) Jones (1746-1794) wrote to his erstwhile pupil Viscount Althorp in August 1775, he described looking out over Conway Bay towards Anglesea, "the ancient Mona" and the village of his father's childhood, Llandabo. William Jones senior had by dint of intellect and hard work escaped the narrow confines of Anglesea, aided by his first patron Lord Bulkeley and by talent and adroit patronage had become well-established in London. A similar mixture of intellect and determination had served not only Jones's patrons, Lords Macclesfield and Hardwicke, but also the great Newton. Law and learning have ever served as vehicles for social, and sometimes financial, advancement; as Dean Gaisford put it, "the study of Greek literature refines the intellect, elevates above the common herd and not infrequently leads to positions of considerable emolument".

It was Philip Yorke, later first Earl Hardwicke (1690-1764) and himself Lord Chancellor for nineteen years, who was in 1708 or so tutor to the Parker children, who introduced William Jones to Thomas Parker; and it was Thomas Parker's heir, George, the second Earl, who had been Jones's pupil, and who succeeded his father as patron and ultimately the owner of Jones's library and papers when Jones died in 1749. In 1708 Jones had acquired the books and papers that had belonged to Collins, by this time dead some twenty years.

JOHN COLLINS

John Collins had become, as it were, the mathematical adviser to Oldenburg in 1667, the year in which he was elected Fellow of the Royal Society, and furnished him with mathematical gossip and information, which Oldenburg put into Latin (Oldenburg was a competent mathematician, and needed to be in order to act as a suitable conduit). In 1668 Collins was seeing Barrow's Lucasian lectures through the press, and he told Oldenburg what Barrow had told him of Newton's discoveries.

The recently published second volume of Wallis's letters contains a number of letters to and from Collins, all now printed with commentary from the autographs once at Shirburn (and printed by Rigaud), now in Cambridge, of which the editors remark, "Wallis's correspondence with Collins covers almost as equally large and varied a number of themes as that with Oldenburg. Many of the letters contain details of recent scientific publications on the Continent…". A fine example of Wallis's use of Collins is the letter dated 10/[20] September 1668 (letter 248) where Wallis asks Collins to transcribe "two or three propositions out of my papers… to send away with the enclosed letter to Lalovera… These you may please to transcribe (carefully)… They will contain (I suppose) about two sheets of paper or more… I shall send you by Moor the carrier, one of my books de Cycloide to be sent with it; that being too big to come by the Post. If the thing

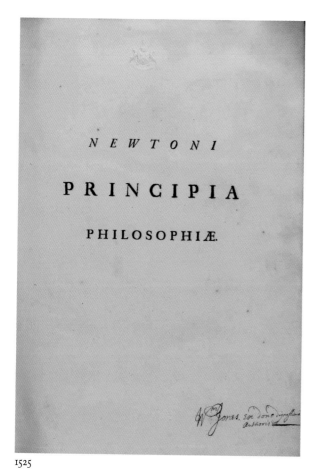

N E W T O N I

P R I N C I P I A

PHILOSOPHIÆ.

1525

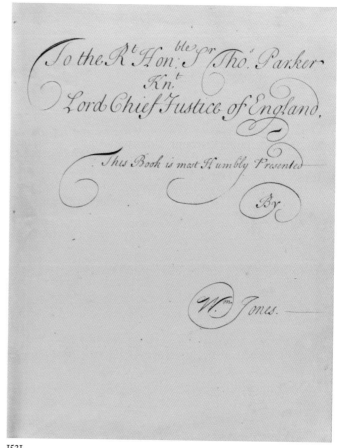

1521

be dispatched time inough, it may bee sent by the same hand that carryes my letter to Mr Hugens [31.viii/10.ix, 1668 = Huygens, *Oeuvres* VI, pp.251-257, letter 1659], which perhaps my Lord Broucker may have shewed you. One Theodorus Riccius [Dirck de Rycke (1650-1690)], who lyes at Mr Edward Robert's house, near York-house; & takes in Post-letters. This Riccius is suddenly going directly to Paris…".

In 1669 Collins had read Newton's early *De analysi*, about which he wrote enthusiastically to Sluse (via Oldenburg) in 1670. In 1670 when Tschirnhaus came to London, Collins met him, as did John Wallis. Oldenburg and Tschirnhaus corresponded during the time the latter was in Paris, Oldenburg for the most part acting as international intermediary for mathematical information passed on by Collins. It was thus that Leibnitz, whose own mathematical prowess was rapidly increasing, learned of Newton's method of determining tangents to complex curves (a subject which Sluse had also discussed, but differently), and something of Newton's work on infinite series. In 1671/2 Collins wrote to Oldenburg about the readiness for the press of Newton's "introduction to algebra, his generall method of analyticall Quadratures, and 20 Dioptick lectures". It was also through Collins that Newton and Sluse, the Liège mathematician, knew of each other's work and methods, Newton even conceding that Sluse had anticipated him (cf. *Principia*, 3rd edition, p. 246).

1523

Early in 1676 Newton composed a lengthy letter, the *Epistola prior*, in which he described what he had done with reference to the development of infinite series and the binomial theorem. This was copied and sent to Leibnitz by Oldenburg in July 1676, and the original returned to Newton. In early October 1676 Leibnitz came to London on his way back to Germany and met Collins, and it was at this point that Collins showed him copies of some of Newton's papers. Newton had been working on, but had not completed, his *Epistola posterior*, a copy of which Leibnitz received at length in June 1677, and about which he was greatly excited, writing twice to Oldenburg. Neither Newton nor Collins was in London in early August 1677, but at the end of August, Collins returned to London and sent copies of Leibnitz's letters to Newton. We do not know of Newton's reactions, and the death of Oldenburg in early September put an end to the exchange of letters between the two. When the subject was revived years later, it caused the most bitter personal animosity and a major controversy.

Collins's legacy lived on. In the third edition of *Principia* we find a change in the text (p.246 = I, 368 in Koyré & Cohen), and what had been printed in the first and second editions (beginning "in literis quae mihi cum geometra peritissimo G.G. Leibnitio…") is now changed to "in epistola quadam ad D.J. Collinium nostratem 10 decemb. 1672 data, cum descripsissem" (= *Correspondence* I, 247 onwards, letter 94; the original was at Shirburn and is now in Cambridge).

WILLIAM JONES

The acquisition in 1708 by Jones of Collins's papers (the date is given in the preface to *De analysi*, 1711, which was written in 1710 "Etenim secundus iam agitur annus…") came at a fortunate time as Newton was then concerned with the question of Leibnitz's primacy in the discovery of the calculus, and Collins's papers were of great use. In 1712 Jones made them available to the Royal Society for the publication of *Commercium epistolicum*, but he retrieved them in the 1730s and in 1741 returned the bulk of them, but not all, in a bound volume to the Society.

When Jones published *De analysi* with no indication of Newton's authorship other than in the preface, he made ample use, with Newton's agreement, of these papers, and added, in addition to *De quadratura*, *Enumeratio linearum tertii ordinis* and *Methodus differentialis*, fragments of four letters to Oldenburg, Wallis and Collins. In this preface he attempted to give a very brief history of Newton's mathematical evolution. Jones also penned for Thomas Birch a fuller English account of Newton's mathematics, which remains unpublished (the autograph is CUL Add. 3960.2; see *Mathematical Papers*, viii, xxii, no. 34) and is dismissed by Professor Whiteside as "unscholarly" and "a mere historical curiosity". Be that as it may, Jones's importance is obvious.

De quadratura was famously published with *Opticks* in 1704, but the presence of the completely unknown manuscript leaf with two pages of text in Newton's own hand, inserted into the copy of the book, shows that Jones's was no simple reprint.

The *Methodus differentialis* was printed in 1711 from Jones's transcription of Newton's own autograph, which does not survive (*Mathematica Papers*, viii, 236, no.1), but some fragments of a "preliminary augmentation of 1676 parent text" are printed by Whiteside from the originals in CUL (dating from just before 1710). Whiteside also prints the full text of Jones's transcription (*Mathematical Papers*, viii, 244 onwards).

Jones's edition of these texts earned him the fellowship of the Royal Society and praise at home and abroad. On the home front Roger Cotes wrote on 15 February 1711 congratulating him, and it was to Jones that Cotes, who was editing the second edition of *Principia*, was to send the text of the Index to that (completed April 1713). Cotes wrote on 3 May 1713 delighted that Jones had approved the index but stating "that it was not design'd to be of any use to such readers as your self, but to those of ordinary capacity".

That these transcripts of Jones were circulated and read we know from the treatise on fluxions (dating from 1671), which served as the text from which Colson in 1736 produced an English translation; and Horsley in 1779 used a copy of the Jones transcript (as well as the autograph, now in Cambridge) when he published *Geometria analytica* for the first time. This copy was communicated to Horsley by Charles Cavendish "cum ipse eum olim a Jonesio acceperat" which seems to suggest that it was a second copy and not Jones's own (*pace* Whiteside; Lord Charles Cavendish (1704-83) was the third son of William, second Duke of Devonshire, himself an amateur of natural philosophy, and father of Henry Cavendish the scientist, 1731-1810).

It can therefore be seen that at different periods in Newton's life, first Collins and then Jones played important roles, and the Macclesfield Library, as the final recipient of their books and papers, is a quite extraordinary link with Newton. In 1752 William Stukeley, the historian of Druids and archaeologist, and like Newton a Lincolnshire man, wrote an account of Newton in which he recounted how after his election to the Royal Society in March 1717/18 at the recommendation of Dr Richard Mead, the physician and collector (who attended Newton in his final illness), he often visited Newton "sometime with Dr. Mead, Dr. Halley, or Dr. Brook Taylor, Mr. W. Jones or Mr. Folkes and others". Jones was the intimate of many British men of science, a respected correspondent of foreign savants (the copy of a letter to Maupertuis in lot 1281 is of great interest particularly for the light it casts on Newton), a member of the group of "infidels" which gathered around Martin Folkes (also President of the Royal Society) and a Freemason, as indeed was J.T. Desaguliers. It was to Jones's pupil and patron, George Parker, second Earl of Macclesfield, and himself President of the Royal Society, that Stukeley most fittingly dedicated his memoir of Newton.

P.R. Quarrie

NOTE ON THE CATALOGUE

All of the books in the library carry the Macclesfield bookplate (see illustration on p. 12); the first or second leaf of each volume also has a small embossed stamp of similar design (see illustration on p. 311). Many of the books were bound up in the eighteenth century and sometimes, notably with the tract volumes, this has resulted in some cropping.

The Library of the
Earls of Macclesfield
removed from Shirburn Castle

Part Five: Science I-O

Session One Lots 1091-1362
Thursday 14 April 2005 at 10 am

1091 Iamblichus (*c.* 250-*c.* 330 AD). In Nicomachi Geraseni arithmeticam introductionem, et de fato. Nunc primum editus, in Latinam sermonem conversus, notis perpetuis illustratus, a Samuele Tennulio. Accedit Joachimi Camerarii explicatio in duos libros Nicomachi, cum indice rerum & verborum locupletissimo. *Arnhem: Wilhelmus Wier for Johann Friedrich Hag, 1668*

4to (204 x 157mm.), [12], 181, [3], 190, [2 (blank)], 191-239, [1 (blank)] pp., title-page in red and black, ILLUSTRATION: engraved frontispiece, woodcut initials and diagrams, BINDING: contemporary calf, red morocco lettering-piece, *some quires browned, extremities slightly rubbed*

References: Wellcome III, p.325

£300-400
€450-600

1092 Iamblichus. In Nicomachi Geraseni arithmeticam introductionem, et de fato. Nunc primum editus, in Latinam sermonem conversus, notis perpetuis illustratus, a Samuele Tennulio. Accedit Joachimi Camerarii explicatio in duos libros Nicomachi, cum indice rerum & verborum locupletissimo. *Arnhem: Wilhelmus Wier for Johann Friedrich Hag, 1668*

4to (193 x 148mm.), [12], 181, [3], 239, [1 (blank)] pp., title-page in red and black, ILLUSTRATION: engraved frontispiece, woodcut initials and diagrams, BINDING: contemporary vellum with gilt centrepiece, gilt edges, *some quires browned, lacking two pairs of silk ties*

This is a commentary on one of only two extant works by Nicomachus of Gerasa (*fl. c.* 100 AD), which "deals with number per se, relative number, plane and solid numbers, and proportions" (*DSB* X, p.113).

References: Wellcome III, p.325

£300-400
€450-600

1093 Iamblichus, *pseudo-.* Τα θεολογουμενα της αριθμητικης. *Paris: Christian Wechel, 1543*

4to (224 x 142mm.), 65, [3]pp., ILLUSTRATION: woodcut printer's device on title-page and final verso, woodcut initials, BINDING: eighteenth-century calf gilt, spine gilt in compartments, morocco lettering-pieces, *slight damp-staining in lower corner with some loss (not affecting text), first and last leaves soiled, extremities slightly rubbed*

FIRST EDITION. This anonymous treatise on the Greek theory of numbers is sometimes ascribed to the Neopythagorean Iamblichus.

References: Smith p.223

£300-400
€450-600

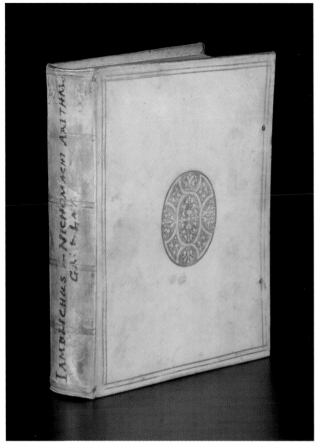

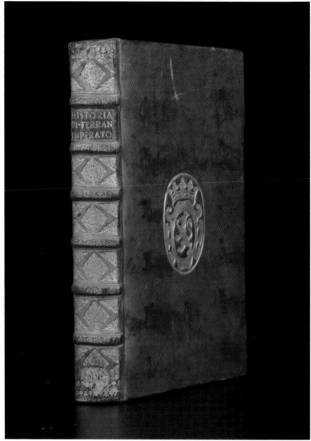

1092

1094

1094 Imperato, Ferrante (1550-1625). Historia naturale... nella quale ordinatamente si tratta della diversa condition di minere, pietre pretiose, ed altre curiosità... Seconda impressione. *Venice: Combi & la Noù, 1672*

folio (316 x 213mm.), [8], 696, [8]pp., title printed in red and black, ILLUSTRATION: engraved illustration on title-page, woodcut initials and headpieces, woodcut illustrations, woodcut printer's devices on Hh4 verso and last verso of index, BINDING: contemporary calf, gilt arms of Nicolas-Joseph Foucault on covers, spine gilt in compartments, red morocco lettering-piece, red edges, *lacking folding engraved plate, index bound between quires Hhh and Iii, extremities slightly rubbed*

Originally printed in 1599, this edition has additional notes by Giovanni Maria Ferro. Imperato was an apothecary in Naples who gathered together a cabinet of natural history specimens, one of the earliest of its kind in Italy.

References: Hunt 321; Nissen *ZBI* 2111; Wellcome IV, p.328

Provenance: Nicolas-Joseph Foucault, armorial bookplate and arms on covers

£1,000-1,500
€1,450-2,200

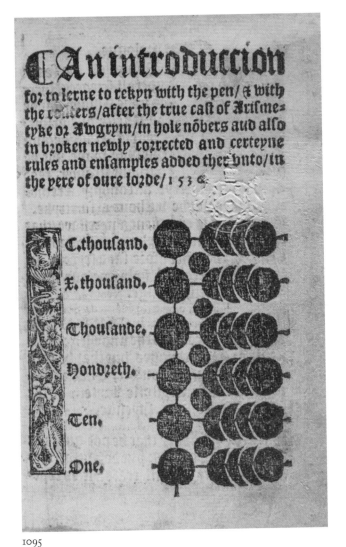

1095

1095

1095 An Introduccion for to lerne to rekyn with the pen & with the counters after the true cast of Arismetyke or Awgrym in whole nombers and also in broken newly corrected and certeyne rules and ensamples added therunto in the yere of oure lorde 1536. *[St Albans: J. Herford for R. Stevenage], (1537)*

8vo (145 x 92mm.), ff. [152], a-s⁸, Black Letter, ILLUSTRATION: woodcut initials and illustrations, woodcut printer's device with letters R.S. on final verso (McKerrow 84), BINDING: eighteenth-century mottled calf, spine gilt in compartments, red morocco lettering-piece, red edges, *small marginal tears on d2-3, r2 torn and repaired with slight loss, joints weak, head of spine chipped*

UNIQUE COMPLETE COPY of this edition of *Introduction for to learn to reckon.* STC records several editions, this being the first listed, although the title-page wording implies that perhaps there was an earlier edition, no longer extant.

Robert Stevenage, the publisher, was abbot of St Albans, and funded a press there between the years 1534 and 1539. STC lists only two products of this press, the present work and John Gwynneth's *The confutacyon of the fyrst parte of Frythes boke* from 1536 (STC 12557). John Herford, a foreign printer, also worked in London from *c.* 1542 until his death in *c.* 1548.

References: STC 14117.7 (BL only, comprising only the final leaf)

£8,000-10,000
€11,600-14,500

1096 Issautier, Nicolò (1657-1676). Geometria. *Turin: heirs of Gianelli, 1679*

3 volumes in one, 8vo (182 x 106mm.), xvi, 184; 152; 176, [48]pp., one half-title, ILLUSTRATION: woodcut diagrams in the text, BINDING: contemporary speckled calf, spine gilt in compartments, *joints weak*

FIRST EDITION, EXTREMELY RARE. As Donato Rossetti explains in his address to the reader, Issautier, professor of mathematics at the Accademia di Piemonte, died during the printing of the second volume, at the age of only 19.

References: Riccardi iii, 176

Provenance: William Jones, signature on half-title

£800-1,000
€1,200-1,450

1097 Jack, Richard (d. 1759). Elements of conic sections in three books: in which are demonstrated the principal properties of the parabola, ellipse, and hyperbola. *Edinburgh: Thomas Wal and Thomas Ruddimans, 1742*

8vo (199 x 114mm.), [4], xi, [1], 331pp., ILLUSTRATION: woodcut vignette on title, woodcut initials, head- and tailpieces, 9 folding engraved plates, BINDING: eighteenth-century smooth calf gilt, spine gilt in compartments with morocco lettering-piece, red speckled edges

£400-600
€600-900

1098 Jacobaeus, Holger (1650-1701). Museum regium, seu catalogus rerum tam naturalium, quam artificialium, quae in basilica bibliothecae augustissimi Daniae Norvegiaeque monarchae, Friderici Quarti asservantur. *Copenhagen: Royal and University Printer, [1710]*

folio (360 x 224mm.), [478]pp., title printed in red and black, ILLUSTRATION: engraved device on title-page, engraved and woodcut initials, head- and tailpieces, 53 engraved plates (2 double-page), BINDING: contemporary mottled calf, spine gilt in compartments, *lacking one plate, title-page torn without loss, a few paper flaws and repairs (some affecting text), 12L2 & 3 transposed, some plates frayed in margin, one plate detached, occasional slight browning, joints worn, extremities rubbed, covers scraped with some loss of covering*

A catalogue of the Danish royal cabinet of curiosities, from natural history specimens to coins and medals. It was originally published in 1696 in the reign of Christian V.

References: Nielsen V, col.239; Nissen *ZBI* 2081 (specifying ff. [260]); Wellcome III, p.338

£500-700
€750-1,050

1098

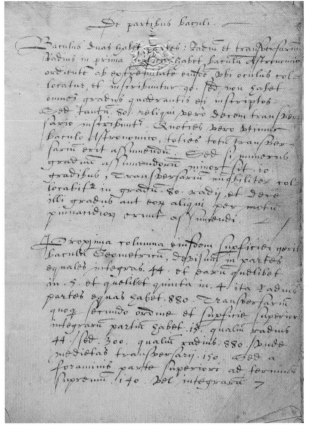

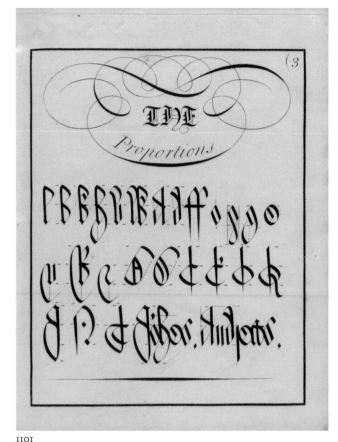

1099

1101

1099 Jacob's Staff or Cross Staff. Manuscript account in Latin. *[England, c. 1600]*

4to (200 x 150mm.), ff. [31] with 61 pages of text, manuscript on paper written in ink in Latin, ILLUSTRATION: ink diagrams, BINDING: later vellum-backed blue boards, *boards a little soiled*

The work is divided into chapters, the first twelve being Propositions (such as "De partibus baculi; Propositio prima. In triangulo equilatero centrum gravitates reperire...") followed by a section, "De longitudine capienda per instrumentum" and various other chapters, and their demonstrations.

The Jacob's Staff or Cross Staff was a tool widely used by astronomers and navigators before the invention of the telescope, and for a while afterwards. It consists of a main staff with a perpendicular crosspiece, attached at its middle to the staff and able to slide up and down along it.

£2,000-3,000
€2,900-4,350

1100 Jannson, François [Frans Jansszoon] (*fl.* 2nd half 17th century). Les cinq ordres d'architecture. *[Holland], 1690*

8vo (187 x 120mm.), manuscript on paper, 34 leaves (the last two leaves and all the versos blank except for ink-drawn frames), comprising title, frontispiece and 30 ink drawings in black and red ink (some with slight text in French) of various aspects of the Orders, BINDING: contemporary mottled calf, *spine rubbed*

A Frans Jannssz is recorded by Thieme-Becker but with no details.

£500-600
€750-900

1101 Jarman, John (*fl.* 1698-1723). A System of the court-hands: wherein the characters are justly and completely demonstrated... Together with the ingrossing, running secretary, and text-hands. By John Jarman, late of Hatton Garden. Published for the use of the Academy in Tower-Street: where clerks are qualified after this method. *London: for the author and J. Walthoe, 1723*

4to (209 x 168mm.), [4]pp., ILLUSTRATION: 23 engraved plates, BINDING: eighteenth-century vellum-backed boards, *occasional small ink-stains*

John Jarman appears to have been writing-master at Thomas Watts' academy in Little Tower Street, for which an advertisement appears on p. [4].

References: Heal p. 177

£800-1,000
€1,200-1,450

1102 Jeake, Samuel (1623-1690). Λογιστικηλογια, or Arithmetick surveighed and reviewed, in four books [edited by Samuel Jeake the younger]. *London: J.R. and J.D. for Walter Kettilby and Richard Mount, 1696*

folio (320 x 198mm.), [18], 376, 405-664, [22]pp., ILLUSTRATION: woodcut diagrams, folding engraved table, BINDING: contemporary sprinkled calf gilt, spine gilt in compartments, red morocco lettering-piece, *extremities slightly rubbed*

FIRST EDITION. Jeake, who came of Puritan stock, was a nonconformist of Rye in Sussex, extremely active in the affairs of the town and its nonconformist congregation. He amassed a substantial library. His son Samuel, to whom the work is dedicated, was know as a practising astrologer, and a number of his manuscripts survive.

This work is "clearly indebted to his extensive holdings of mathematical books, as he explains in his preface, where, indeed, he describes the work as a 'complete collection of the cream of other authors'".

References: Wing J499; M. Hunter and others, editors, *A radical's books: the library catalogue of Samuel Jeake of Rye* (Woodbridge, 1998), especially page lii

£1,000-1,500
€1,450-2,200

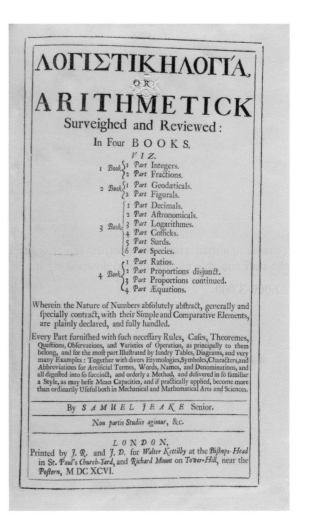

1102

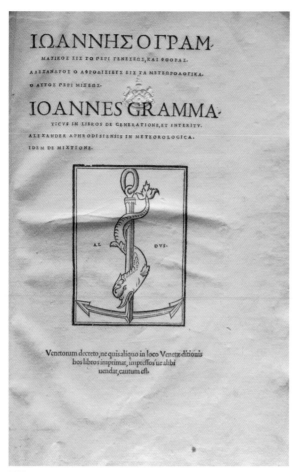

1103

1103

1103 Joannes Philoponus (6th century AD), *of Alexandria.* Ιωαννες ο γραμματικος εις το περι γενεσεως, και φθορας... In libros de generatione, et interitu. Alexander Aphrodisiensis in Meteorologica. Idem de mixtione [with the text of the first two works]. *(Venice: Aldus Manutius & A. Torresanus, September, 1527)*

folio (312 x 212mm.), ff. [2], 147, [1], Greek letter, last leaf with colophon and device, ILLUSTRATION: woodcut diagrams in text of *Meteorologica* commentary, BINDING: contemporary Venetian binding of brown rough calf, covers decorated in blind, with an outer panel of a diapered roll and fillets enclosing a similar central panel enclosing a pattern of arabesques, half-moon corner decorations, gilt edges, *rubbed, bands and corners worn, lacking ties*

The Aristotelian commentaries of late antiquity, particularly those of Alexander of Aphrodisias and Joannes Philoponus, were much studied in the late fifteenth and early sixteenth centuries, and it was part of the Aldine 'plan' to print these as well as the Aristotelian corpus itself. Aldus began with the commentary on Ammonius in 1503, and started again with Torresani in 1513 with Alexander's commentary on part of the *Organon*. In 1527 two volumes were produced, the present work and Simplicius *De anima*.

References: Censimento 16 CNCE 37733; UCLA 215; Renouard 1527/7; Texas 225

£2,500-3,500
€3,650-5,100

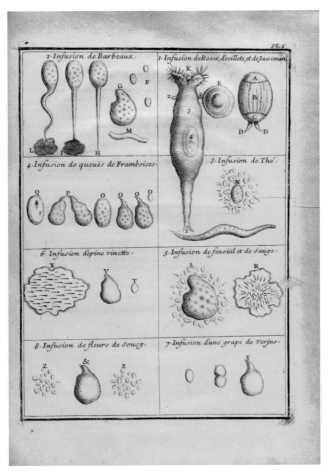

1104

1104 Joblot, Louis (1645-1723). Descriptions et usages de plusieurs nouveaux microscopes, tant simples que composez, avec des nouvelles observations faites sur une multitude innombrable d'insectes, & d'autres animaux de diverses especes, qui naissent dans les liqueurs préparées, & dans celles qui ne le sont point. *Paris: Jacques Collombat, 1718*

2 parts in one volume, 4to (247 x 185mm.), [12], 78; 96, [6]pp., ILLUSTRATION: woodcut device on title, woodcut initials, head- and tailpieces, first page of text engraved, 34 engraved plates, BINDING: contemporary sprinkled calf, spine gilt in compartments with morocco lettering-piece, *joints breaking, extremities rubbed*

Joblot's work with microscopes is better known from the later (and more common) 1754 edition. This is the first treatise on Protozoa, which were discovered a few years earlier by Anton van Leeuwenhoek.

"The publication of the *Descriptions* established Joblot as the first French microscopist. The first part of the book described several microscopes and their construction and introduced some improvements, including the use of stops (diaphragms) in compound microscopes to correct for chromatic aberration" (*DSB* VII, p.110).

References: Cole 1265; Nissen *ZBI* 2113

£1,500-2,000
€2,200-2,900

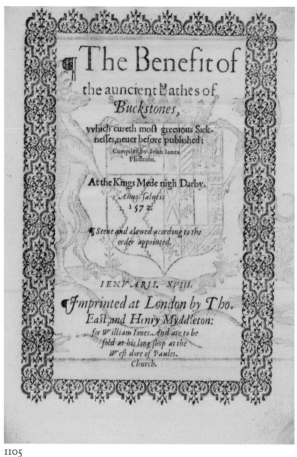

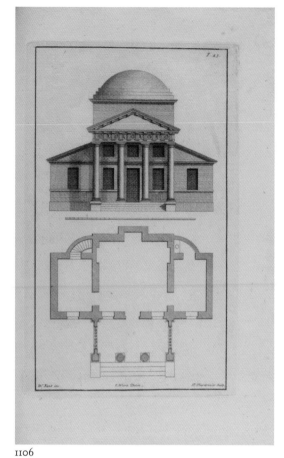

1105

1106

1105 Jones, John (*fl. 1579*). The bathes of Bathes ayde: wonderfull and most excellent, agaynst very many sicknesses... *London: (Thomas East) for William Jones, 13 May 1572*, ff. [8], 35 (i.e. 34), [4], ILLUSTRATION: woodcut border on title-page, woodcut initials and headpieces, woodcut illustrations, 2 folding tables, *both tables laid down, paper flaw in final leaf*

Ibid. The benefit of the auntient bathes of Buckstones, which cureth most greevous sicknesses, never before published. *London: Thomas East and Henry Myddleton for William Jones, 18 January 1572*, ff. [8], 20, [1], ILLUSTRATION: woodcut border on title-page, woodcut coat-of-arms of dedicatee, George Talbot, earl of Shrewsbury, woodcut initials, *lacking last 3 leaves, a few marginal paper repairs*

2 works in one volume, 4to (172 x 127mm.), BINDING: eighteenth-century mottled calf gilt, spine gilt in compartments, red edges, *some headlines and margins shaved*

BOTH FIRST EDITIONS. Jones was a Welsh physician who frequented the baths at Buxton and Bath. His patrons, Henry Herbert, earl of Pembroke and George Talbot, earl of Shrewsbury, are the dedicatees of these two works.

References: STC 14724a.3 & 14724a.7; Wellcome 3475 & 3476

£1,000-1,500
€1,450-2,200

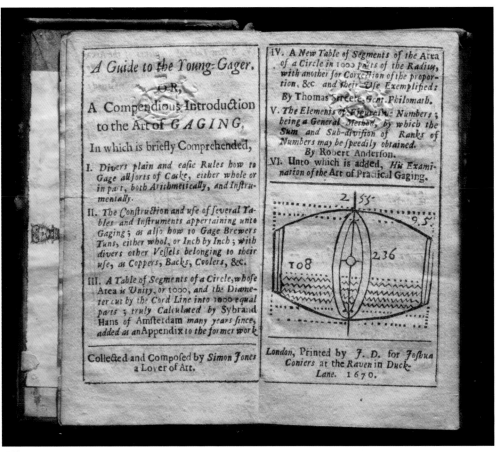

1107

1106 Jones, Inigo (1573-1652). Designs of Inigo Jones and others. *[London]: Isaac Ware, [1731]*

4to (253 x 162mm.), engraved throughout, ILLUSTRATION: engraved title-page and 6-page list of plates, 48 engraved plates (6 double-page), BINDING: contemporary calf gilt, spine gilt in compartments, morocco lettering-piece, red speckled edges

This collection of designs by Inigo Jones, William Kent and Lord Burlington contains fireplaces, porticoes, ceiling panels and architectural plans. "Most of these Designs are already Executed; & the rest, are at Burlington House" (verso of title-page). An extremely important volume in the Palladian revival.

References: BAL RIBA 1622; Fowler 437; Harris 909

£1,500-2,000
€2,200-2,900

1107 Jones, Simon. A guide to the young gager, or, a compendious introduction to the art of gaging (The art of practical gaging examined... by Robert Anderson). *London: J.D. for Joshua Coniers, 1670*

12mo (125 x 65mm.), [8], 168, [6], 18pp., ILLUSTRATION: woodcut diagrams, BINDING: contemporary calf, gilt fillets with corner fleurons, flat spine gilt, *both covers detached, extremities rubbed*

FIRST EDITION. For other works by Anderson on gauging, see Macclesfield Science A-C lot 166.

References: Wing J990A (one copy only, in Cambridge)

£600-800
€900-1,200

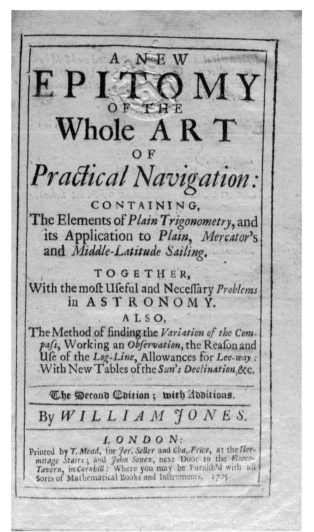

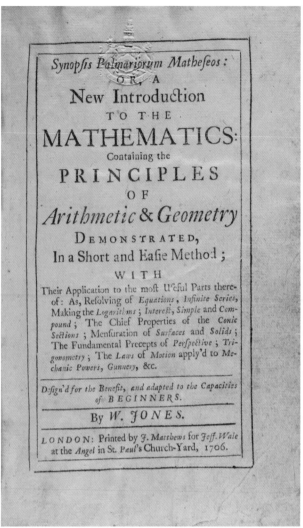

1108

1109

1108 Jones, William (1675-1749). A new epitomy of the whole art of practical navigation: containing, the elements of plain trigonometry, and its application to plain, Mercator's and Middle-Latitude sailing... The second edition, with additions. *London: T. Mead for Jer. Seller, Cha. Price and John Senex, 1705*

8vo (158 x 92mm.), [4], 151, [1]pp., ILLUSTRATION: woodcut diagrams, BINDING: contemporary calf gilt, spine gilt in compartments, red morocco lettering-piece, *slightly browned, a few leaves shaved, extremities rubbed*

VERY RARE. The only copy recorded by ESTC is in Boston Public Library.

This work was originally published in 1702 with the title *A new compendium of the whole art of practical navigation*. Another edition, seemingly identical to the second, was published in 1706 with the title *A new epitomy of the art of practical navigation*. According to Taylor, "the only known copy of [the 1706 edition] was recently found among books from Sir Isaac Newton's library" (p.417), which is now in Trinity College Cambridge (Harrison 858). The 1706 edition contains a plate which not present in the Boston or Shirburn copies of the 1705 edition.

£1,500-2,000
€2,200-2,900

1109 Jones, William. Synopsis palmariorum matheseos: or, a new introduction to the mathematics: containing the principles of arithmetic & geometry demonstrated, in a short and easie method. *London: J. Matthews for Jeff. Wale, 1706*

8vo (195 x 118mm.), [12], 304pp., ILLUSTRATION: woodcut diagrams and headpiece, 3 engraved plates (loose), engraved table entitled "The cases of interest" pasted to inside front cover, BINDING: contemporary calf, spine gilt in compartments, red morocco lettering-piece, numerous manuscript annotations (some probably autograph), both on the pages and on inserted slips of paper, *joints partly split, extremities rubbed*

FIRST EDITION of Jones's second published work which "attracted the attention of Newton and Halley. Although the book was designed essentially for beginners in mathematics, it contained a fairly comprehensive survey of contemporary developments, including the *method of fluxions* and the *doctrine of series*" (*DSB* VII, p.162).

£500-700
€750-1,050

1110 Johnstone, John (1603-1675). An history of the constancy of nature. Wherein... it is maintained that the world doth not decay universally, [etc.]. *London: Printed for John Streater, and are to be sold by the booksellers, 1657*

8vo (143 x 87mm.), [16], 180, [2 (adverts)] pp., first leaf a blank (lacking), BINDING: contemporary sheep, *slightly rubbed*

References: Wing J1016

£600-800
€900-1,200

1111 Jordaine, Joshua. Duodecimal arithmetick... practically applied to the measuring of all sorts of superficies, and solids, as board, glass, &c., timber, stone... But chiefly to the gauging of all sorts of brewers tuns and casks. *London: John Richardson for the author, 1687*

8vo (182 x 114mm.), [28], 303, [1]pp., folding table at p. 268, ILLUSTRATION: folding engraved slip, woodcut diagrams in text, BINDING: contemporary speckled calf, *outer corner of licence leaf torn away (affecting a rule line but not text), some light damp marking, binding rubbed*

FIRST EDITION. RARE: WING RECORDS ONLY ONE COPY.

References: Wing J1018c; not in Taylor

£500-700
€750-1,050

1112 Jordanus (*fl.* 1230), *Nemorarius* and **Jacques Le Fèvre d'Etaples (d. 1536).** In hoc opera contenta Arithmetica decem libris demonstrata Musica libris demonstrata quattuor Epitome in libros arithmeticos divi Severini Boetij Rithmimachie ludus que et pugna numerorum appellatur. *Paris: J. Higman & W. Hopyl, 22 July 1496*

folio (270 x 193mm.), 72 leaves, types 82G and 63G (commentary), 51 lines of text, initial spaces mostly with guide-letters, ILLUSTRATION: woodcut on i8 recto and small diagrams in text, BINDING: nineteenth-century half calf by Hatton, *small tear in title-page with loss of a few letters, last leaf soiled on verso*

FIRST EDITION. Jordanus's work on the theory of numbers is in ten books, edited by Le Fèvre. This edition also includes: Le Fèvre's own treatise on music; his epitome of Boethius's arithmetic; and an anonymous tract about the arithmetical game of Rithmimachia, attributed variously to Le Fèvre and John Shirwood, Bishop of Durham (d. 1494).

Of Jordanus *Nemorarius* (or of Nemore) very little is known, but he was the author of several works including *De numeris datis*, the first western European treatise on advanced algebra, a text known in the sixteenth century to Scheubel and Riese, but not printed, unlike his other works which were frequently printed in Paris and elsewhere.

References: HC 9436; BMC viii 137; Polain 2323; Goff J472; Smith I, p. 62; Stillwell II.187; Klebs 563.1

£20,000-30,000
€29,000-43,500

1113 Jordanus, *Nemorarius* and **Jacques le Fèvre d'Etaples.** In hoc opere contenta Arithmetica decem libris demonstrata. Musica libris demonstrata quatuor. Epitome in libros arithmeticos divi Severini Boethij. Rithmimachie ludus qui et pugna numerorum appellatur. *Paris: H. Estienne, (7 September 1514)*

folio (275 x 195mm.), ff. [72], a-i⁸, ILLUSTRATION: marginal diagrams etc., BINDING: nineteenth-century half calf by Hatton, *a few marginal worm holes*

See lot 1112 for the first edition of this work.

References: Renouard, *Estienne* p.16 no.4; Moreau II 885

Provenance: Estienne Baluze (his sale, 1713)

£1,500-2,000
€2,200-2,900

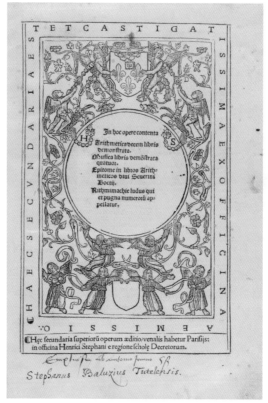

1113

¶ Minores victorias ppaucas posui:vt vos venatoribus similes relinquã:qui magis fere inuẽtione
q̃ oblata sine venatione gaudere solent . Ex tribus tamen Bathille preceptis minozum victoriarum
cognitio pendet.
¶ Primum. Datos duos campozũ numeros iunge : lũctozũ dimidium est inter eos in Arithmetica
medietate medius numerus.
¶ Secundum. Datis itidem duobus nũeris:duc primũ in scõm:et pducti accipe latus tetragonicũ.
et illud est eozum rationis geometrice medius numerus.
¶ Tertium. Datos duos numeros aggrega:et qui aggregatus est serua.duc primũ in scõm/et pdu
ctum dupla/et duplatũ diuide per seruatum aggregatũ:et qui puenit est illoz numerozũ harmonice
pportiõalitatis medius . Et si hoc pacto quẽadmodũ hec tria docẽt precepta integros numeros non
repias:numeri dati nullos habebũt in illa rõne/ pportiõalitatez medios.et nõ modo minorezvicto:
rias/seu sint ex Arithmetica et Geometrica/seu ex Arithmetica et Harmonica/seu ex Geometrica et
Harmonica reperias:sed et si volueris maximas.Verũ solent o Bathille aliter cãpos/acierũ duces/
comitesgozdinare.vt area sit campozũ sexagintaquattuoz.aut limite campozum medio acienvtranq̃
dirimẽtesuperadiecto duozum atq̃ septuaginta.

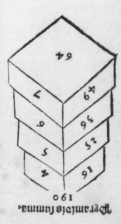

Pyramidis summa.
191
I

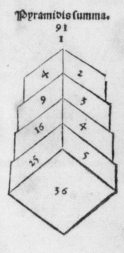

Pyramidis summa.
190

¶ Et campis hoc modo digestis rudes adhuc et quos ad mysteria ipse cetus silẽtium candidissimus
pater nondum admittit ex supiozibus preceptis inter se concertant.mox po puerilibus actis/iocisq̃
reiectis ad silentia hymnosq̃ assuefacti:presentia preceptozis tanq̃ numinis cuiusdã fruũtur/solan

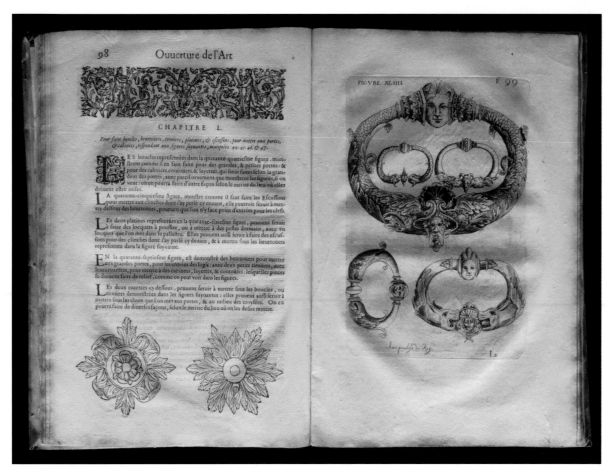

1114

1114 Jousse, Mathurin (1607-1692). La fidelle ouverture de l'art de serrurier...
Ensemble un petit traicté de diverses trempes. *La Flèche: George Griveau, 1627*

folio (306 x 210mm.), [8 (including engraved title)], 152pp., ILLUSTRATION:
engraved title, numerous engraved and woodcut illustrations (some full-page),
woodcut head-pieces and initials, BINDING: contemporary vellum, *occasional light
staining, covers lightly soiled*

FIRST EDITION. Jousse was a silversmith by trade and the present work contains
fine illustrations of designs for locks, keys, door-handles, bolts, bells, brackets,
well-heads, window-grilles, a rolling-chair and prosthetics. This book may well
have been intended as a companion volume to Jousse's *Le Théâtre de l'art de
charpentier*, first published by Griveau in the same year. A supposed 1624 edition
of the present work is unsubstantiated.

References: Berlin Catalogue 1333

£5,000-7,000
€7,300-10,200

1115 Jousse, Mathurin. Le Secret d'architecture découvrant fidelement les traits
géometriques, couppes, et dérobemens nécessaires dans les bastiments. *La Flèche:
Georges Griveau, 1642*

folio (336 x 228mm.), 8, 227, [1 (blank)] pp., ILLUSTRATION: woodcut device on
title, 100 (of 112) woodcut diagrams in text (some full-page), woodcut head- and
tail-pieces and initials, BINDING: eighteenth-century vellum-backed boards, *lacking
12 folding woodcut plates, short tear in D5 and T2 without loss, O2 & 5 browned*

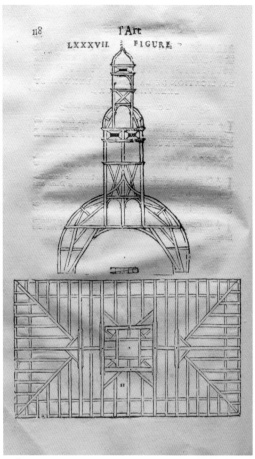

1116

FIRST EDITION. One of the earliest treatises on the construction of stone vaults. It was quickly superseded by François Derand's *L'Architecture des voûtes* which was published the following year. Because of their size, twelve of the woodcuts were issued as folding plates; they are not present in this copy. The copy described by Millard is the dedication copy and contains a variant title-page, with reset text and the woodcut arms of the dedicatee.

References: BAL RIBA 1638; Fowler 160; Millard i 82; Berlin Catalogue 2538

£800-1,000
€1,200-1,450

1116 Jousse, Mathurin. L'Art de charpenterie... Corrigé & augmenté de ce qu'il y a de plus curieux dans cet art, & des machines les plus nécessaires à un charpentier.
Paris: Thomas Moette, 1702

folio (314 x 195mm.), [4], 208pp., ILLUSTRATION: 7 engraved plates, woodcut vignette on title, numerous woodcut illustrations in text (most full-page), woodcut head- and tail-pieces and initials, BINDING: contemporary vellum, *last 2 engraved plates and a few full-page woodcuts very slightly shaved*

First published in 1627 entitled *Le Théâtre de l'art de charpentier*, this work was the first devoted entirely to carpentry. Three further editions were published in the seventeenth century before the present edition, which was expanded by Philippe de La Hire. As well as additional text, it contains a revised introduction, a *Table de matières* and seven engraved plates.

References: BAL RIBA 1639

£1,000-1,500
€1,450-2,200

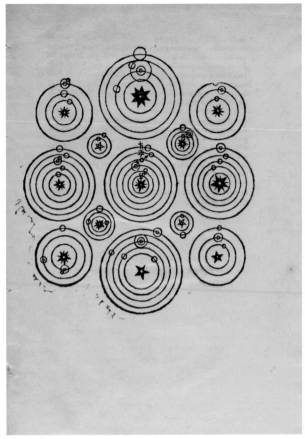

1117   1118

1117 Jouvin, -. Solution et esclaircissement de quelques propositions de mathematiques, entr' autres de la duplication du cube, & de la quadrature du cercle. *Paris: Jacques Langlois, 1658*

4to (232 x 174mm.), [8], 76, [4 (the last 3 blank)] pp., ILLUSTRATION: woodcut diagrams (some full-page), BINDING: eighteenth-century vellum-backed boards, *diagram on p. 30 cropped at foot*

The dedication of this anonymous work is signed by Jouvin.

£1,000-1,500
€1,450-2,200

1118 Jungenickel, Andreas (*fl.* 1661-1683). Schlüssel zur Mechanica. Das ist: gründliche Beschreibung der vier haupt Instrumenten der Machination. *Nuremberg: Christoff Gerhard for Paul Fürsten, [1661]*

FIRST EDITION, 4to (188 x 147mm.), [8 (including additional engraved title)], 368, [16]pp., ILLUSTRATION: engraved title-page, woodcut diagrams in text, typographical ornaments, BINDING: eighteenth-century speckled calf

References: VD17 3:3026145

£1,000-1,500
€1,450-2,200

1119 Jüngken, Johann Helfrich (1648-1726). Chymia experimentalis curiosa, ex principiis mathematicis demonstrata. *Frankfurt: Johann Andreae for Hermann von Sand, 1681*

FIRST EDITION, 8vo (173 x 95mm.), [20], 898pp., title printed in red and black, text in Latin and German, ILLUSTRATION: engraved frontispiece by Johann Philip Aubry, woodcut initials, head- and tailpieces, engraved plate, BINDING: contemporary mottled calf, spine gilt in compartments, red morocco lettering-piece, *lacking additional engraved title-page, some browning or staining, frontispiece laid down, extremities rubbed*

References: Krivatsky 6300; Wellcome III, p.370; Partington II, 303; VD17 23:241505P

£200-300
€300-450

1120 Kahle, Ludwig Martin (1712-1775). Elementa logicae probabilium methodo mathematica in usum scientiarum et vitae adornata. *Halle: Officina Rengeriana, 1735*

8vo (210 x 160mm.), [10], XXII, 245, [31]pp., title-page in red and black, ILLUSTRATION: woodcut initials and headpieces, BINDING: contemporary calf, blind roll-tooled border within a double gilt fillet, spine gilt in compartments with the emblem of the dauphin, red speckled edges, *joints weak, extremities slightly rubbed, spine a little chipped at head and foot*

FIRST EDITION. Kahle became professor of philosophy at the University of Göttingen in 1737 and after further study became professor of law at the same university in 1747.

£150-200
€250-300

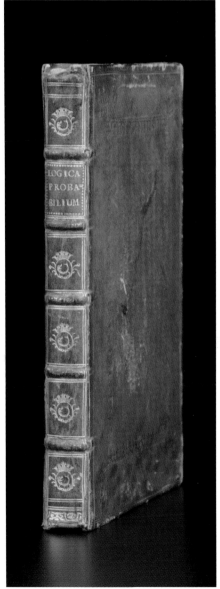

1120

1121 Keckermann, Bartholomaeus (1573-1609). Systema physicum, septem libris adornatum, et anno Christi MDCVII publice propositum in Gymnasio Dantiscano. *Hanau: Petrus Antonius, 1617*, 8vo (170 x 98mm.), [16], 854, [42]pp., ILLUSTRATION: woodcut device on title-page, engraved portrait of Keckermann on verso of title, woodcut initials, head- and tailpieces, BINDING: contemporary calf with blind-stamped centrepiece, red edges, printer's waste used as endpapers (cut away at the front), *some browning, a few wormholes (some touching text), extremities slightly rubbed*

Ibid. Systema compendiosum totius mathematices, hoc est, geometriae, opticae, astronomiae et geographiae, publicis praelectionibus, anno 1605, in celeberrimo Gymnasio Dantiscano propositum. *Hanau: P. Antonius, 1617*, 8vo (162 x 96mm.), 607, [9]pp., ILLUSTRATION: woodcut initials and headpieces, woodcut diagrams, woodcut printer's device on section titles, BINDING: contemporary calf, red edges, *some browning, woodcut on final leaf cropped, extremities slightly rubbed, upper joint splitting at head, spine chipped at foot*

Ibid. Systema physicum... Editio tertia... *Hanau: P. Antonius for Johann Stockel, 1623*, 8vo (168 x 95mm.), [16], 853, [11]pp., ILLUSTRATION: woodcut device on title-page, woodcut initials, head- and tailpieces, BINDING: contemporary calf, manuscript diagram inserted between pp.136-167, *flyleaf and title-page torn without loss of text, some staining or browning, binding rubbed, upper joint splitting*

together 3 volumes

Keckermann was professor of philosophy at the Gdansk Gymnasium from 1602 until his death in 1609. He attempted to introduce a curriculum along Ramist principles, whereby students would complete a comprehensive education after three years. His influence was considerable and his books were used all over Europe.

£500-800
€750-1,200

1122 Kegel, Johann Michael. Neu-vermehrte arithmetica vulgaris, et practica italica. *[Frankfurt]: Johann Valentin Schäller, [1696]*

12mo (159 x 88mm.), [16 (including frontispiece)], 276, [12]pp., title printed in red and black, ILLUSTRATION: engraved frontispiece, woodcut initials, head- and tailpieces, BINDING: eighteenth-century mottled calf, spine gilt in compartments, red morocco lettering-piece, red edges, *some page numerals shaved, title-page cropped at foot*

Provenance: R. Cotter, inscription on final verso dated 1712

£300-400
€450-600

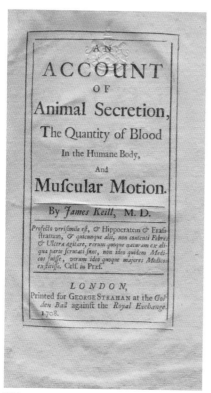

1123

1123 Keill, James (1673-1719). An account of animal secretion, the quantity of blood in the humane body, and muscular motion. *London: for George Strahan, 1708*

FIRST EDITION, 8vo (192 x 117mm.), xxviii, 187, [1]pp., ILLUSTRATION: woodcut diagrams, BINDING: contemporary panelled calf, spine gilt in compartments, red morocco lettering-piece, *upper joint weak, lower cover detached*

References: Wellcome III, p.381

£300-400
€450-600

1124 Keill, James. Essays on several parts of the animal oeconomy. The fourth edition. To which is added, A dissertation concerning the force of the heart, by James Jurin, with Dr Keill's answer, and Dr Jurin's reply. Also Medicina statica Britannica, or statical observations, made in England, by James Keill, explained and compared with the aphorisms of Sanctorius, by John Quincy. *London: for George Strahan, 1738*

8vo (197 x 120mm.), xlviii, 295, [1]pp., ILLUSTRATION: woodcut printer's device on title-page, woodcut initials, head- and tailpieces, woodcut diagrams, BINDING: contemporary speckled calf gilt, red morocco lettering-piece, *marginal tear in H2, extremities rubbed, joints cracking*

References: Wellcome III, p.381

£100-150
€150-250

1125 Keill, John (1671-1721). Introductio ad veram physicam: seu lectiones physicae habitae in schola naturalis philosophiae Academiae Oxoniensis An. Dom. 1700. Quibus accedunt Theorematum Hugenianorum de vi centrifuga & motu circulari demonstrationes. Editio quarta. *London: Henry Clements, 1719*

8vo (195 x 118mm.), [18], 274pp., ILLUSTRATION: woodcut printer's device on title-page, woodcut diagrams, BINDING: contemporary panelled calf, spine gilt in compartments, red morocco lettering-piece, *tear in preliminaries, occasional foxing, extremities rubbed*

First published in 1702. John Keill was the brother of James Keill and a pupil of David Gregory. He was a dedicated propagator of Newton's ideas, being among the first to lecture on the subject at Oxford. He was elected a fellow of the Royal Society in 1700 and was Savilian professor of astronomy from 1712 until his death.

The preliminaries seem to have been printed incorrectly; there should only be 14 pages. A3 appears twice with different text on the versos, and the first page of preface also appears twice.

References: Houzeau & Lancaster 9241; Wallis 102.3

Provenance: T. Clark, Trinity College Cambridge, inscription on flyleaf

£100-150
€150-250

1126 Keill, John. An introduction to natural philosophy: or, philosophical lectures read in the University of Oxford, Anno Dom. 1700. To which are added, the demonstrations of Monsieur Huygens's theorems, concerning the centrifugal force and circular motion. Translated from the last edition of the Latin. *London: H[enry] W[oodfall] for William and John Innys and John Osborn, 1720*

8vo (193 x 115mm.), xii, 306, [2]pp., ILLUSTRATION: woodcut initials, head- and tailpieces, woodcut diagrams, BINDING: contemporary panelled calf, spine gilt in compartments, morocco lettering-piece, eighteenth-century manuscript annotations in a neat cursive hand, interleaved with a series of loosely inserted pages of eighteenth-century manuscript notes and mathematical calculations, by way of annotation and commentary on the text in numerous pages of this book

First English edition of *Introductio ad veram physicam*.

References: Wallis 103

£200-300
€300-450

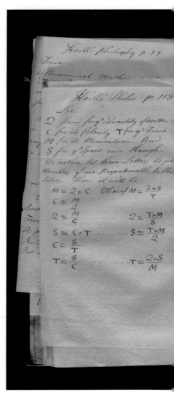

1126

1127 Keill, John. Introductio ad veram astronomiam, seu lectiones astronomicae habitae in schola astronomica Academiae Oxoniensis. Editio secunda, multo auctior & emendatior. *London: W. Strahan & W. Mears, 1721*

8vo (200 x 120mm.), [8], xvi, 316, 337-513, [1 (blank)] pp., ILLUSTRATION: woodcut printer's device on title-page, woodcut diagrams, 2 folding engraved plates, BINDING: contemporary panelled calf, spine gilt in compartments, red morocco lettering-piece, *occasional foxing, extremities rubbed, upper joint cracking at head*

Originally published in Oxford in 1718. An English edition was first published in 1721 (see following lot).

References: Houzeau & Lancaster 9244; Wallis 103.171

£200-300
€300-450

1128 Keill, John. An introduction to the true astronomy: or, astronomical lectures, read in the astronomical school of the University of Oxford. *London: for Bernard Lintot, 1721*

8vo (199 x 115mm.), [8], xv, [1], 396, [12]pp., ILLUSTRATION: woodcut device on title-page, woodcut initials, head- and tailpieces, 28 folding engraved plates, BINDING: contemporary mottled calf gilt, spine gilt in compartments, red morocco lettering-piece, *a few plates shaved, extremities slightly rubbed*

References: Wallis 103.172

£300-400
€450-600

1129 Keill, John. An introduction to the true astronomy: or, astronomical lectures, read in the astronomical school of the University of Oxford. The second edition. *London: for Bernard Lintot, 1730*

8vo (199 x 118mm.), [6], xiv ,[4], 396, [12]pp., ILLUSTRATION: woodcut device on title-page, woodcut initials, head- and tailpieces, 28 folding engraved plates, BINDING: contemporary speckled calf, spine gilt in compartments, morocco lettering-piece, *a few plates shaved, extremities slightly rubbed*

References: Wallis 103.173

£120-150
€200-250

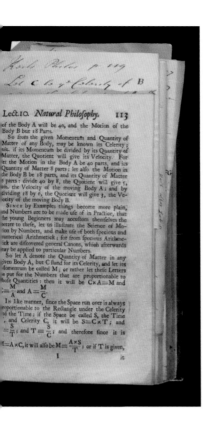

1130 Keill, John. An introduction to the true astronomy: or, astronomical lectures, read in the astronomical school of the University of Oxford. The third edition, corrected. *London: for Henry Lintot, 1739*

8vo (194 x 118mm.), [6], xiv, [4], 396, [12]pp., ILLUSTRATION: woodcut device on title-page, woodcut initials, head- and tailpieces, 28 folding engraved plates, BINDING: contemporary morocco-backed boards, *one plate loose, some plates creased at fore-edge, extremities rubbed*

References: Wallis 103.174

£100-150
€150-250

1131 [Keill, John] Institutions astronomiques, ou leçons élémentaires d'astronomie, pour servir d'introduction à la physique céleste, & à la science des longitudes... [translated by Pierre Charles le Monnier]. *Paris: Hippolyte-Louis Guerin & Jacques Guerin, 1746*

4to (255 x 193mm.), [8], lxiv, 660pp., ILLUSTRATION: woodcut initials, head- and tailpieces, woodcut diagrams, 15 folding engraved plates, BINDING: contemporary smooth calf gilt, spine gilt in compartments, morocco lettering-piece, red speckled edges, *small hole in Eee2 with loss of 2 letters, spine a little frayed at foot*

References: Wallis 103.185

£1,000-1,500
€1,450-2,200

1132 Keill, John. An examination of Dr Burnet's Theory of the Earth: with some remarks on Mr Whiston's New Theory of the Earth. Also an examination of the reflections on the Theory of the Earth; and a defence of the remarks on Mr Whiston's New Theory. The second edition corrected, and all the figures (25 in number) engraved on copper plates. To the whole is annexed a dissertation on the different figures of the coelestial bodies, &c... by Mons. de Maupertuis. *Oxford and London: H. Clements and S. Harding, 1734*

8vo (209 x 125mm.), [8], 347, [1 (blank)], 67, [1]pp., ILLUSTRATION: woodcut initial, head- and tailpieces, woodcut diagram, 13 engraved plates, BINDING: contemporary mottled calf gilt, spine gilt in compartments, morocco lettering-piece, red edges, *Y8 loose, extremities slightly rubbed*

Originally published in 1698, this was Keill's first work. It is "an attack on the cosmogonical treatises then being widely debated by many members of the Royal Society... Besides those of Burnet and Whiston, Keill attacked the ideas of Richard Bentley, who had tried to use Newtonian principles as the foundation for his physicotheology in his famous Boyle lectures in 1692" (*DSB* VII, p.275).

References: Wellcome III, p.381

£100-150
€150-250

JOHANN KEPLER

O curas hominum, o quantum est in rebus inane (Persius *Satires* 1.1)

Johann Kepler, who used this sentence as a motto, is a fascinating mixture of an empirical scientist who saw into the heavens "mentis oculo". A devout Protestant, like Novalis (who greatly admired him), a "Gott-trunckener Mensch" with strongly Neoplatonist leanings, a follower of Tycho Brahe, and a humanistic scholar with a deeply bookish knowledge, he was faced by confessional and personal problems. Unlike Newton, who went nowhere other than Lincolnshire, Cambridge and London, Kepler typified the itinerant savant dependent on the patronage of others. He travelled widely across Europe: from Weil der Stadt, where he was born, to Tübingen; from Graz to Prague, where in 1600 he succeeded Tycho as Imperial Astronomer, and where he spent twelve productive years; then to Linz; and finally to Regensburg. Not for him a comfortable birth at Rome in the bosom of an international order, a Torún canonry, a private island, or a Cambridge fellowship followed by a well-paid government position. It was, as Caspar puts it in the opening sentence of his biography, "in a spiritually and politically rent and divided period of German history that Johannes Kepler carried out his lifework".

Kepler was enormously productive: his own autograph list of his works up to 1622 (the so-called Graz Catalogue) is long, and the bibliography of works up to 1634 (including the posthumously published *Somnium*) lists eighty-six items (some long, some short), printed at Tübingen, Heidelberg, Leipzig, Frankfurt, Augsburg, Prague, Linz, and Sagan. Equally, Kepler's own involvement in the actual production of his books was very considerable, in the provision of type, of paper and of much else.

Kepler's works circulated widely, and not just amongst mathematicians and astronomers: John Donne in *Ignatius his conclave* (first published in 1611) refers to his *De stella in cygno* (1606) saying that Kepler "ever since Tycho Brahe's death, hath received it into his care, that no new thing should be done in heaven without his knowledge" ("Tychone iam mortuo, equidem haec me cura incessit, ne quid fortasse novi existeret in coelo, me inscio"; *Ignatius his conclave*, ed. T. S. Healy, Oxford, 1969, pp.6-7). Again in England, Robert Burton, author of *The Anatomy of Melancholy*, owned a copy of the posthumous *Somnium*. Andrew Fletcher of Saltoun (1653-1716) owned thirteen works.

The present sale contains thirteen titles by Kepler, all under his name, except for one at lot 1405. Five further titles were in Macclesfield Science A-C (lots 199, 232, 249, 263 and 264). There is, revealingly, one major work lacking, the great *Astronomia nova* (1609), a book, one must assume, difficult to find even three hundred or more years ago; its absence from this library cannot really be explained otherwise. Caspar says that few copies were printed. In the mid-seventeenth century Constantijn Huygens (1628-1697), the brother of Christiaan, owned a number of works by Kepler, including the *Astronomia nova*, bought by him in 1655 (sold in September 1701 by Vander Aa in The Hague; see Huygens, *Oeuvres* 22, pp.454-455). The mathematician Franz von Schooten found it for him, "having searched nearly all the booksellers", finally purchasing it from Cornelis Hack for three florins.

Newton knew of Kepler's work and Kepler's laws, and his Rudolphine Tables were part of Newton's intellectual make-up; as Caspar puts it (p.138), "Kepler did not reach the high goal of celestial mechanics which he was the first to set up and perceive. It was reserved for Newton's genius, by stating the law of gravity, to crown the structure which Kepler had begun…".

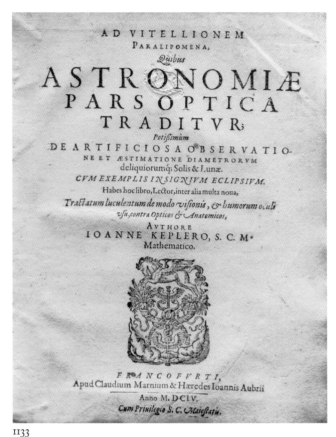

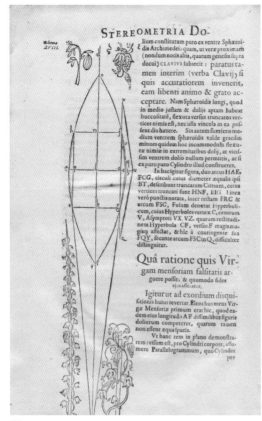

1133   1134

1133 Kepler, Johann (1571-1630). Ad Vitellionem paralipomena, quibus astronomiae pars optica traditur. *Frankfurt: Claude Marne and the heirs of Jean Aubry, 1604*

4to (207 x 163mm.), [16], 176, [2], 177-449, [19]pp., ILLUSTRATION: woodcut printer's device on title-page, woodcut initials and headpieces, woodcut diagrams, engraved plate, 2 folding tables, BINDING: contemporary vellum, *some browning, vellum warped at edges*

FIRST EDITION, dedicated to Rudolph II. "The six astronomical chapters include not only a discussion of parallax, astronomical refraction, and his eclipse instruments but also the annual variation in the apparent size of the sun" (*DSB* VII, p.298). Kepler continued his study of optics with the publication of *Dioptrice* in 1611.

References: Caspar 18

£1,500-2,000
€2,200-2,900

1134 Kepler, Johann. Nova stereometria doliorum vinariorum... et usus in eo virgae cubicae... Accessit stereometriae archimedeae supplementum. *Linz: J. Planck, for the author, 1615*

folio (295 x 190mm.), ff. [57], the last leaf being the rare list of errata (printed on recto only of a leaf measuring 205 x 150mm.), ILLUSTRATION: woodcut figures and diagrams, BINDING: eighteenth-century vellum-backed boards

FIRST EDITION. This copy has the rare list of errata.

References: Caspar 48

£6,000-8,000
€8,700-11,600

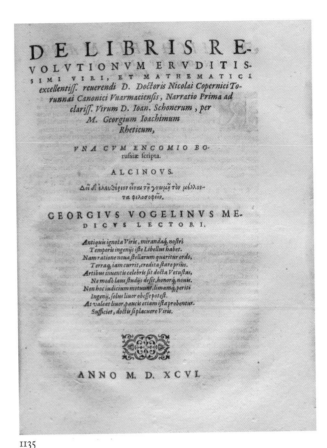

DE LIBRIS RE-
VOLVTIONVM ERVDITIS-
SIMI VIRI, ET MATHEMATICI
excellentiss. reuerendi D. Doctoris Nicolai Copernici To-
runnai Canonici Vuarmaciensis, Narratio Prima ad
clariss. Virum D. Ioan. Schonerum, per
M. Georgium Ioachimum
Rheticum.

VNA CVM ENCOMIO BO-
russiæ scripta.

ALCINOVS.

Δεῖ δὲ ἐλευθέριον εἶναι τῇ γνωμῇ τὸν μέλλον-
τα φιλοσοφεῖν.

GEORGIVS VOGELINVS ME-
DICVS LECTORI.

Antiquis ignota Viris, mirandáq́ nostri
Temporis ingenijs iste Libellus habet.
Nam ratione noua stellarum quæritur ordo,
Terráq, iam currit, credita stare prius.
Artibus inuentis celebris sit docta Vetustas,
Ne modò laus studijs desit, honoŕq, nouis.
Non hoc iudicium metuunt, limamq, periti
Ingenij, solus liuor obesse potest.
At valeat liuor, pauci etiam ista probentur.
Sufficiet, doctis si placuere Viris.

ANNO M. D. XCVI.

1135

Prodromus
DISSERTATIONVM COSMOGRA-
PHICARVM, CONTINENS MYSTE-
RIVM COSMOGRAPHI-
CVM,
DE ADMIRABILI
PROPORTIONE ORBIVM
COELESTIVM, DEQVE CAVSIS
cœlorum numeri, magnitudinis, motuúmque pe-
riodicorum genuinis & pro-
prijs,
DEMONSTRATVM, PER QVINQVE
regularia corpora Geometrica,
A
M. IOANNE KEPLERO, VVIRTEM-
bergico, Illustrium Styriæ prouincia-
lium Mathematico.

Quotidiè morior, fateórque: sed inter Olympi
Dum tenet assiduas me mea cura vias:
Non pedibus terram contingo: sed ante Tonantem
Nectare, diuina pascor & ambrosiâ.

Addita est erudita NARRATIO M. GEORGII IOACHIMI
RHETICI, de Libris Reuolutionum, atq; admirandis de numero, ordine, & distantijs Sphærarum Mundi hypothesibus, excellentissimi Mathematici, totiúsq, Astronomiæ Restauratoris D. NICOLAI
COPERNICI.

TVBINGÆ
Excudebat Georgius Gruppenbachius,
ANNO M. D. XCVI.

1135

1135

1135

1135 Kepler, Johann. Prodromus dissertationum cosmographicarum, continens mysterium cosmographicum, de admirabili proportione orbium coelestium, deque causis coelorum numeri, magnitudinis, motuumque periodicorum genuinis & proprijs... Addita est narratio M. Georgii Ioachimi Rhetici, de libris revolutionum [etc.]. *Tübingen: G. Gruppenbach, 1596,* [2], 181pp., ILLUSTRATION: folding woodcut diagrams numbered II (p.18), IV (p.48) and V (p.51), large woodcut schema on p.9, woodcut diagrams in text, *without engraved diagram III at p.24*

Ibid. De stella nova in pede serpentarii, et qui sub ejus exortum de novo iniit, trigono igneo... Accesserunt I. De stella incognita cygni: narratio astronomica. II. De Jesu Christi servatoris vero anno natalitio [etc.]. *Prague: Paul Sessius, 1606* (part 2 *Frankfurt: Wolfgang Richter, 1606*), [10], 212; 35, [5 (last leaf blank)], ILLUSTRATION: folding engraved stellar plate at p.76 of part 1

Ibid. Phaenomenon singulare seu Mercurius in Sole, [etc.]. *Leipzig: (typis T. Beyeri, Valentin am Ende excudebat for) T. Schurer, 1609,* ff. [20], last leaf a blank, ILLUSTRATION: small woodcut diagram with letterpress pasted to C4verso

Ibid. Dissertatio cum nuncio sidereo nuper ad mortales misso a Galilaeo Galilaeo mathematico patavino. *Prague: Daniel Sedesanus, 1610,* [6], 34, [2]pp., *corner of title-page torn away with loss of a couple of letters*

Ibid. Dioptrice... Praemissa epistola Galilaei de ijs, quae... nova & admiranda in coelo deprehensa sunt, [etc.]. *Augsburg: D. Franck, 1611,* [8], 28; 80pp., ILLUSTRATION: woodcut diagrams

5 works in one volume, 4to (187 x 148mm.), BINDING: English panelled calf *c.* 1700, gilt ornaments on spine, lettering piece, edges coloured

A very interesting *Sammelband* of some of Kepler's works, clearly all in England from an early date.

References: Caspar 6, 27, 30, 34, 40

Provenance: There are various strands of English annotation in the volume, some of it attributable to John Collins, and some to Jones, most of it contemporary and therefore predating these. The second tract (which has an inscription on the title, which seems to suggest that it was a gift, although the price of 3s.6d. is also written there) and the last in particular are heavily annotated in both ink and pencil (both are also used elsewhere) and clearly by the same person. On the final blank of the tract on the true year of the birth of Christ is a whole series of short notes. The *Dissertatio cum nuncio sidereo* is heavily marked in pencil and some notes in ink are written over these marks. Here and elsewhere the expression 'my Astraea' is used.

£60,000-80,000
€87,000-116,000

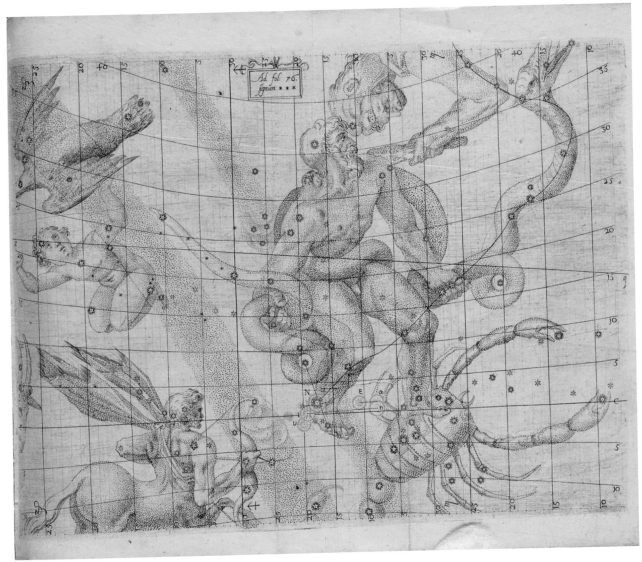

1136

1136 Kepler, Johann. De stella nova in pede serpentarii, et qui sub eo exortum de novo iniit, trigono igneo…. Accesserunt I. De stella incognita cygni: narratio astronomica. II. De Jesu Christi servatoris vero anno natalitio, [etc.]. *Prague: P. Sessius (Frankfurt: W. Richter), 1606*

4to (200 x 153mm.), [12], 212; 35, [3]pp., ILLUSTRATION: folding engraved plate at p. 76, woodcut figures in text, BINDING: contemporary vellum over pasteboard, spine lettered

FIRST EDITION. Kepler announced in this work a new star (Kepler's *nova*) seen in October 1604 in the constellation Serpentarius, which he showed had to be located in the unchangeable region of the "fixed stars".

Who vagrant transitory Comets sees,
Wonders, because they are rare: but a new starre
Whose motion with the firmament agrees,
Is miracle, for there no new things are.

(John Donne, 'To the Countesse of Huntingdon', vv. 5-8)

References: Caspar 27; Zinner 4097

£25,000-35,000
€36,200-51,000

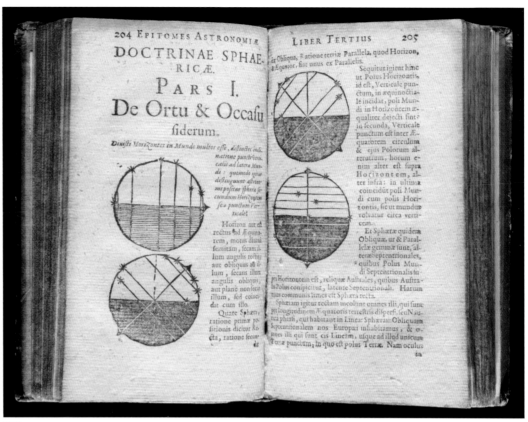

1137

1137 Kepler, Johann. Epitome astronomiae Copernicanae usitata forma quaestionum & responsionum conscripta, inque VII libros digesta, quorum tres hi priores sunt de doctrina sphaerica (...Liber quartus, doctrinae theoricae primus, quo physica coelestis, hoc est, omnium in coelo magnitudinum, motuum, proportionumque, causae vel naturales vel archetypicae explicantur...; Libri V. VI. VII. quibus proprie doctrina theorica... comprehenditur). *Linz: Johannes Plancus, 1618 (Frankfurt: Johann-Friedrich Weiss for Godefrid Schönwetter, 1621-1635)*

3 parts in 2 volumes, 8vo (157 x 90mm.), [12], 400, 409-417, [17]; [2], 419-622, [2]; [12], 641-932, [14]pp., ILLUSTRATION: woodcut diagrams, typographical and woodcut initials, head- and tailpieces, folding letterpress table, BINDING: non-uniform contemporary calf, spines gilt in compartments, red morocco lettering-pieces, *lacking errata leaf in final part, paper flaw in V1 with loss of a few letters, a few headlines shaved, bindings rubbed, spines chipped, joints of vol.1 weak*

FIRST EDITION of books I-III and V-VIII, with the second edition of book IV.

"Despite its title, Kepler's *Epitome astronomiae Copernicanae* was more an introduction to Keplerian than to Copernican astronomy. Cast in a catechetical form of questions and answers typical of sixteenth-century astronomy textbooks, it treated all of heliocentric astronomy in a systematic way, including the three relations now called Kepler's laws. Its seven books were issued in three installments. Taken together, they constitute a squat, unprepossessing octavo volume whose physical appearance scarcely marks it as Kepler's longest and most influential work. J.L. Russell has maintained that from 1630 to 1650 the *Epitome* was the most widely read treatise on theoretical astronomy in Europe" (*DSB* VII, p.302).

References: Caspar 55, 66 & 87; Houzeau & Lancaster 11831

£5,000-7,000
€7,300-10,200

1138 Kepler, Johann. Harmonices mundi libri V quorum primus geometricus... Secundus architectonicus... tertius proprie harmonicus... Quartus metaphysicus, psychologicus & astrologicus... Quintus astronomicus & metaphysicus... Appendix habet comparationem huius operis cum Harmonices Cl. Ptolemaei libro III. cumque Roberti de Fluctibus, dicti Flud medici oxoniensis speculationibus harmonicis, operi de macrocosmo & microcosmo insertis. *Linz: J. Plannk for G. Tampach, 1619*

folio (300 x 195mm.), [8], 66, 255pp., first state of title-page with woodcut device, and without text beginning 'Accessit nunc...', ILLUSTRATION: 5 engraved plates on 4 leaves at p. 52, woodcut illustrations and diagrams, printed music, BINDING: contemporary vellum, *title and first few leaves slightly foxed*

FIRST EDITION, with the dedication to James I of England which was later suppressed.

This work is a cosmological treatise, encompassing Kepler's view of the world, and contains Kepler's third law of planetary motion (the square of a planet's periodic time is proportional to the cube of its mean distance from the sun). Dating from the late sixteenth century in its origins, for a variety of domestic and other reasons Kepler did not complete the work until 1618, three months after the death of his daughter Katherine and a few days after the Defenestration of Prague. It is his hymn to the universe. As Koestler says, "the *Harmony of the world* is a mathematician's Song of Songs 'to the chief harmonist of creation'; it is Job's daydream of a perfect universe... [it is]... the climax of his lifelong obsession. What Kepler attempted here is, simply, to bare the ultimate secret of the universe in an all-embracing synthesis... It was the first attempt of this kind since Plato, and it is the last to our day..." (*The Sleepwalkers*, Penguin: Arkana, 1989, p. 394).

References: Caspar 58; Zinner 4737; Dibner 6; Horblit 58; Norman 1207

£70,000-100,000
€102,000-145,000

Ioannis Keppleri
HARMONICES
MVNDI
LIBRI V. QVORVM

Primus GEOMETRICVS, De Figurarum Regularium, quæ Proportiones Harmonicas constituunt, ortu & demonstrationibus.
Secundus ARCHITECTONICVS, seu ex GEOMETRIA FIGVRATA, De Figurarum Regularium Congruentia in plano vel solido:
Tertius propriè HARMONICVS, De Proportionum Harmonicarum ortu ex Figuris: deque Natura & Differentiis rerum ad cantum pertinentium, contra Veteres:
Quartus METAPHYSICVS, PSYCHOLOGICVS & ASTROLOGICVS, De Harmoniarum mentali Essentia earumque generibus in Mundo; præsertim de Harmonia radiorum, ex corporibus cœlestibus in Terram descendentibus, eiusque effectu in Natura seu Anima sublunari & Humana:
Quintus ASTRONOMICVS & METAPHYSICVS, De Harmoniis absolutissimis motuum cœlestium, ortuque Eccentricitatum ex proportionibus Harmonicis.
Appendix habet comparationem huius Operis cum Harmonices Cl. Ptolemæi libro III. cumque Roberti de Fluctibus, dicti Flud. Medici Oxoniensis speculationibus Harmonicis, operi de Macrocosmo & Microcosmo insertis.

Cum S. C. Mtis. Priuilegio ad annos XV.

Lincii Austriæ,
Sumptibus GODOFREDI TAMPACHII Bibl. Francof.
Excudebat IOANNES PLANCVS.
ANNO M. DC. XIX.

1138

CAPVT XIII.
Quid sit Cantus naturaliter Concinnus & aptus.

Nihil dicemus de stridulo illo more canendi, quo solent uti Turcæ & Vngari pro classico suo: brutorum potius animarum voces incondiras, quàm humanam Naturam imitati.

Videtur omninò primus author hausisse melodiam huiusmodi incondicam ab instrumento min apte conformato, eamq; consuetudine diuturnâ, cum ipsi instrumenti facturâ, transmisisse ad posteros, totiq; gentem. Interfui Pragæ precib, quas Legati Turcici sacerdos horis statis ingeniculatus, terramq; fronte crebro feriens, decantare solebat: apparuit facile, ipsum ex disciplina canere, exercitationemq; & promptitudinem labore comparasse, nihil enim hæsitavit: at intervallis usus est miris, insolitis, concisis, abhorrentibus, ut nemo proprio naturæ ductu & ex seipso ultrò simile quid constanter unquam meditari posse videatur. Conabor aliqd proximù illi per nostras notas Musicas exprimere.

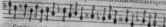

Concinus igitur & humanarum aurium iudicio aptus cantus est, qui exorsus à certo quodam sono; ab eo per intervalla concinna tendit ad sonos consonos & primo illi, & plerumq; etiam inter se mutuò; dissona cursim pervolitans intervalla, in consonis verò immorans, seu mensurâ temporis, Syllabarumq; longitudine, seu crebro ad illos reditu, veluti duarum vocum inter se consonantiam affectans, unica vocis traductione à loco uno Systematis ad alium. Exemplum.

Hic sonus initialis est in clavi G, cum quâ in cantu molli concordant h, e, d, g. Excurrit igitur Cantus (primùm flexu deorsùm facto) ad clavem e, consonam, & transilit plane dissonum locum A; fuisset autem idem, si attigisset ipsum sed brevi mora: tota verò series reliqua potissimùm in locis h, d, g, intonat, sed eò octavæ tale exprimens, in d, creberrimè rediens, post in h, in superius verog, se interdum efferens, in hæc omnia loca signanter: non sic in e, vel in f, loca primo dissona: tandemq; redit ad G, ibiq; finit.

Circa traditam cantus definitionem multa veniunt nobis annotanda.

I. Partes Cantus, ex quibus vel omnibus vel aliquibus constat omnis Cantus, Euclides nominat has quatuor, Ἀγωγὴν, Τονὴν, Πετϊείαν,

H 3   Πλο-

1138

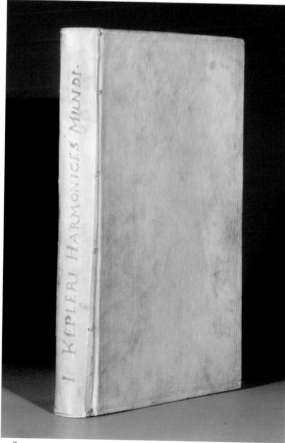

1138

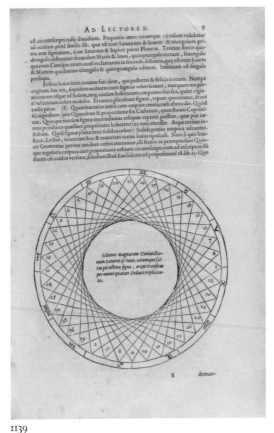

1139 Kepler, Johann. Prodromus dissertationum cosmographicarum, continens mysterium cosmographicum de admirabili proportione orbium coelestium... demonstratum per quinque regularia corpora geometrica... Addita est erudita narratio M. Georgii Ioachimi Rhetici, de libris revolutionum... Item, eiusdem Ioannis Kepleri pro suo opere harmonices mundi apologia adversus demonstrationem analyticam... Roberti de Fluctibus. *Frankfurt: Erasmus Kempfer for Godefrid Tampach, 1621 (-1622)*

folio (290 x 186mm.), [8], 114, 119-163, [1 (blank)]; [50]pp., ILLUSTRATION: woodcut initials and headpieces, woodcut diagrams, 3 folding woodcut plates, woodcut device on second title-page, BINDING: contemporary speckled calf, spine gilt in compartments, *some browning, extremities and joints rubbed*

Kepler's *Mysterium cosmographicum* was originally published in 1596, and "was essentially the first unabashedly Copernican treatise since *De Revolutionibus* itself... notwithstanding its faults, [it] had thrust him into the front rank of astronomers". Robert Fludd and Kepler were on opposite sides in the debate between "the new, quantitative mathematical approach to nature" and "the qualitative, symbolical, alchemical tradition" (*DSB* VII, pp.291-293). The appendix to this second edition of the *Mysterium cosmographicum* contains Kepler's defence against Fludd.

References: Caspar 67 & 68; Houzeau & Lancaster 2841

£25,000-30,000
€36,200-43,500

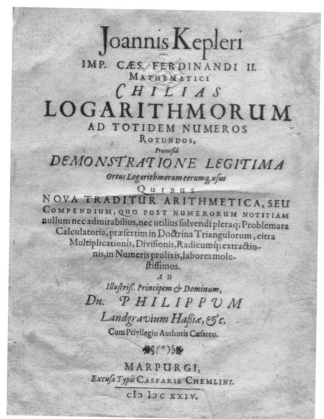

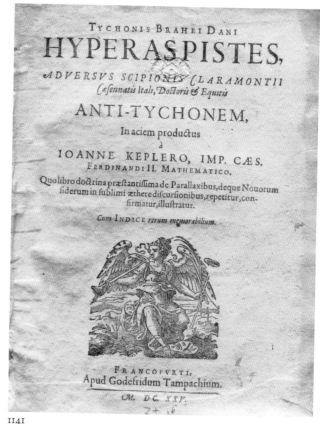

1140   1141

1140 Kepler, Johann. Chilias logarithmorum ad totidem numeros rotundos, praemissa demonstratione legitima ortus logarithmorum eorumque usus... *Marburg: Caspar Chemlin, 1624*, 55, [53]pp., ILLUSTRATION: woodcut initials, head- and tailpieces, 1 folding table, woodcut diagrams, *some browning*

Ibid. Supplementum chiliadis logarithmorum, continens praecepta de eorum usu. *Marburg: Caspar Chemlin, 1625*, [2], 113-216pp., ILLUSTRATION: woodcut initials, head- and tailpieces, *browned*

FIRST EDITIONS, 2 works in one volume, 4to (191 x 145mm.), BINDING: seventeenth-century speckled calf with blind fillets, flat spine blind-tooled then gilt in the eighteenth century, morocco lettering-piece, *extremities rubbed (particularly spine), upper hinge broken, joints weak*

"Kepler had seen John Napier's *Mirifici logarithmorum canonis descriptio* (1614) as early as 1617; but he did not study the new procedure carefully until by chance, the following year, he saw Napier's tables reproduced in a small book by Benjamin Ursinus. Kepler then grasped the potentialities offered by the logarithms; but lacking any description of their own construction, he re-created his own tables by a new geometrical procedure" (*DSB* VII, p.304).

References: Caspar 74 & 75

£5,000-6,000
€7,300-8,700

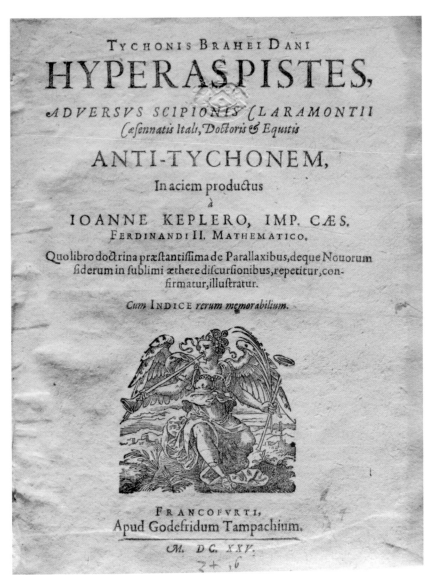

TYCHONIS BRAHEI DANI
HYPERASPISTES,
ADVERSVS SCIPIONIS CLARAMONTII
(æsennatis Itali, Doctoris & Equitis

ANTI-TYCHONEM,
In aciem productus
à
IOANNE KEPLERO, IMP. CÆS.
FERDINANDI II. MATHEMATICO,

Quo libro doctrina præstantissima de Parallaxibus, deque Nouorum
siderum in sublimi æthere discursionibus, repetitur, con-
firmatur, illustratur.

Cum INDICE *rerum memorabilium.*

FRANCOFVRTI,
Apud Godefridum Tampachium.
M. D C. XXV.

1141

1141 Kepler, Johann. Tychonis Brahei Dani Hyperaspistes adversus Scipionis
Claramontii… Anti-Tychonem, in aciem productus a Ioanne Keplero, [etc.].
Frankfurt: G. Tampach, 1625

4to (203 x 155mm.), [8], 202, [12]pp., ILLUSTRATION: woodcut diagrams,
BINDING: contemporary vellum, *somewhat browned in parts*

This work was answered by Chiaramonti in 1626 (*Apologia pro Antitychone suo*
etc.).

References: Caspar 76; Zinner 5008; Kepler, *Gesammelte Werke* 8, pp. 470-477, gives
an excellent *Entstehungsgeschichte* of the controversy

£15,000-20,000
€21,800-29,000
See also illustration on previous page

1142

1142 Kepler, Johann. Tabulae Rudolphinae, quibus astronomicae scientiae, temporum longinquitate collapse restauratio continentur. *Ulm: Jonas Saur, 1627*

2 parts in one volume, folio (338 x 228mm.), [16], 125, [3]; 119pp. (p.118 misnumbered 115), 3rd issue of first 2 quires, ILLUSTRATION: engraved frontispiece by Georg Celer, woodcut diagrams in text, BINDING: modern half calf

FIRST EDITION. In 1601, shortly before his death, Tycho Brahe asked Kepler to complete his *Rudolphine tables* of planetary motion. Kepler's completed work, based both on his discovery of the laws of planetary motion and on his introduction to logarithms, produced far more accurate positions than those in previous tables.

Caspar identifies three issues of the first two quires of this first edition. The present copy contains the third issue of each quire. Some copies of this edition contain an engraved world map of 1630.

References: Caspar 79; Houzeau & Lancaster 12754; Norman 1208; Zinner 5063

£15,000-20,000
€21,800-29,000

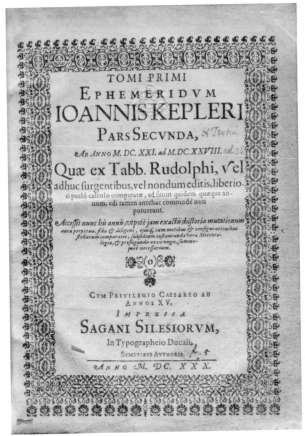

1143   1144

1143 Kepler, Johann. Tabulae Rudolphinae, or the Rudolphine Tables, supputated to the meridian of Uraniburge, first, by John Kepler, from the observations of the tres noble Ticho Brahe, afterwards digested into a most accurate, and easie compendium, by the famous Johannes Baptista Morinus. *London, 1675,* [2], 103, [1 (blank)] pp.

Coley, Henry (1633-1704). [Clavis astrologiae eliminata... second edition. *London: Benj. Tooke and Tho. Sawbridge, 1676*], 357-478, 609-696pp. only, replacement printed text pasted over p.609, ILLUSTRATION: woodcut illustrations, *incomplete*

2 works in one volume, 8vo (180 x 117mm.), BINDING: contemporary calf, spine gilt in compartments, astrological chart of Henry Coley and an engraved portrait pasted to inside front cover, *occasional slight browning, joints cracking at head, extremities rubbed*

FIRST ENGLISH EDITION, published as part of Coley's *Clavis astrologiae eliminata,* with a separate title-page and separate pagination.

The *Tabulae Rudophinae,* a continuation of Tycho's planetary observations, were originally published in 1627, although Kepler had been working on them since 1601. The book "did not contain sequential positions of planets for specific days; rather, it provided perpetual tables for calculating such positions for any date in the past or future" (*DSB* VII, p.304).

Jean-Baptiste Morin (1583-1656) was professor of mathematics at the Collège de France, and an opponent of Gassendi (see lot 1449).

References: Wing K332 & C5099; Caspar 97; Houzeau & Lancaster 12754

£800-1,000
€1,200-1,450

1144 Kepler, Johann. Tomi primi ephemeridum… pars secunda, ab anno 1621 ad 1628 (pars tertia, complexa annos a 1629 in 1636… opera… Iacobi Bartschii). *Sagan: in typographeio ducali, for the author, 1630*, 4to (225 x 170mm.), ILLUSTRATION: woodcut diagrams etc., BINDING: mid-seventeenth-century English calf, *text browned, joints worn*

Ibid. Ad epistolam… Jacobi Bartschii… praefixam Ephemeridi in annum 1629, responsio: de computatione et editione ephemeridum. *[Sagan]: typis Sanagensibus, 1629*, 4to (188 x 142mm.), 11pp., loose inside the previous volume

References: Caspar 84 & 80

£2,000-3,000
€2,900-4,350

1145 Kersey, John (1616-1677). The elements of that mathematical art commonly called algebra, expounded in four books (The third and fourth books of the elements of algebra). *London: William Godbid for Thomas Passinger and Benjamin Hurlock, 1673 (-1674)*

2 volumes in one, folio (317 x 197mm.), [10], 323, [1 (blank)]; [4], 416pp., title-pages in red and black, ILLUSTRATION: woodcut initials and headpieces, woodcut diagrams, BINDING: contemporary panelled calf with blind-stamped corner fleurons, spine gilt in compartments, morocco lettering-piece, red edges, manuscript leaf inserted entitled "Errata… corrected in the late edition by W.J." [i.e. William Jones], *lacking engraved frontispiece portrait, margin of D1 torn without loss, binding rubbed, joints weak*

FIRST EDITION. Kersey was a teacher of mathematics in London, and a friend of Edmund Wingate. This work was reissued in 1717 together with lectures on geometry by Halley.

References: Wing K352 & K353

£300-400
€450-600

1146 Kinckhuysen, Gerard (*fl.* 1645-1663). Algebra ofte Stel-Konst, beschreven tot dienst van de Leerlinghen. *Haarlem: (Isaac van Wesbusch for) Passchier van Wesbusch, 1661*

4to (197 x 140mm.), 110, [2]pp., last leaf with errata on recto and imprint on verso, ILLUSTRATION: engraving on title-page, woodcut initials, head- and tailpieces, BINDING: contemporary vellum over pasteboard

FIRST EDITION AND A FINE COPY. Collins, who had a higher regard for the work than it deserves, sent Newton a copy of what must have been a Latin translation of this book (see Newton, *Correspondence* I, 23 n. 14), and Newton intended to produce a revision to be published in Cambridge. In the event this was declined in 1676. Newton abandoned the project but because he had intended to prefix to it his *Methodus fluxionum et serierum infinitarum*, 'the results of this lost opportunity were deplorable in no common degree'. There is a copy of the Latin version (1663) by Mercator amongst the Macclesfield papers now in Cambridge. Newton's own material was published in volume II of the *Mathematical Papers.*

£1,000-1,500
€1,450-2,200

1147 Kinckhuysen, Gerard. Geometria ofte meet-konst, beschreven tot dienst der ghene die haer in dese konst zijn oeffenende. *Haarlem: Passchier van Wesbusch, 1663,* 165, [1]pp., ILLUSTRATION: engraved diagram on title-page, woodcut initials, head- and tailpieces, woodcut diagrams

Ibid. De grondt der meet-konst, ofte een korte verklaringe der keegel-sneeden, met een by-voeghsel. *Haarlem: Passchier van Wesbusch, 1660,* [4], 91, [1]pp., ILLUSTRATION: engraved diagram on title-page, woodcut initials, head- and tailpieces, engraved diagrams

Ibid. Algebra ofte stel-konst, beschreven tot dienst van de Leeringhen. *Haarlem: Passchier van Wesbusch, 1661,* 110, [2]pp., engraved diagram on title-page, woodcut initials, head- and tailpieces, engraved diagram

[Ibid.] Hey ghebruyck des quadrants, zijnde seer nut voor veel persoonen, ende vermakelijck voor alle lief hebbers. *Haarlem: Passchier van Wesbusch, 1643,* ff. 10, ILLUSTRATION: engraved diagram on title-page, woodcut initial and tailpiece, engraved plate, *plate loose*

Ibid. Verklaringe end ghebruyck van den altijdt-duerenden maen-wyser. *1645,* 59, [1 (blank)] pp., ILLUSTRATION: engraved diagram on title-page, woodcut initials and tailpieces, engraved and woodcut diagrams

5 works in one volume, 4to (198 x 148mm.), BINDING: contemporary mottled calf gilt, large gilt centrepiece, roll-tooled gilt border with internal corner-pieces, spine gilt in compartments, gilt edges, *extremities rubbed*

References: 5th work: Houzeau & Lancaster 10373

£800-1,000
€1,200-1,450

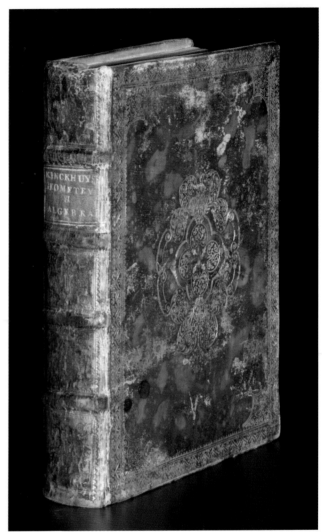

1147

1148 Kirch, Gottfried (1639-1710). Annus I (-X) ephemeridum motuum coelestium ad annum aerae christianae 1681 (-1690) cum ortu & occasu diurno planetarum... ex tabulis rudolphinis, ad meridianum Uranoburgicum, in freto cimbrico supputatus. Cui accessit catalogus novus stellarum australium clariss. Edmundi Halleii... *Leipzig: heirs of Lanckisius and the widow of Johann Bauer for the author, [1681-1690]*

10 parts in one volume, 4to (214 x 161mm.), [52]; [48]; [48]; [48]; [48]; [48]; [48]; [48]; [48]; [48]pp., ILLUSTRATION: woodcut initials and headpieces, woodcut diagrams, 9 engraved plates (3 folding, 3 cut out and pasted to margin), BINDING: contemporary vellum, *some browning*

Kirch's tables were responsible for introducing Halley's *Catalogus stellarum australium* of 1679 to Germany. Kirch was appointed the first royal astronomer in Berlin in 1700, although the observatory there was not completed until 1711.

References: Houzeau & Lancaster 15342

£400-600
€600-900

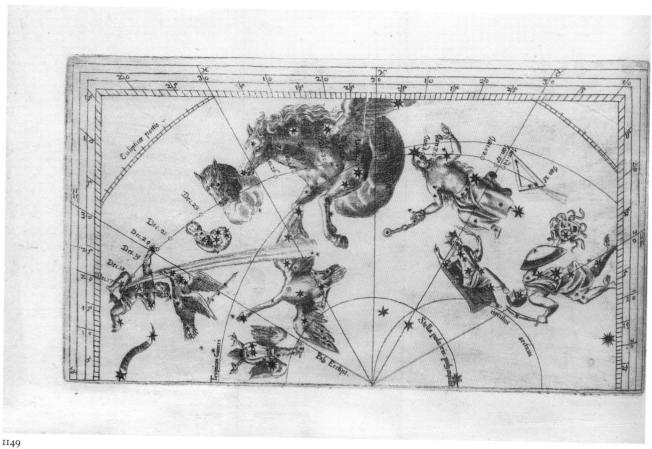

1149

1149 Kirch, Gottfried. Neue Himmels-Zeitung darinnen sonderlich und ausführlich von den zweyen neuen grossen im 1680 Jahr erschienenen cometen... *Nuremberg: Wolfgang Moritz Endter and Johann Andreas Endter, 1681*, [8], 84, 81-144pp., ILLUSTRATION: woodcut initials and tailpieces, 6 engraved plates (4 folding), *one plate detached, L3 torn without loss*

Zimmermann, Johann Jakob (1644-1693). Cometo-scopia oder Himmel-gemäser Bericht mit müglichstem Fleiss darstellende beedes die nach der Trigonometria Spharica, astronomische Calculation, als auch Astro-Theologische Aussdeutung dess mittem im Novembri 1680.sten Jahrs entstandenen und biss in den Anfang Februarii 1681. erschienenen grossen Wunder-Sterns und Cometens... (Cometo-scopiae pars altera...). *Stuttgart: Johann Gottfridt Zubrodt, 1681*, [18], 20, [2]; 105, [13]pp., ILLUSTRATION: woodcut device on first title-page, 4 folding engraved plates (one pasted to a page edge), *one plate shaved at bottom*

2 works in one volume, 4to (202 x 163mm.), BINDING: contemporary speckled calf, spine gilt in compartments, morocco lettering-pieces, red edges, *occasional slight browning, extremities slightly rubbed*

FIRST EDITIONS of two rare works on the comets of 1680 and 1681. Kirch's work was used by both Halley and Newton, the latter incorporating Kirch's observations into the third edition of his *Principia*.

References: BL STC German XVIIc. K251 & Z228; neither in Houzeau & Lancaster

£2,000-3,000
€2,900-4,350

ATHANASIUS KIRCHER

Athanasius Kircher, the Jesuit polymath and prolific author, is one of the great learned figures of the seventeenth century. Born at Fulda on 2nd May 1602, he died in Rome on 28th November 1680. Educated under the care of the Benedictines, he joined the Jesuits in October 1618, and from then on his life was closely intertwined with the Society.

His journey to France in 1631, first to the Jesuit house at Lyon and then to Avignon (this visit commemorated in a book published there), led to an immense change in his life. It was in Provence that he met Claude-Nicolas Fabri de Peiresc (d. 1637), the enormously important spider at the centre of the web of European intellectual life and erudite correspondence. Kircher was destined for the imperial court at Vienna, but Peiresc engineered his transfer to Rome, and it was there, with brief travels to Malta and elsewhere, that Kircher spent the rest of his life, although posthumously his name (with those of a number of fellow Jesuits) is also recorded on the face of the moon.

Papal patronage and protection were useful: contacts with the Barberini family (Urban VIII was pontiff when he arrived) served him well. He co-operated with the great architect and sculptor Gianlorenzo Bernini, who provided the frontispiece for Urban's *Poemata* (Rome, 1632) on the creation of the fountain in Piazza Navona, into which was placed the Egyptian obelisk described by Kircher in his *Obeliscus Pamphilius* (1650). His journey to Malta in 1638 with Fabio Chigi (1599-1667), who became Pope Alexander VII in 1655, and the Vatican librarian Lucas Holstenius, accompanying a young German convert the Landgrave of Hessen, was the catalyst for important work both scientific and linguistic. His connection with Chigi in the longer term provided papal support, not least in the publication of books outside Italy, a task eased by subventions also from Vienna. Papal protection may also have extended to his citation of dangerous and condemned works, like those of Giordano Bruno.

Kircher wrote some forty works on a wide variety of subjects from the study of Coptic to China (where he had wished to be a missionary) and from ancient Latium to music, many of a scientific nature. Some were published more than once, like his *Iter exstaticum*, and some were repetitious: like many composers he used the same tune more than once. Other works were translated into various languages, either in part or in whole. His books were generally handsomely illustrated and it has been suggested by Ingrid Rowland that on occasions his illustrations contained a message which his words could not. The Museum Kircherianum in Rome was a huge draw for tourists, and various artefacts from it may still be seen in Rome, and Kircher himself was always delighted to entertain visitors.

When John Evelyn visited the Gesù and other Jesuit buildings on 8 November 1644 he met "Father Kercherus... [who] shew'd us many singular courtesies, leading us into their Colledge... and finaly... into his owne study, where he with Dutch patience shew'd us his perpetual motions, Catoptrics, Magnetical experiments, models, and a thousand other crotches & devises..." (*Diary*, ed. E. de Beer, II (Oxford, 1955) p.230).

1150

1150 Kircher, Athanasius (1602-1680), *S.J.* Primitiae gnomonicae catoptricae hoc est horologiographiae novae specularis. *Avignon: Jean Piot, 1635*

4to (210 x 160mm.), [12 (including engraved frontispiece)], 228, [16]pp., last leaf with privilege, ILLUSTRATION: engraved frontispiece, full-page engraved illustration entitled "horologium catoptricon" on p.142, woodcut diagrams, BINDING: contemporary English speckled calf, spine gilt in compartments, later morocco lettering-piece, *some damp-staining and wormholes in first few quires, last leaf of preface slightly shaved and coming loose, engravings shaved, extremities rubbed*

FIRST EDITION. Kircher was sent from Lyon to Avignon in 1632, and described how he had the idea of decorating the blank walls of a tower at the Jesuit college there with pictures of the heavens, and of how there was a huge gap between the conception and its execution. Eventually by use of a small fragment of a mirror carefully positioned, he was able to reflect onto the internal walls of the building the light of both the sun and the moon so that "ipsius caeli iura legesque astrorum id invasisse diceres". The megacosm was reduced to a microcosm, plain for all to see. "For whatever the sun by day and the moon by night describes and shows in the heavens, so here below all was shown by means of the mirror, devised by a Promethean skill...". The liminary verses all bear witness to Kircher's ingenuity: "Cuncta haec monstrantur solis splendore reflexo, Doctos quem in muros specula fixa vibrant".

References: Houzeau & Lancaster 11442; Dünnhaupt/Kircher 2; Sommervogel IV, 1047

£2,000-2,500
€2,900-3,650

1151 Kircher, Athanasius, *S.J.* Musurgia universalis, sive ars magna consoni et dissoni in X libros digesta. *Rome: (Luigi Grignani) for the heirs of Francesco Corbelletti, 1650*

2 volumes in one, folio (317 x 210mm.), [20], 690; [2], 462, [38]pp., errata leaf at the end, numerous typeset musical examples, ILLUSTRATION: engraved portrait of Archduke Leopold, 2 engraved frontispieces, 21 engraved plates on 20 sheets (4 folding), woodcut devices on titles, woodcut illustrations and diagrams in text, woodcut tail-pieces, typographic head-pieces, BINDING: contemporary calf, spine gilt in compartments, *second frontispiece tipped in and slightly shaved at head and foot, occasional light off-setting from plates, a few headlines trimmed, inscription erased from first title, joints weak*

FIRST EDITION. The *Musurgia universalis* is one of the most important of all musical treatises, influencing musical theorists well into the next century. Kircher recorded the first, imperfect, description of a speaking trumpet.

References: Merrill 8; Sommervogel IV, 1051.11; Caillet 5785; Dünnhaupt/Kircher 8; RISM Écrits p. 449; Gregory & Bartlett i, 135

£4,000-6,000
€5,800-8,700

1152 Kircher, Athanasius, *S.J.* Obeliscus pamphilius, hoc est, interpretatio nova & hucusque intentata obelisci hieroglyphici... *Rome: Luigi Grignani, 1650*

folio (323 x 212mm.), [64], 560, [30]pp., ILLUSTRATION: woodcut arms of the dedicatee, Innocent X [Pamphilj] on title-page, large folding engraved plate of the obelisk, woodcut initials, head- and tailpieces, woodcut illustrations (2 full-page), 5 full-page engraved illustrations, BINDING: contemporary mottled calf, spine gilt in compartments, speckled edges, *lacking engraved title and portrait, plate repaired (just affecting image), binding slightly rubbed*

FIRST EDITION. Kircher was encouraged by Fabri to study hieroglyphics and in 1646 he produced a Coptic grammar. This work is a description of the Pamphilj obelisk in Piazza Navona in Rome, which was redesigned for Innocent X as a monument to his family, who owned buildings on the piazza. The obelisk itself was originally erected by the Emperor Domitian in 80AD; its remains were discovered in 1648 and after repair it was placed upon Bernini's fountain of the four rivers in the centre of the piazza.

References: Caillet 5787; Cicognara 2526; Rossetti 5886; Dünnhaupt/Kircher 9; Sommervogel IV, 1052

£2,000-3,000
€2,900-4,350

1151

1152

1153 Kircher, Athanasius, *S.J.* Itinerarium exstaticum quo mundi opificium (Iter extaticum II. Qui & mundi subterranei prodromus dicitur). *Rome: Vitale Mascardi, 1656-1657*

2 parts in one volume (the second part bound first), 4to (236 x 172mm.), [8], 464, [24]; [24], 237, [15 (the last 2 blank)] pp., BINDING: contemporary vellum

FIRST EDITION. The work is cast in the form of a dream dialogue between Theodidactus (taught by God = Kircher) and his guardian angel Cosmiel (the Greek stem kosm (as in kosmos) and the Hebrew termination as in Uriel), in which an account is given of traditional cosmology by Theodidactus (with no great enthusiasm) and by Cosmiel of the Copernican system. The work attracted criticism and was unfavourably viewed by the censors. Schott however was able without hindrance to produce his second edition (in which he referred to all manner of condemned books).

References: Dünnhaupt/Kircher 12

Provenance: Thomas More, early signature on first title

£1,000-1,500
€1,450-2,200

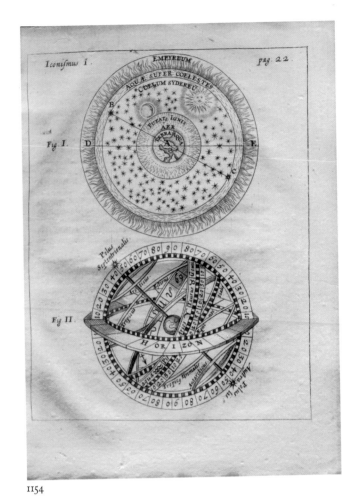

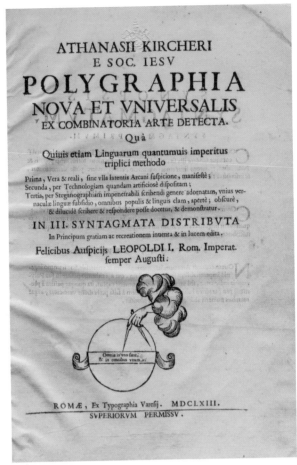

1154

1156

1154 Kircher, Athanasius, *S.J.* Iter exstaticum coeleste... secunda editione [edited by Gaspar Schott]... accessit eiusdem auctoris iter exstaticum terrestre, & synopsis mundi subterranei. *Würzburg: Johann Andreas Endter & the heirs of Wolfgang Endter, 1671*

second edition, 4to (212 x 160mm.), [22], 689, [15]pp., ILLUSTRATION: engraved frontispiece, engraved coat-of-arms of the dedicatee (Joachim, abbot of Fulda) on verso of title, woodcut initials, head- and tailpieces, 12 engraved plates, BINDING: contemporary vellum with blind-stamped centrepiece, spine gilt in compartments, morocco lettering-piece, *occasional slight browning, binding slightly soiled, lacking 2 pairs of ties*

References: Caillet 5776; Dünnhaupt/Kircher 12.I.b; Sommervogel IV, 1056; see Ingrid D. Rowland, *The ecstatic journey* (Chicago, 2000), no. 28

£1,500-2,000
€2,200-2,900

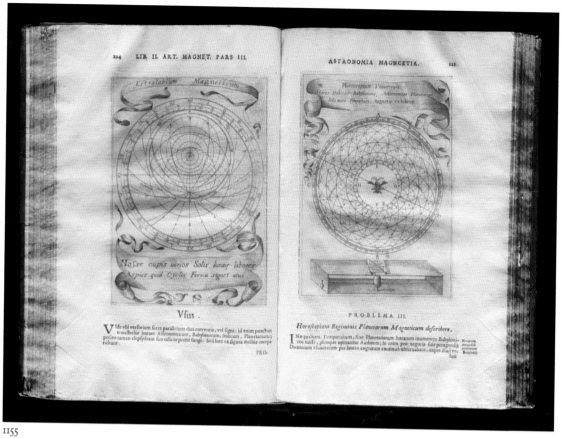

1155

1155 Kircher, Athanasius, *S.J.* Magnes sive de arte magnetica opus tripartitum... Editio tertia. *Rome: Vitale Mascardi for Blasius Deversin & Zanobius Masotti, 1654*

folio (341 x 225mm.), [16 (including engraved title-page)], 618, [28]pp., title printed in red and black, ILLUSTRATION: additional engraved title-page, engraved printer's device on title-page, woodcut initials, head- and tailpieces, full-page engraved arms of the dedicatee, Ferdinand IV, on +3 verso, woodcut and engraved illustrations (some full-page), BINDING: contemporary calf with blind fillets and corner fleurons on covers, spine gilt in compartments over original blind tooling, red speckled edges, *Ll1 torn without loss, binding rubbed, joints cracking, spine chipped at head*

Originally published in 1641, this is the third edition, greatly expanded. Kircher examines all aspects of magnetism, from that of the earth to animals, music and love.

References: Caillet 5780; Wheeler Gift 116a; Dünnhaupt/Kircher 5b; Sommervogel IV, 1049

£2,000-3,000
€2,900-4,350

1156 Kircher, Athanasius, *S.J.* Polygraphia nova et universalis ex combinatoria arte detecta... *Rome: Varese, 1663*

folio (333 x 222mm.), 148, 23, [1 (blank)] pp., ILLUSTRATION: woodcut on title-page, woodcut initials and tailpieces, 1 engraved and 2 letterpress tables (1 folding), BINDING: nineteenth-century calf with black fillets by Hatton of Manchester, red edges, *folding table repaired and rebacked with linen*

FIRST EDITION of Kircher's treatise on combining all languages to form one language.

References: Dünnhaupt/Kircher 15; Sommervogel IV, 1059

£1,000-1,500
€1,450-2,200

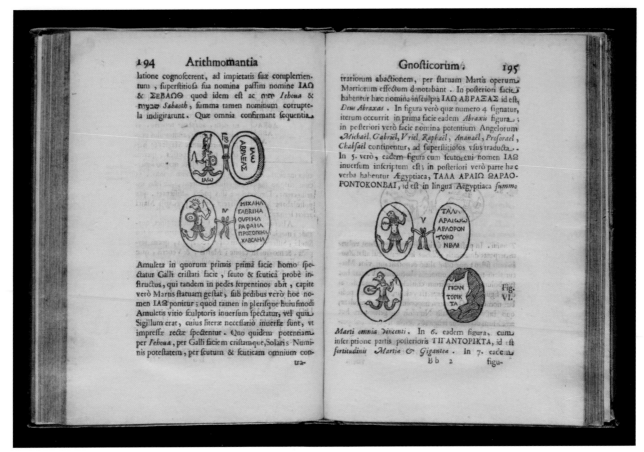

1157

1157 Kircher, Athanasius, *S.J.* Arithmologia, sive de abditis numerorum mysteriis qua origo, antiquitas & fabrica numerorum exponitur; abditae... proprietates demonstrantur; fontes superstitionum in amuletorum fabrica aperiuntur... *Rome: Varese, 1665*

FIRST EDITION, 4to (240 x 173mm.), [16 (including frontispiece)], 301, [11]pp., 3 folding printed tables (one in red and black), ILLUSTRATION: engraved frontispiece, full-page woodcut arms of dedicatee on verso of title-page, woodcut initials, tailpieces and illustrations, BINDING: contemporary calf, spine gilt in compartments, morocco lettering-piece, *without final blank, extremities rubbed*

References: Merrill 19; Caillet 5769; Dünnhaupt/Kircher 18; Sommervogel IV, 1063

£1,000-1,500
€1,450-2,200

1158 Kircher, Athanasius, *S.J.* Ars magna lucis et umbrae in X libros digesta... Editio altera priori multo auctior. *Amsterdam: Joannes Jansson a Waesberge and the heirs of Eliza Weterstraet, 1671*

folio (385 x 242mm.), [34 (including frontispiece and portrait)], 424, 525-810, [10]pp. (425-524 omitted in pagination), ILLUSTRATION: engraved frontispiece, engraved portrait of the dedicatee, Johann Friedrich, count of Waldstein, woodcut initials and tailpieces, engraved and woodcut illustrations (some full-page), 2 engraved tables, large folding engraved plate entitled "Horoscopium Catholicum Societ. Iesu", another engraved plate, BINDING: contemporary calf, spine gilt in compartments, morocco lettering-piece, *occasional browning, binding rubbed, joints splitting at head and foot*

1158

1159

Second edition of Kircher's work on optics and horology, originally published in Rome in 1646. The large folding plate represents a hierarchy of the Society of Jesus, each branch containing a small sundial, the whole plate designed to be cut out and used in sunlight to tell the time in each particular branch.

References: Caillet 5770; Dünnhaupt/Kircher 7a; Sommervogel IV, 1050; Wellcome III, p.394

£4,000-5,000
€5,800-7,300

1159 Kircher, Athanasius, *S.J.* Latium. Id est, nova & parallela Latii tum veteris tum novi descriptio. *Amsterdam: J. Janssonius van Waesberg & heirs of E. Weyerstraet, 1671*

folio (380 x 238mm.), [20], 263, [11]pp., ILLUSTRATION: additional engraved title by Romeyn de Hooghe, engraved portrait of Clement X, 25 engraved plates and maps (some folding), engraved illustrations in text, woodcut tail-pieces and initials, BINDING: contemporary mottled calf, spine gilt in compartments, *short tear in one plate (without loss), some light spotting and browning (heavier at beginning and end), joints partly split*

FIRST EDITION. Kircher's topographical description of the area around Rome includes the history of its development. The illustrations show ruins, villas, gardens and coins.

References: Cicognara 3758; Rossetti G-848 & 5890; Dünnhaupt/Kircher 24; Sommervogel IV, 1067

£1,500-2,000
€2,200-2,900

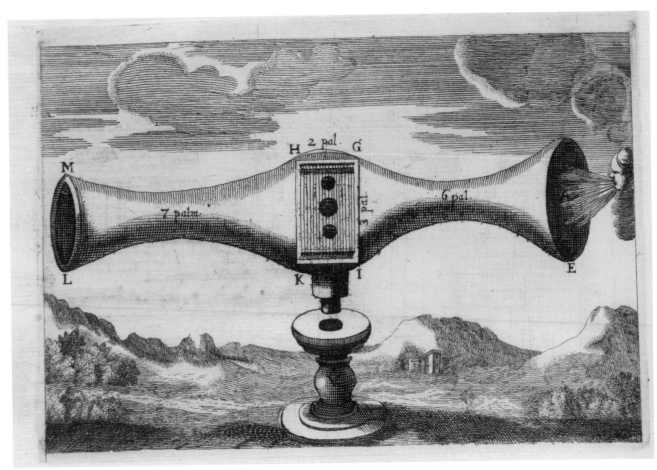

1160

1160 Kircher, Athanasius, *S.J.* Phonurgia nova, sive conjugium mechanico-physicum
artis & naturae paranympha phonosophia concinnatum. *Kempten: Rudolph
Dreherr, 1673*

folio (335 x 211mm.), [42], 229, [1], [16]pp., ILLUSTRATION: engraved frontispiece
by G.A. Wolfgang after F. Chevrier, engraved vignette on title, engraved portrait
of Emperor Leopold I by Wolfgang after F. Herman, 2 engraved plates, 17
engraved illustrations in text (at pp.69, 74, 79, 90, 99, 100, 120, 127, 138, 141,
143, 144, 150, 158, 162, 168 & 206), woodcut diagrams, initials, head- and
tailpieces, BINDING: contemporary speckled calf, spine gilt in compartments,
binding slightly rubbed

FIRST EDITION. The *Phonurgia*, the first work published in Europe devoted to
acoustics, deals with echoes and the amplification of sound. In it Kircher responds
to the claim by Sir Samuel Morland to have invented the "tuba stentorophonica",
or speaking trumpet (*Tuba stentoro-phonica*, 1671; see lot 1492). Kircher himself
had first described such an instrument in his *Musurgia universalis* of 1650, and
had been using it to call worshippers to the shrine of St Eustace at Mentorella.
The *Phonurgia* contains supportive testimonials from people such as Kircher's
pupil Schott and James Alban Gibbs, who may be a relation of the architect James
Gibbs, who was of a Catholic family. It also contains descriptions of inventions
such as eavesdropping devices, an Aeolian tuba, talking statues and curiously-
shaped trumpets.

References: Dünnhaupt/Kircher 26; Wellcome III, p.395

£4,000-5,000
€5,800-7,300

1161

1162

1161 Kircher, Athanasius, *S.J.* Arca Noë, in tres libros digesta. *Amsterdam: J. Janssonius van Waesberge, 1675*

folio (374 x 239mm.), [14], 240, [16]pp., ILLUSTRATION: additional engraved title, engraved portrait of Charles II of Spain, 19 engraved plates and maps (most folding or double-page), engravings and woodcuts in text, BINDING: contemporary mottled calf, *some browning and spotting, joints rubbed*

FIRST EDITION. Kircher's fanciful explanation of the biblical flood was dedicated to Charles II, King of Spain, who was only twelve years old at the time. "The most famous and elaborate account of the Ark produced in the seventeenth century... Not only was [Kircher] concerned to construct the story of the Ark in every detail, but he came to personify the impulse for collecting natural history - given sacred purpose through Noah - as he brought together and accommodated the extraordinary *Museum Kircherianum* in Rome. The connection was evident for Kircher; he described Noah's Ark as the first museum" (J. Bennett and S. Mandelbrote, *The Garden, the ark, the tower, the temple*, Oxford 1998, no. 37).

References: Merrill 26; Sommervogel IV, 1068-69.33; Nissen *ZBI* 2195; Caillet 5768; Dünnhaupt/Kircher 29

£2,000-3,000
€2,900-4,350

1162 Kircher, Athanasius, *S.J.* Sphinx mystagoga, sive diatribe hieroglyphica, qua mumiae, ex Memphiticis pyramidum adytis erutae, et non ita pridem in Galliam transmissae, juxta veterum hieromystarum mentem, intentionemque, plena fide & exacta exhibetur interpretatio. Ad inclytos, abstrusiorumque cognitionum peritia instructissimos Galliae philologos directa. *Amsterdam: Jansson-Waesberge, 1676,* [16], 72, [6]pp., ILLUSTRATION: woodcut device on title-page, woodcut initials, engraved and woodcut illustrations, 5 engraved plates (3 folding)

Ibid. Romani Collegii Societatis Jesu musaeum celeberrimum: cujus magnum antiquariae rei, statuarum, imaginum, picturarumque partem ex legato Alphonsi Donini, S.P.Q.R., a secretis, munifica liberalitate relictum... *Amsterdam: Jansson-Waesberge, 1678,* FIRST EDITION, [10 (including frontispiece and portrait], 66, [6]pp., ILLUSTRATION: engraved frontispiece, engraved portrait of Kircher, woodcut initials, 17 engraved plates (9 folding), engraved and woodcut illustrations

Kestler, Johann Stephan (*fl.* **1675).** Physiologia Kircheriana experimentalis, qua summa argumentorum multitudine et varietate naturalium rerum scientia per experimenta physica, mathematica, medica, chymica, musica, magnetica, mechanica, comprobatur atque stabilitur. Quam ex vastis operibus Adm. Revd. P. Athanasii Kircheri extraxit, & in hunc ordinem per classes redegit Romae, anno M.DC.LXXV. *Amsterdam: Jansson-Waesberge, 1680,* [6], 248, [8]pp., ILLUSTRATION: engraved frontispiece, woodcut initials and tailpieces, engraved and woodcut illustrations

3 works in one volume, folio (385 x 243mm.), BINDING: contemporary vellum, blind-stamped centrepiece, morocco lettering-pieces, red edges, *binding very slightly soiled and warped, small chip in spine*

The first work, of which another edition was printed in Rome in the same year, is an interpretation of the hieroglyphics traced on two mummies brought from Egypt, now located in the Château d'Ussé in Touraine. The second work is a catalogue of Kircher's Chinese and Egyptian antiquities and scientific instruments, and the third is a summary of Kircher's experiments, compiled by one of his students.

References: 1st work: Merrill 27; Caillet 5796; Dünnhaupt/Kircher 30a; Sommervogel IV, 1069; *2nd work:* Caillet 5784; Dünnhaupt/Kircher 31; Sommervogel IV, 1076; *3rd work:* Krivatsy 6404

£6,000-8,000
€8,700-11,600
See illustration on previous page

1163 Kircher, Athanasius, *S.J.* Mundus subterraneus, in XII libros digestus... Editio tertia. *Amsterdam: Joannes Jansson a Waesberge and sons, 1678*

2 volumes, folio (382 x 246mm.), [22 (including engraved title-page and portrait)], 366, [6]; [10 (including engraved title-page)], 507, [9]pp., ILLUSTRATION: 2 additional engraved title-pages, engraved device on first title-page, engraved portrait of Kircher, woodcut initials and tailpieces, 21 engraved maps and plates (12 double-page, 1 folding), 2 plates each containing 2 volvelles (uncut), woodcut and engraved illustrations, 5 letterpress tables (2 double-page, 1 folding), BINDING: contemporary speckled calf, spines gilt in compartments, morocco lettering-pieces, speckled edges, *occasional slight foxing, one plate loose, one small wormhole in gutter of vol.2, bindings slightly rubbed and scraped*

Third edition of Kircher's lengthy work on subterranean earth, covering subjects as diverse as volcanoes and fanciful monsters. His observations about volcanoes were based on a visit to Sicily where he saw the eruptions of Etna and Stromboli in 1637-1638.

References: Caillet 5783; JCB 678/76; Sabin 37967; Dünnhaupt/Kircher 16b; Sommervogel IV, 1060

£5,000-7,000
€7,300-10,200

1164 Kircher, Athanasius—Buonanni, Filippo (1638-1725). Musaeum Kircherianum, sive musaeum a P. Athanasio Kirchero in Collegio Romano Societatis Jesu iam pridem incoeptum nuper restitutum, auctum, descriptum & iconibus illustratum. *Rome: Giorgio Plachi, 1709*

folio (370 x 237mm.), [12], 522 [i.e. 395], [8]pp. (pp.40-60, 80-83, 116-127, 147-160, 184-197, 225-226, 248-252, 284-300, 313-316, 320-321, 362-391 & 412 are all single engraved sheets), ILLUSTRATION: 172 engraved plates, woodcut tail-pieces and initials, BINDING: contemporary speckled calf, spine gilt in compartments, *upper joint partly split*

The Musaeum Kircherianum, founded on the collections of Alfonso Donnino left to the Society of Jesus in Rome, was administered for many years by Kircher, who also added greatly to the collections. A first catalogue of the collection, written by Giorgio de Sepi, was published in 1678.

References: Nissen *ZBI* 2198; Cicognara 3372; Caillet 5784; Rossetti 1377

£3,000-4,000
€4,350-5,800

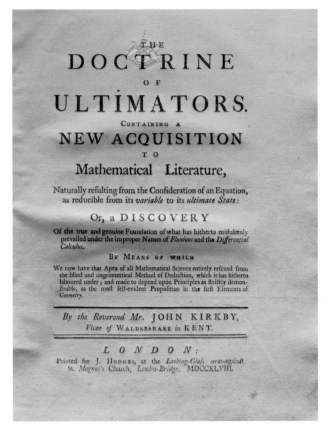

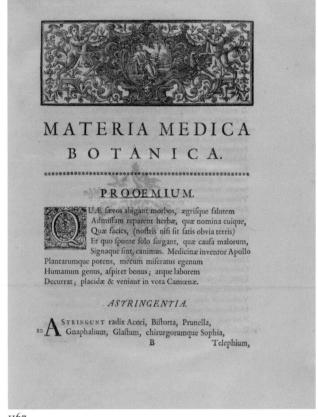

1166   1167

1165 Kirkby, John (1705-1754). Arithmetical institutions. Containing a compleat system of arithmetic natural, logarithmical, and algebraical in all their branches. *London: for B. Motte and J. Clark, 1735*

4to (232 x 169mm.), [8], 48, 68, 40, 72, 93, [1 (blank)], 59, [3]pp., ILLUSTRATION: woodcut initials, head- and tailpieces, folding table, BINDING: contemporary mottled calf gilt, spine gilt in compartments, red morocco lettering-piece, red edges

£200-300
€300-450

1166 Kirkby, John. The doctrine of ultimators. Containing a new acquisition to mathematical literature, naturally resulting from the consideration of an equation as reducible from its variable to its ultimate state: or, a discovery of the true and genuine foundation of what has hitherto mistakenly prevailed under the improper names of fluxions and the differential calculus. *London: for J. Hodges, 1748*

FIRST EDITION, 4to (262 x 202mm.), [2 (half-title)], viii, [4], 146pp., ILLUSTRATION: woodcut diagrams, BINDING: vellum-backed patterned paper boards

£500-700
€750-1,050

1167 Knowles, Gilbert (1667-1734). Materia medica botanica; in qua symptomata variorum morborum describuntur, herbaeque iisdem depellendis aptissimae apponuntur... *London: William Bowyer for William Lewis, 1723*

4to (283 x 220mm.), [14], 256, [20]pp., ILLUSTRATION: woodcut initials, head- and tailpieces, BINDING: contemporary speckled calf, roll-tooled floral gilt border on both covers, spine gilt in compartments, morocco lettering-piece, gilt edges, *upper joint cracking at head*

FIRST EDITION. Gilbert's treatise on various diseases and associated medicinal plants is written in Latin hexameters. Bowyer printed 250 copies for subscribers.

References: Wellcome III, p.406; *Bowyer Ledgers* 880; Nichols, *Anecdotes* VIII, 442

£300-400
€450-600

1168 Krüger, Peter (1580-1639). Synopsis trigonometriae sive doctrinae triangulorum, cum canone trigonometrico hoc est tabulis sinuum, tangentium, secantium, [etc.] (Eine Aussgabe den jenign Landmessern... welche ermeinen die Vollkomenheit ihrer Kunst könne wol bestehen ohne doctrina triangulorum). *Gdansk: typis Hunefeldianis, sumptibus autoris, 1612*

8vo (155 x 85mm.), [8], 240, [4]pp., ILLUSTRATION: small woodcut diagrams, BINDING: eighteeenth-century English mottled calf, gilt spine, red morocco lettering-piece

Krüger was Hevelius's teacher in the Gymnasium at Gdansk and gave him private lessons on planetary astronomy and other subjects. It was to Krüger that Hevelius sent letters when he was journeying in England and France in 1631-1634 (see Macpike, *Hevelius, Flamsteed & Halley*, 1937, pp. 1-2).

£400-600
€600-900

1169 Krüger, Peter. Doctrina astronomiae sphaericae... explicata... cum tabulis ad eam pertinentibus. *Gdansk: Andreas Hünefeldt, 1635*

8vo (160 x 95mm.), [16], 175, 95, [1]pp., ILLUSTRATION: woodcut diagrams in text, BINDING: contemporary vellum

£500-700
€750-1,050

1170 [La Caille, Nicolas Louis de (1713-1762)] Leçons élémentaires de mathématiques, ou élémens d'algèbre et de géométrie. *Paris: Hippolyte-Louis Guerin & Jacques Guerin, 1747*

FIRST EDITION, 8vo (199 x 122mm.), [8], 252, [4]pp., ILLUSTRATION: 5 folding engraved plates, BINDING: contemporary polished calf gilt, spine gilt in compartments

£150-200
€250-300

1171 La Caille, Nicolas Louis de. Ephemerides des mouvemens celestes, pour dix années, depuis 1745 jusqu'en 1755 et pour le meridien de la ville de Paris. *Paris: Jacques-François Collombat, 1744*, 4to (258 x 193mm.), lxxii, 259, [3]pp., ILLUSTRATION: engraved frontispiece, woodcut diagrams, 3 engraved plates, BINDING: contemporary smooth calf gilt, spine gilt in compartments, morocco lettering-pieces, red speckled edges

Ibid. Leçons élémentaires d'astronomie géometrique et physique. *Paris: les freres Guerin, 1746*, 8vo (202 x 125mm.), [4], 355, [1]pp., ILLUSTRATION: woodcut device on title-page, woodcut initials, head- and tailpieces, 9 folding engraved plates, BINDING: contemporary smooth calf gilt, spine gilt in compartments, red morocco lettering-piece, red speckled edges

together 2 volumes

FIRST EDITIONS. La Caille's volume of ephemerides follows on from the three volumes by Desplaces (for the first of which see Macclesfield Science D-H, lot 624). He also published two more, for 1755-1764 and 1765-1744.

References: Houzeau & Lancaster 15522 & 9254

£400-500
€600-750

1172 La Chambre, Marin Cureau de (1594-1669). Nouvelles observations et coniectures sur l'iris. *Paris: Pierre Rocolet, 1650*

4to (245 x 186mm.), [6], 340, [6]pp., ILLUSTRATION: engraved device on title-page, woodcut and engraved initials, head- and tailpieces, engraved diagrams, BINDING: contemporary calf, spine gilt in compartments, speckled edges, *without initial blank, a few marginal wormholes (occasionally touching a diagram), binding rubbed, upper cover detaching, sewing broken in a few places*

FIRST EDITION. La Chambre was physician to Chancelier Séguier and Louis XIII, and entered the Académie royale in 1666. Most of his writings were of a medical nature.

References: Krivatsy 3017

£600-800
€900-1,200

1173 La Condamine, Charles Marie de (1701-1774). Mesure des trois premiers degres du Méridien dans l'hemisphere austral, tirée des observations de M.rs de l'Academie Royale des Sciences, envoyés par le Roi sous l'Équateur. *Paris: Imprimerie Royale, 1751*, [12], 266, x pp., ILLUSTRATION: engraved vignette on title-page, woodcut initials and headpieces, engraved headpieces, woodcut diagrams, 3 folding engraved plates

Ibid. Supplément au journal historique du voyage a l'Équateur, et au livre de la mesure des trois premiers degrés du meridien: servant de réponse à quelques objections. *Paris: Durand & Pissot, 1752*, [4], viii, 52pp., ILLUSTRATION: woodcut vignette on title-page, woodcut head- and tailpieces, *part one only*

2 works in one volume, 4to (251 x 152mm.), BINDING: contemporary mottled calf, spine gilt in compartments, red morocco lettering-piece

BOTH FIRST EDITIONS.

References: Sabin 38483 & 38490; *1st work:* Norman 1249

£600-800
€900-1,200

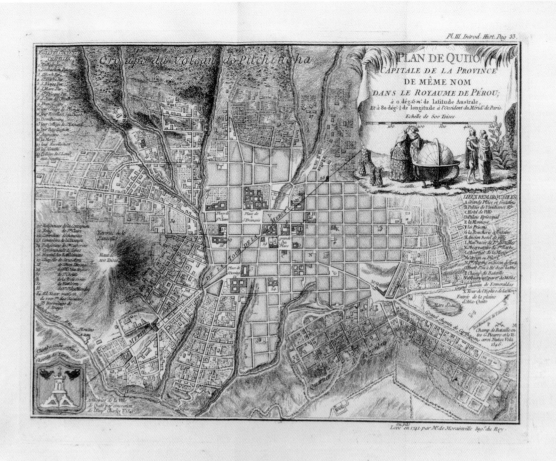

1174

1174 La Condamine, Charles Marie de. Journal du voyage fait par ordre du Roi, a l'Équateur, servant d'introduction historique a la mesure des trois premiers degres du méridien. *Paris: Imprimerie Royale, 1751*

4to (248 x 190mm.), [2], xxxvi, 280, xv, [1 (blank)] pp., ILLUSTRATION: woodcut device on title-page, 3 folding engraved maps (including one large map of the province of Quito by d'Anville), engraved headpiece, 3 engraved plates (2 folding), woodcut tailpieces, folding letterpress leaf, BINDING: contemporary mottled calf, spine gilt in compartments, red morocco lettering-piece, red edges, *map of Quito a little creased, extremities slightly rubbed*

FIRST EDITION. La Condamine went to Peru as part of an expedition which "had as its goal the verification of Newton's hypothesis on the flattening of the terrestrial globe in the polar regions and, thereby, the resolution of the controversy regarding the form of the earth that was then dividing French scientists. Maupertuis, Clairaut and Le Monnier went to Lapland to measure several degrees of meridian at the arctic circle, while Godin, Bouguer, and La Condamine were sent to Peru, territory belonging to Philip V of Spain, in order to make the same measurement in the vicinity of the equator" (*DSB* XV, p.270). La Condamine spent ten years in South America, returning with copious natural history specimens. He was also able to report that Newton was correct in his supposition regarding the shape of the earth.

References: Norman 1250; Sabin 38479

£600-800
€900-1,200

1175 Laet, Johannes de (1593-1649). De gemmis et lapidibus libri duo. Quibus praemittitur Theophrasti liber de lapidibus Graece & Latine cum brevibus annotationibus. *Leiden: Joannes Maire, 1647*, [64], 210 [6]pp., ILLUSTRATION: woodcut device on title-page, woodcut initials and illustrations, 2 folding letterpress tables

Boodt, Anselmus Boetius de (?1550-1634). Gemmarum et lapidum historia... Tertia editio longe purgatissima. *Leiden: Joannes Maire, 1647*, [8], 576, [22]pp., ILLUSTRATION: woodcut device on title-page, woodcut initials and illustrations

2 works in one volume, 8vo (182 x 110mm.), BINDING: contemporary calf, spine gilt in compartments, morocco lettering-piece, *binding rubbed, upper cover detached*

FIRST EDITION of Laet's work, and the third edition of that of de Boodt. These two works were issued together, usually with the de Boodt bound first as the title-page for that part mentions Laet's treatise.

References: Wellcome II, p.202

£500-700
€750-1,050

1176 La Faille, Jean Charles de (1597-1662), *S.J.* Theoremata de centro gravitatis partium circuli et ellipsis. *Antwerp: Jean Meursius, 1632*

4to (247 x 180mm.), [8], 53, [3]pp., ILLUSTRATION: engraved device on title-page, woodcut initials, woodcut diagrams, BINDING: eighteenth-century vellum-backed blue boards, *binding slightly soiled*

FIRST EDITION. La Faille was professor of mathematics in Madrid.

£400-600
€600-900

1177 La Fontaine, *sieur de.* La geometrie universelle, avec un compendion de perspective, la contruction des cadrans solaires, l'usage du cadran analytique, & autres diverses choses contenuës en cet oeuvre. *Paris: Estienne Loyson, 1666*

8vo (160 x 93mm.), [6], 150pp., ILLUSTRATION: woodcut vignette on title-page, woodcut initials and headpieces, 26 folding engraved plates, BINDING: contemporary mottled calf, spine gilt in compartments, red morocco lettering-piece, marbled edges, *spine rubbed*

FIRST EDITION. La Fontaine was "ingenieur ordinaire du Roy".

£500-700
€750-1,050

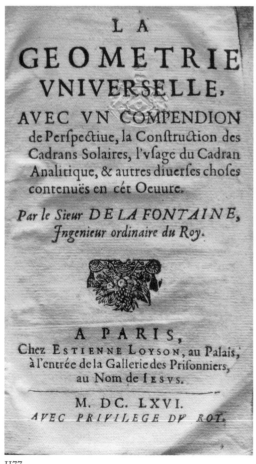

1177

1178 Lagny, Thomas Fantet de (1660-1734). Nouveaux elemens d'arithmetique et d'algebre, ou introduction aux mathematiques. *Paris: Jean Jombert, 1697*

FIRST EDITION, 12mo (169 x 95mm), [40], 527, [7]pp., ILLUSTRATION: woodcut device on title-page, woodcut initials, head- and tailpieces, BINDING: contemporary calf, spine gilt in compartments, *binding rubbed*

£100-150
€150-250

1179 La Hire, Philippe de (1640-1718). Nouvelle méthode en géometrie pour les sections des superficies coniques, et cylindriques, qui ont pour bases des cercles, ou des paraboles, des elipses, & des hyperboles. *Paris: chez l'autheur et Thomas Moette, 1673*

4to (206 x 163mm.), [8], 94; 6pp., ILLUSTRATION: 25 folding engraved plates, woodcut vignette on title, woodcut initials, head- and tail-pieces, BINDING: contemporary mottled calf, spine gilt in compartments with small double-headed eagle, *some light soiling, binding slightly worn, upper joint split*

LA HIRE'S FIRST WORK ON CONIC SECTIONS, a comprehensive study which clearly shows the influence of Desargues. The last six-page work is entitled *Phil. de la Hire De cycloide lemma.*

£800-1,000
€1,200-1,450

1180 La Hire, Philippe de. Nouveaux elemens des sections coniques, les lieux geometriques, la construction, ou effection des equations. *Paris: André Pralard, 1679*

12mo (152 x 88mm.), [12], 452pp., ILLUSTRATION: woodcut diagrams in text, BINDING: contemporary mottled calf, *upper joint partly split*

FIRST EDITION. La Hire's exposition of the properties of conic sections provides a useful summary of the advances made in analytic geometry, and contains ideas such as the possible extension of space to more than three dimensions.

£200-250
€300-400

1181 La Hire, Philippe de. Sectiones conicae in novem libros distributae... Adjecta demum est brevis expositio propositionum septem librorum conicorum Apollonii Pergaei... *Paris: Estienne Michallet, 1685*

folio (367 x 235mm.), [8], 245, 248-249, [1]pp., ILLUSTRATION: woodcut vignette on title-page, woodcut initials, head- and tailpieces, woodcut diagrams, BINDING: contemporary calf with black roll-tooled border, spine gilt in compartments, morocco lettering-piece, *marginal tear in M1-2, quires Xx and Ddd slightly browned, binding rubbed, joints weak*

FIRST EDITION of La Hire's extensive treatise on conic sections.

£1,000-1,500
€1,450-2,200

1182 La Hire, Philippe de. Gnomoniques, or the art of drawing sun-dials on all sorts of planes by different methods... Rendred into English... by John Leek. *London: for Richard Northcott, 1685*

FIRST EDITION IN ENGLISH, 8vo (152 x 95mm.), [16], 108, [44], 15pp., ILLUSTRATION: 17 engraved plates, BINDING: contemporary calf, *a few plates trimmed at head, spine rubbed*

References: Wing L181A; Houzeau & Lancaster 11534

£300-400
€450-600

1183 La Hire, Philippe de. La Gnomonique, ou l'art de tracer des cadrans ou horloges solaires sur toutes sortes de surfaces, par differentes pratiques. *Paris: Estienne Michallet, 1682*

FIRST EDITION, 12mo (155 x 84mm.), 194, [54]pp., ILLUSTRATION: 6 folding engraved plates, BINDING: contemporary calf, *light soiling on title*

References: Houzeau & Lancaster 11534

£700-900
€1,050-1,350

1184 La Hire, Philippe de. La gnomonique, ou methodes universelles pour tracer des horloges solaires ou cadrans sur toutes sortes de surfaces. *Paris: Thomas Moette, 1698*

12mo (145 x 79mm.), [24], 274 [i.e. 275], [1 (blank)] pp., ILLUSTRATION: engraved frontispiece and 9 plates (8 folding), BINDING: contemporary calf, spine gilt in compartments

Second edition, enlarged by the author. The first edition was published in 1682 (see lot 1183).

£400-500
€600-750

1185 [La Hire, Philippe de] L'Ecole des arpenteurs, où l'on enseigne toutes les pratiques de géometrie... Seconde édition, reveuë, corrigée & augmentée. *Paris: Thomas Moette, 1692*

12mo (162 x 88mm.), [12], 154 [i.e. 354], [2]pp., ILLUSTRATION: woodcut illustrations and diagrams, BINDING: contemporary speckled calf, spine gilt in compartments, *joints rubbed*

£250-300
€400-450

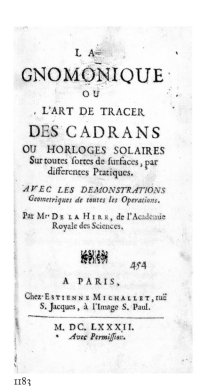

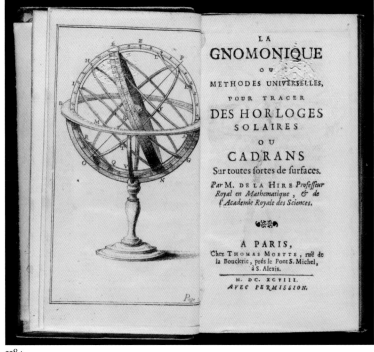

1183   1184

1186 La Hire, Philippe de. Tabulae astronomicae Ludovici Magni jussu... in quibus solis, lunae reliquorumque planetarum motus ex pisis observationibus... traduntur. *Paris: Jean Boudot, 1702*

4to (253 x 188mm.), [12], 102, [2]; [2], 80pp., ILLUSTRATION: 4 folding engraved plates, woodcut diagrams in text, BINDING: contemporary speckled calf, spine gilt in compartments, *short tear in lower margin of title, some light soiling, binding slightly rubbed*

FIRST EDITION. The second of two sets of astronomical tables published as the result of La Hire's observations of the movements of the sun, moon and planets at the Paris observatory. The first set, entitled *Tabularum astronomicarum*, was published in 1687.

£300-400
€450-600

1187 La Hire, Philippe de. Tables astronomiques... dans lesquelles on donne les mouvemens du soleil, de la lune, & des autres planètes... Troisième édition. *Paris: Montalant, 1735*

4to (256 x 190mm.), xx, 198; [2], 83, [1]pp., ILLUSTRATION: 4 folding engraved plates, woodcut diagrams in text, BINDING: contemporary mottled calf, spine gilt in compartments

The first French edition of La Hire's *Tabulae astronomicae* of 1702 (see lot 1186).

£300-400
€450-600

1188 La Hire, Philippe de. Description et explication des globes qui sont placés dans les pavillons du Château de Marly. *Paris: L.V. Thiboust, 1704*

8vo (192 x 130mm.), [10], 96pp., BINDING: contemporary speckled calf, spine gilt in compartments, *binding slightly rubbed*

£400-500
€600-750

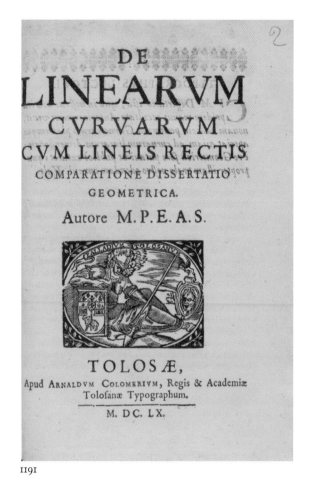

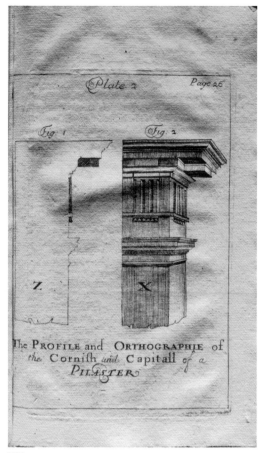

1191   1193

1189 La Lande, Joseph Jérôme le Français de (1732-1807). Astronomie... Seconde
édition revue et augmentée. *Paris: widow Desaint, 1771*

3 volumes, 4to (253 x 188mm.), [4], lvi, 608, 248; [4], 830; [4], 840pp.,
ILLUSTRATION: woodcut vignette on title-pages, woodcut initials, head- and
tailpieces, 42 folding engraved plates, BINDING: contemporary polished calf, spines
gilt in compartments, red morocco lettering-pieces, *quire Kkk of vol.2 stained, one
plate creased, extremities slightly rubbed*

Lalande studied under the Jesuits at the Collège de Lyon, and as a student in
Paris he followed the astronomical lectures of Delisle and the mathematical ones
of Le Monnier. He became a member of both the Prussian and French academies
of science. This textbook was originally published in 1764 and a third edition
appeared in 1791.

References: Houzeau & Lancaster 9258

£400-600
€600-900

1190 Laloubère, Antoine de (1600-1664), *S.J.* Quadratura circuli et hyperbolae
segmentorum... demonstrata, etc. *Toulouse: Pierre du Bosc, 1651*

8vo (170 x 100mm.), [14], 624, [16]pp., ILLUSTRATION: numerous engraved
geometrical diagrams in text, some full-page, BINDING: contemporary Cambridge
binding of brown calf, gilt double fillet on covers with small rosettes at corners,
flat spine with gilt ornaments, *offsetting on end-leaves from a Cambridge Greek Bible*

£700-1,000
€1,050-1,450

1191 Laloubère, Antoine de (1600-1664), *S.J.* Veterum geometria promota in septem de cycloide libris, et in duabus adiectis appendicibus. *Toulouse: Arnauld Colomere, 1660*, [16], 404pp., ILLUSTRATION: woodcut device on title-page, woodcut initials, head- and tailpieces, 7 engraved plates

[Fermat, Pierre de (1601-1665)] De linearum curvarum cum lineis rectis comparatione dissertatio geometrica. Autore M.P.E.A.S. *Toulouse: Arnauld Colomere, 1660*, 26, [2 (blank)], 27-39, [1 (blank)] pp., ILLUSTRATION: woodcut device on title-page, woodcut initial and tailpiece, typographical headpieces, 2 engraved plates

2 works in one volume, 4to (235 x 163mm.), BINDING: contemporary mottled calf gilt, spine gilt in compartments, red morocco lettering-piece, *binding rubbed, joints worn*

FIRST EDITION. Laloubère was professor of humanities, rhetoric and mathematics at the Jesuit college in Toulouse and was a friend of Fermat, who also lived in Toulouse. The tract by Fermat is the only work published during his lifetime.

£1,000-1,500
€1,450-2,200

1192 Lamy, Bernard (1640-1715). Traitez de mechanique, de l'equilibre des solides et des liqueurs. Où l'on découvre les causes des effets de toutes les machines dont on mesure les forces d'une maniere particuliere; on y en propose aussi qulques nouvelles. *Paris: André Pralard, 1679*

12mo (148 x 83mm.), [2], 242, 143-163, [1]pp., ILLUSTRATION: woodcut device on title-page, woodcut initials, head- and tailpieces, woodcut diagrams, BINDING: contemporary calf, spine gilt in compartments, speckled edges, *lacking folding plate, binding slightly rubbed*

FIRST EDITION. Lamy, an Oratorian priest, was a close follower of the work of Descartes, which led to his expulsion from his teaching position at the Collège of Angers in 1676.

£150-200
€250-300

1193 Lamy, Bernard. A treatise of perspective; or, the art of representing all manner of objects, as they appear to the eye in all situations. Containing the elements of designing and painting. Illustrated with above 50 figures in copper. Written originally in French... and faithfully translated into English, by an officer of His Majesties Ordnance [A. Forbes]. *London: Printed, and sold by most booksellers, 1702*

8vo (186 x 115mm.), [18], 174pp., ILLUSTRATION: woodcut diagrams, 31 engraved plates (some printed back-to-back), of which 1 folding, BINDING: contemporary panelled calf, spine gilt in compartments with morocco lettering-piece, *a few quires browned, binding rubbed*

FIRST EDITION IN ENGLISH, originally published in French the previous year. Lamy's work on mathematics was used right through the eighteenth century and into the nineteenth century.

£500-700
€750-1,050

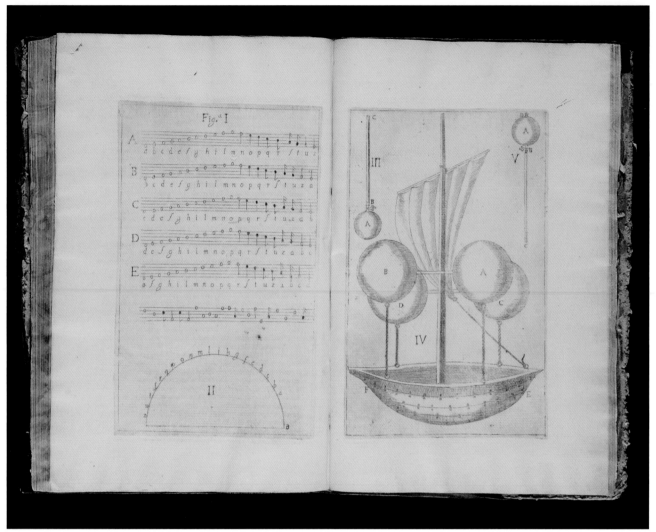

1195

1194 Lana Terzi, Francesco (1631-1687), *S.J.* Magisterium naturae, et artis. Opus physico-mathematicum... in quo occultiora naturalis philosophiae principia manifestantur, et multiplici tum experimentorum, tum demonstrationum serie comprobantur... *Brescia: Giovanni Maria Ricciardi, 1684-1686 (vol.3: Parma: Ippolito Rosati, 1692)*

3 volumes, folio (365 x 237mm.), [16], 48, 51-54, 57-256, 265-344, 353-494, 497-526; [34], 512, [18]; [8], 23, [1], 571, [1 (blank)] pp., ILLUSTRATION: woodcut vignette on title-pages, woodcut initials, head- and tailpieces, 57 engraved plates, BINDING: contemporary calf gilt, spines gilt in compartments, morocco lettering-pieces, red speckled edges, *small hole in A2 of vol.1 with loss of a few letters, lacking G1&4, quires Kk and Xx in vol.1, without final blank in vols. 1 & 2, lacking e2 in vol.2, extremities rubbed, upper cover of vol.2 torn, calf detaching from board edges*

This work was projected in 9 volumes, but only 3 appeared.

References: Riccardi ii, 13; Caillet 6093

£800-1,000
€1,200-1,450

1195 Lana Terzi, Francesco, *S.J.* Prodromo ouero saggio di alcune inuentiuoni nuoue... per mostrare li piu reconditi principij della naturale filosofia... Dedicato alla sacra maesta cesarea... Leopoldo I. *Brescia: Rizzardi, 1670*

folio (314 x 204mm.), [8], 252pp., ILLUSTRATION: 20 engraved plates with figures numbered I-LXX, woodcut initials, BINDING: contemporary English mottled calf over pasteboard, spine gilt, spine label wrongly titled ("Fausti Veranti Machinae Novae", a copy of which is elsewhere in the library), mottled edges, *end-papers and first 3 leaves slightly chewed at edges, calf becoming detached at board edges*

FIRST EDITION. Lana Terzi was a pupil of Kircher in Rome. This *Prodromo* is an introduction to his main work, *Magisterium naturae et artis*. The *Prodromo*, which is deliberately written in Italian and not in Latin, stresses in its dedication to the Emperor Leopold the importance of empiricism and the role of learning in helping mankind ("a fine di giovare al genere humano").

Oldenburg, writing to Malpighi (20 December 1670, *Correspondence* VII, 332-334), mentions the *Prodromo* which he was sent by John Dodington from Venice, and of which Oldenburg wrote an account in the *Philosophical Transactions* (25 March 1671), and asks for information about the author, of whose abilities Malpighi was critical in his reply (*Correspondence* VII, 429-431). This copy probably belonged to John Collins.

The book is chiefly famous for "Lana's little canoe... [It] is as captivating... as Godwin's gansas or Cyrano's rocket. Yet here was no Lucianic fantasy. This was straightforward science... although his ship never flew, it is no exaggeration to say that in the idea Lana had in mind lay the principle of the later balloon in which man was to conquer the air... The real novelty... lay not in the sail and oars, but in the four evacuated globes the size of which Lana carefully demonstrated, attached to the ship by four ropes of equal length... Whatever may be... the importance of Lana's *Prodromo* in the history of science, Lana's influence upon literature is indisputable..." (M. Hope Nicolson, *Voyages to the Moon*, New York, 1960, p.168).

References: Riccardi ii, 12; Norman 1272; Dibner 176

£4,000-5,000
€5,800-7,300

1196 Lando, Giovanni Giacomo. Aritmetica mercantile... nella quale si vede, come si hanno da fare li conti, per li cambi, che si fanno nelle città principali della christianità. *Venice: the heirs of Imberti, 1645*

4to (212 x 150mm.), [12], 270pp., ILLUSTRATION: woodcut device on title, woodcut initials, head- and tailpieces, BINDING: eighteenth-century panelled calf, spine gilt in compartments, *small hole in title-page (not affecting text), paper flaw in D2, ink stains on N2 (obscuring a few letters), upper joint cracking, extremities rubbed*

This is the fourth edition of a work which was first published in Naples in 1604. It is a handbook of rates of exchange across the major Italian cites of the time, Antwerp and Barcelona. This edition is quite rare; only two copies are recorded in Italian libraries.

References: cf. Michel V, p.17

£300-500
€450-750

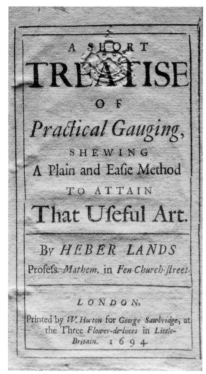
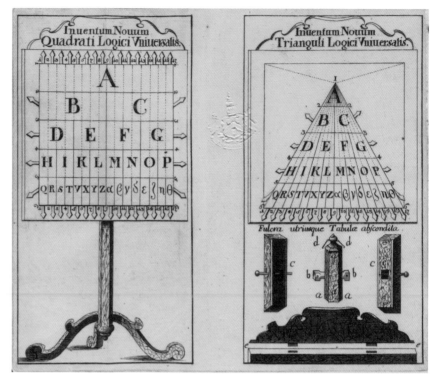

1197   1198

1197 Lands, Heber (*fl.* 1694-1738). A short treatise of practical gauging, shewing a plain and easie method to attain that useful art. *London: W. Horton for George Sawbridge, 1694*

8vo (145 x 85mm.), [10], 98, [2]pp., ILLUSTRATION: woodcut diagrams, BINDING: contemporary speckled calf with blind fillets and corner fleurons, spine gilt in compartments, *joints worn, spine chipped*

FIRST EDITION, RARE.

References: Wing L323A

£500-700
€750-1,050

1198 Lange, Johann Christian (1669-1756). Inventum novum quadrati logici universalis: in trianguli quoque formam commode redacti... Accedit dissertatio apologetica pro logica Aristotelica genuina, maxime logica... *Hesse: Johann Müller, 1714*

8vo (169 x 100mm.), [12], 176, 63, [1]pp., ILLUSTRATION: folding engraved frontispiece, woodcut initials and headpieces, woodcut diagrams, BINDING: contemporary speckled calf, spine gilt in compartments, red morocco lettering-piece, red and gold patterned paper pastedowns

FIRST EDITION. Lange was a Protestant theologian, preacher and hymn writer from Leipzig. He became professor of philosophy in Giessen in 1697 and then professor of logic and metaphysics in 1707. This work is dedicated to the Royal Society of London.

£300-400
€450-600

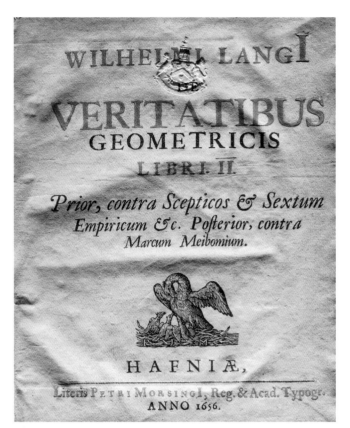

1199 Lange, Villum (1624-1682). De veritatibus geometricis libri II. Prior, contra Scepticos & Sextum Empiricum &c. Posterior, contra Marcum Meibomium. *Copenhagen: Peder Jensen Morsing, 1656*

4to (172 x 140mm.), [4], 373, [19]pp., title printed in red and black, ILLUSTRATION: woodcut device on title-page, woodcut initials and tailpieces, 3 folding engraved plates, BINDING: contemporary calf, spine gilt in compartments, morocco lettering-piece, *extremities rubbed*

FIRST EDITION. Lange was appointed Professor of Mathematics at the University of Copenhagen in 1650.

£500-700
€750-1,050

1200 Langley, Batty (1696-1751). The builder's chest-book; or, a complete key to the five orders in architecture... The second edition, much improv'd. *London: for J. Wilcox and James Hodges, 1739*

12mo (171 x 93mm.), vi, vi, 142pp., ILLUSTRATION: woodcut initials, head- and tailpieces, 7 folding engraved plates, BINDING: slightly later calf-backed marbled boards, spine gilt in compartments, red morocco lettering-piece, red edges

Langley was much interested in freemasonry, which had been founded in England in 1717. "The 'Dialogue' on architecture between M and P, master and pupil, in *The builder's chest-book* (1727), suggests an early form of masonic catechism" (Harris, p.264).

This second edition was also issued together with Isaac Gadsdon's *Geometrical rules*, not present in this copy.

References: Harris 416; cf. BAL RIBA 1730 (1st edition of 1727)

£1,000-1,500
€1,450-2,200

1201 Lansberge, Philip van (1561-1632). Triangulorum geometriae libri quatuor; in quibus nova & perspicua methodo, & αποδειξει, tota ipsorum triangulorum doctrina explicatur. *Leiden: Franciscus Raphelengius, in Officina Plantiniana, 1591*

4to (230 x 173mm.), [12], 207, [1 (blank)] pp., ILLUSTRATION: woodcut device on title-page, woodcut initials and diagrams, BINDING: contemporary carta rustica, uncut, *+6 torn and repaired, H3 torn without loss, binding worn*

FIRST EDITION. Van Lansberge studied mathematics and theology in England and became a Protestant minister in the Netherlands. This treatise was influenced by the *Geometriae rotundi* of Thomas Finck (Basel, 1583; see Macclesfield Science D-F, lot 777).

References: Adams L160

£800-1,000
€1,200-1,450

1202 Lansberge, Philip van. Opera omnia. *Middelburg: Zacharias Roman, 1663*

folio (285 x 180mm.), [12], 118; [10], 74, [2 (blank)]; [6], 53, [1 (blank)]; [8], 34, [2 (blank)]; [12], 41, [1 (blank)]; [2], 180; 181, [3]; [4], 103, [1 (blank)] pp., ILLUSTRATION: engraved title-page, portrait of the author on verso of title, woodcut initials, woodcut diagrams, folding engraved plate, BINDING: contemporary vellum with blind-stamped centrepiece, *pp.9-12 of the "Tabulae motuum caelestium" lacking and supplied in manuscript, lacking 5 plates, binding very slightly soiled*

References: Houzeau & Lancaster 2983

£500-700
€750-1,050

1203 Lantz, Johann (1564-1638), *S.J.* Institutionum arithmeticarum libri quatuor. In quibus, regulis et exemplis practicis, brevissime et clarissime explicantur... cum appendice fractionum astronomicarum... *Munich: Nicolaus Heinrich, 1616*

8vo (157 x 95mm.), [7], 180, [13]pp., ILLUSTRATION: woodcut initials and headpieces, woodcut diagrams, BINDING: eighteenth-century calf-backed marbled paper boards, spine gilt in compartments, red morocco lettering-piece, red edges, *a few leaves shaved*

FIRST EDITION. Lantz was Professor of Mathematics at the University of Tübingen.

References: Houzeau & Lancaster 13059; Zinner 4557

£600-800
€900-1,200

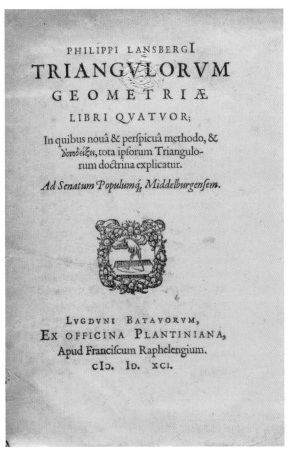

1201

1202

1204 La Roche, Estienne de (*fl. c.* 1520).

Larismethique nouvellement composee... divisee en deux parties... *(Lyon: Guillaume Huyon for) Constantin Fradin, (2 June 1520)*

folio (251 x 165mm.), ff. [4], 230, title printed in red, ILLUSTRATION: elaborate woodcut border and device on title-page, woodcut initials and diagrams, BINDING: nineteenth-century half calf by Hatton of Manchester, marbled edges, *occasional marginal damp-staining*

FIRST EDITION of La Roche's treatise which "introduced into France the Italian knowledge of arithmetic and useful notations for powers and roots" (*DSB* VIII, p.41). La Roche's teacher was Nicolas Chuquet on whose (then unpublished) work this text is based.

References: Rép. bibl. xvie siècle, Lyon III, Huyon 12

£5,000-7,000
€7,300-10,200

1204

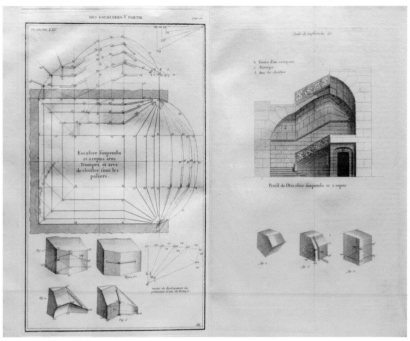

1205

1205 La Rue, Jean Baptiste de (d. 1743). Traité de la coupe des pierres, où par une methode facile & abregée, l'on peut aisément se perfectionner en cette science. *Paris: l'Imprimerie Royale, 1728*

folio (425 x 278mm.), [16], 185, [1 (blank)] pp., ILLUSTRATION: additional engraved title-page, engraved device on title-page, engraved headpieces and initials, woodcut tailpieces, woodcut diagrams, 72 engraved plates (mostly double-sided, some folding), BINDING: contemporary calf, spine gilt in compartments, morocco lettering-piece, red edges, *binding slightly rubbed*

FIRST EDITION and a crisp copy of La Rue's comprehensive work on stone-cutting, designed as a practical treatise for stone-masons. It was reissued in 1738 and 1764.

References: BAL RIBA 1765

£1,000-1,500
€1,450-2,200

1206 Laugier, Marc Antoine (1713-1769). Versuch in der Bau-Kunst. Neue Ausgabe genau übersehen, verbessert, und mit einem Wörter-Buche der darinnen befindlichen Kunst-Wörter... aus dem französischen ins deutsche übersetzet [by Von Schneller]. *Frankfurt and Leipzig: Fischer, 1758*

8vo (160 x 94mm.), [68], 276pp., ILLUSTRATION: woodcut initials, head- and tailpieces, BINDING: contemporary marbled calf, flat spine gilt, red morocco lettering-piece, yellow edges, *leaf *)(8 repaired in margin*

A translation of *Essai sur l'architecture*. "The *Essai sur l'architecture* was published anonymously because of its controversial argument: an advocacy of radical primitivism, epitomised by the hut consisting only of columns, entablature and roof... Laugier's innovation was to write about architectural theory, untrammelled by prolonged consideration of individual buildings, in a forthright and accessible style; and he was read by both architects and the general public" (BAL RIBA 2, p.938).

References: cf. BAL RIBA 1774 (1755 French edition)

£150-200
€250-300

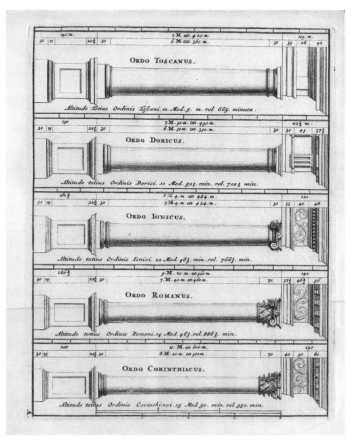

1207

1207 Lauterbach, Johann Balthasar (1660-1694). Abregé de l'architecture civile suivant la juste proportion antique & moderne. *Amsterdam: J. de la Feuille, 1699*

12mo (153 x 95mm.), [2], 32pp., title printed in red and black, ILLUSTRATION: engraved frontispiece, woodcut initials, head- and tailpieces, 3 engraved section-titles, 1 engraved table, 25 engraved plates (one folding), BINDING: contemporary speckled calf, spine gilt in compartments, *extremities rubbed*

FIRST EDITION, later published in German in 1706.

References: Berlin Catalogue 1983

£600-800
€900-1,200

1208 Lavoisier, Antoine Laurent (1743-1794). Essays physical and chemical... volume the first [all published], translated from the French, with notes, and an appendix, by Thomas Henry. *London: Joseph Johnson, 1776*

8vo (214 x 130mm.), xxxii, [2], 475, [1 (blank)] pp., ILLUSTRATION: 3 folding engraved plates, BINDING: nineteenth-century half calf by Hatton of Manchester, red morocco lettering-piece, *without final advertisement leaf*

"In 1774 Lavoisier published the first and only volume of his *Opuscules Physique et Chymiques*, a pioneer work in which he first gives a historical survey of previous workers' efforts and then describes his own experiments on gases and the conclusions to be derived from them" (Duveen & Klickstein, p.94).

References: Duveen & Klickstein, *Lavoisier* 124

£400-600
€600-900

1209 Leadbetter, Charles (1681-1744). Astronomy; or, the true system of the planets demonstrated. Wherein are shewn by instrument, their anomalies, heliocentrick and geocentrick places both in longitude and latitude... Likewise the places of the heavenly bodies and motion of the earth are not only shewn, but... demonstrated... by short and easie rules and new astronomical tables.... *London: for J. Wilcox and T. Heath, 1727*

4to (222 x 169mm.), [4], viii, [4 (advertisements and errata)], 120pp., ILLUSTRATION: woodcut initials and headpieces, engraved illustration, 11 engraved plates (8 folding), BINDING: contemporary speckled calf, spine gilt in compartments, morocco lettering-piece

FIRST EDITION. Leadbetter was a teacher of mathematics in London, and he placed advertisements in his books: "Astronomy in all its parts; with other parts of the Mathematicks, the use of the Globes, Maps, &c. are carefully taught by this Author, at his House the Hand and Pen, in Cock-Lane, near Shoreditch, London: or, at any Gentleman's Appartment".

References: not in Houzeau & Lancaster

£400-600
€600-900

1210 Leadbetter, Charles. Astronomy of the satellites of the Earth, Jupiter and Saturn: grounded upon Sir Isaac Newton's theory of the Earth's satellite. *London: for J. Wilcox, 1729*

FIRST EDITION, 8vo (203 x 122mm.), vii, [1], 96pp., ILLUSTRATION: woodcut diagrams and tailpiece, BINDING: contemporary speckled calf, spine gilt in compartments, morocco lettering-piece

References: Wallis 106.45; not in Houzeau & Lancaster

£300-400
€450-600

1211 Leadbetter, Charles. A treatise of eclipses of the sun and moon, for thirty-five years, commencing anno 1715, ending 1749... The second edition, with additions. *London: for J. Wilcox, 1731*

8vo (175 x 105mm.), [2 (advertisement)], v, [3], 176pp., ILLUSTRATION: woodcut diagrams, BINDING: contemporary speckled calf, spine gilt in compartments, morocco lettering-piece, *binding very slightly rubbed*

This work was originally published in 1727 with the title *Treatise of eclipses for three years, with the transits of Venus and Mercury over the Sun for 79 years, and the conjunctions of Jupiter and Saturn for 120 years.*

References: Houzeau & Lancaster 12122

£300-400
€450-600

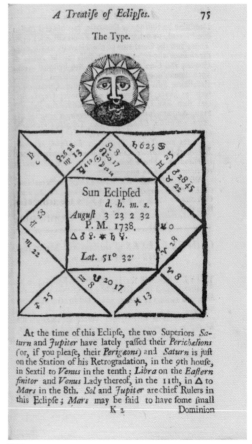

1211

1212

1212 Leadbetter, Charles. Uranoscopia: or, the contemplation of the heavens. Being a demonstration of the equation of time. With the method of observing the solar ingresses into any point of the ecliptic; and the investigation of the aphelions, and eccentricities of the planets. *London: for J. Wilcox, 1735*

FIRST EDITION, 8vo (192 x 118mm.), [6 (including half-title and engraved title-page], viii, [4], 590, [2 (advertisements)] pp., title printed in red and black, ILLUSTRATION: engraved frontispiece portrait of the author, woodcut headpieces and initials, woodcut diagrams, BINDING: contemporary mottled calf gilt, spine gilt in compartments, morocco lettering-piece, red edges, *text not printed on pp.87 and 450*

References: Houzeau & Lancaster 12129; Taylor, *Hanoverian* 84

£300-400
€450-600

1213 Leadbetter, Charles. A compleat system of astronomy, in two volumes. Containing the description and use of the sector... together with all the precepts of calculation... To the whole are prefix'd, astronomical definitions, for the benefit of young students. The second edition, with additions (New tables of the motions of the planets, and the fixed stars, and the first satellite of Jupiter... vol. II). *London: for J. Wilcox, 1742*

2 volumes, 8vo (205 x 122mm.), [24 (including frontispiece)], 486, [2 (advertisements)]; [4], 444pp., titles printed in red and black, ILLUSTRATION: engraved frontispiece portrait, woodcut initials and headpieces, woodcut diagrams, BINDING: contemporary smooth calf gilt, spine gilt in compartments, morocco lettering-pieces, red speckled edges, *O4 in vol. 2 torn without loss*

Originally published in 1728.

References: Houzeau & Lancaster 9249

£500-700
€750-1,050

1214 Le Clerc, Daniel (1652-1728). Histoire de la medecine, où l'on voit l'origine & les progrès de cet art, de siecle en siecle. *Amsterdam: George Gallet, 1702*, 4to (212 x 144mm.), [14], 274; 248; 205, [31]pp., title printed in red and black, ILLUSTRATION: engraved frontispiece, small engraving of Hippocrates on title-page, woodcut initials, head- and tailpieces, 5 engraved plates (2 folding), folding letterpress table, BINDING: contemporary calf, spine gilt in compartments, speckled edges, *binding slightly rubbed, upper joint cracking at foot*

Ibid. Histoire de la medecine... Nouvelle edition... *Amsterdam: aux depens de la Compagnie, 1723*, 4to (252 x 190mm.), [18], 820, [20]pp., title printed in red and black, ILLUSTRATION: engraved frontispiece, engraved vignette on title-page, woodcut initials, head- and tailpieces, 9 engraved plates, folding letterpress table, BINDING: contemporary calf, spine gilt in compartments, morocco lettering-piece, speckled edges, *binding slightly rubbed*

together 2 volumes

Originally published in 1696, "this was the most complete and reliable work on the history of medicine... and may still be consulted with profit" (Eimas, p.243).

References: Wellcome III, p.470; *1st work:* Cole 1106; *2nd work:* Eimas 682

£300-400
€450-600

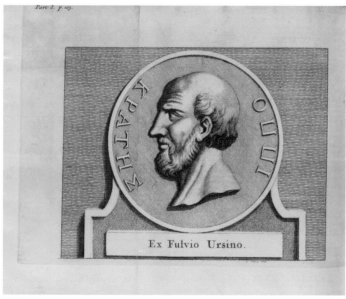

1214

1215 Le Clerc, Daniel. A natural and medicinal history of worms, bred in the bodies of men and other animals... together with an enquiry into the origin of worms, and the remedies which destroy them... [translated by Joseph Browne]. *London: for J. Wilcox, 1721*

FIRST EDITION IN ENGLISH, 8vo (192 x 115mm.), [28], 151, 160-436pp., ILLUSTRATION: woodcut initials and headpieces, 3 folding engraved plates, BINDING: contemporary panelled calf, morocco lettering-piece, *binding rubbed, upper joint weak*

References: Wellcome III, p.470; Cole 1107

Provenance: Edward Mansel, bookplate and inscription on title-page dated 1723

£300-400
€450-600

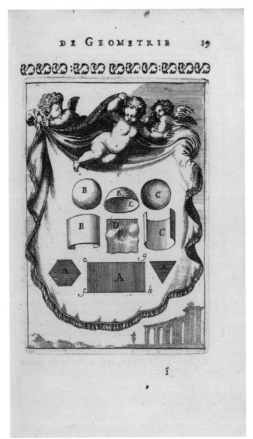

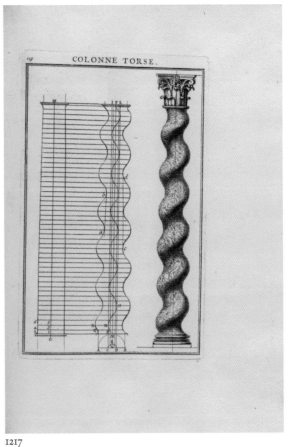

1216   1217

1216 Le Clerc, Sebastien (1637-1714). Pratique de la géometrie, sur le papier et sur le terrain. Avec un nouvel ordre & une methode particulière. *Paris: Thomas Jolly (imprimerie de Jean Cusson, 1668) 1669*

12mo (147 x 85mm.), [6], 4, [3 (2 blank)], 6-41 [1 (blank)], 139, [9]pp., ILLUSTRATION: engraved frontispiece and 82 full-page engravings in text, first leaf of dedication to the marquis de Seignelay partly engraved, BINDING: contemporary mottled calf, engraving on L6 printed upside-down

FIRST EDITION of this influential work.

References: Vagnetti EIIIb60

Provenance: William Herbert, presentation inscription by Herbert on flyleaf, dated 1671

£800-1,200
€1,200-1,750

1217 Le Clerc, Sebastien. Traité d'architecture avec des remarques et des observations très-utiles pour les jeunes gens, qui veulent s'appliquer à ce bel art. *Paris: Pierre Giffart, 1714*

2 volumes in one, 4to (245 x 184mm.), [8], 194, [2]pp.; [184 engraved leaves], ILLUSTRATION: 184 engraved plates (including title and sub-title to volume 2), 2 engraved head-pieces, woodcut head- and tail-pieces and initials, BINDING: contemporary calf, *binding slightly rubbed*

FIRST EDITION, published only a few months before Le Clerc's death.

References: BAL RIBA 1802

£400-500
€600-750

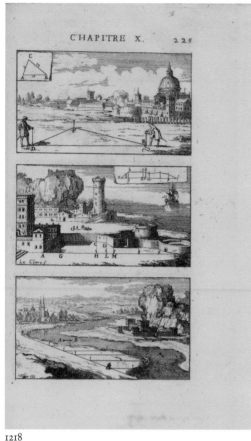

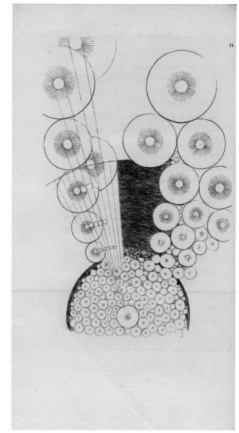

1218   1219

1218 Le Clerc, Sebastien. Traité de géometrie. *Paris: André Cailleau, 1719*

8vo (194 x 123mm.), [4], 229 [but 249]pp., ILLUSTRATION: 16 full-page engravings, woodcut diagrams in text, BINDING: contemporary speckled calf, *tears in G5, I5 & M5 with no loss*

£200-250
€300-400

1219 Le Clerc, Sebastien. Nouveau système du monde, conforme à l'ecriture sainte, où les phénomènes sont expliquez sans excentricité de mouvement... Revû & augmenté. *Paris: André Cailleau, 1719*

8vo (200 x 118mm.), [16], 200, [4]pp., ILLUSTRATION: 60 full-page engravings, one engraved head-piece, BINDING: contemporary speckled calf

£300-400
€450-600

1220 Le Clerc, Sebastien. Discours touchant le point de vue, dans lequel il est prouvé que les choses qu'on voit distinctement, ne sont vues que d'un oeil. *Paris: André Cailleau, 1719*

12mo (155 x 85mm.), [12], 86pp., ILLUSTRATION: one engraved plate, 24 full-page engravings, 9 full-page woodcut diagrams, one engraved head-piece, BINDING: contemporary speckled calf

This work was first published in 1679.

£200-300
€300-450

1221 [Lee, Weyman] An essay to ascertain the value of leases and annuities for years and lives, and to estimate the chances of the duration of lives. Wherein are many observations on bills of mortality... *London: for S. Birt, D. Browne, and J. Shuckburgh, 1737*

8vo (197 x 116mm.), xix, [1], 470, [6 (advertisements)] pp., ILLUSTRATION: woodcut initials, head- and tailpieces, BINDING: contemporary speckled calf gilt, spine gilt in compartments, morocco lettering-piece, *binding slightly rubbed*

FIRST EDITION, quickly reprinted the following year.

References: Kress 4343; not in Goldsmiths

Provenance: Tho. Clarke, inscription on flyleaf (Sir Thomas Clarke 1703-1764)

£400-600
€600-900

1222 Leeuwenhoek, Antoni van (1632-1723). Arcana naturae, ope & beneficio exquisitissimorum microscopiorum detecta... Editio altera. *Leiden: Cornelis Boutestein, 1696*

4to (202 x 148mm.), [10], 56, 49-58; [2], 124; 232, 231-258pp., ILLUSTRATION: additional engraved title-page by Romeyn de Hooghe, woodcut initials, head- and tailpieces, engraved illustrations, 16 engraved plates (7 folding), BINDING: contemporary panelled calf, red morocco lettering-piece, red speckled edges

Antoni van Leeuwenhoek, the founder of microscopy and protozoology, communicated his observations through the microscope in over a hundred letters (originally published in Dutch and later translated into Latin) mostly addressed to the Royal Society of London, which then published them in its *Philosophical Transactions*. He constructed his first microscope in 1671 and presented many specimens to the Royal Society. He was the first to see bacteria and red blood corpuscles, and correctly hypothesised the link between spermatozoa and fertilization.

References: Landwehr, *Romeyn de Hooghe* 69; cf. Norman 1320 (3rd edition of 1708); see also C. Dobell, *Antony van Leeuwenhoek and his "little animals"* (London, 1932), who confusingly states that this is the second edition of *Arcana naturae detecta* (1695), whereas it is in fact the second edition of *Anatomia seu interiora rerum* (1687).

£1,000-1,500
€1,450-2,200

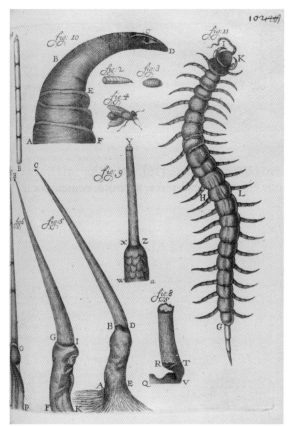

1222

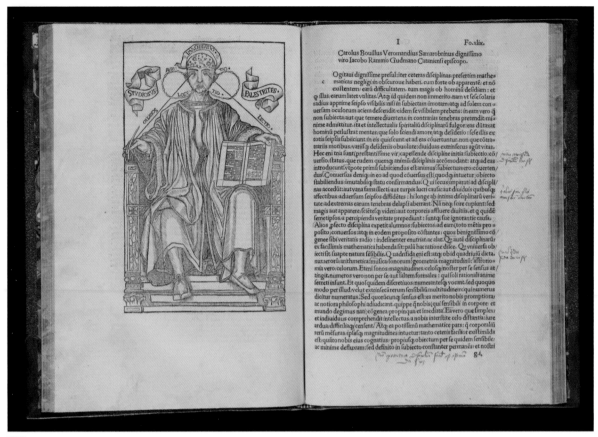

1223

1223 Le Fèvre d'Etaples, Jacques (d. 1536). In hoc libro contenta Epitome compendiosaque introductio in libros arithmeticos divi Severini Boetij: adiecto familiari commentario dilucidata. Praxis numerandi... Introductio in geometriam, [etc.]. *(Paris: Wolfgang Hopyl & Henri Estienne, 27 June 1503)*

folio (275 x 190mm.), ff. cxii, ILLUSTRATION: full-page cut on F8v, numerous woodcut diagrams in margins, woodcut initials, BINDING: nineteenth-century half calf by Hatton, *small repair to title*

One of the earliest books from Estienne's press. There are a few contemporary marginal notes in a French hand.

References: Renouard, *Estienne,* p.1; Moreau 1503/86; Schreiber 1

£1,500-2,000
€2,200-2,900

1224 Le Fèvre d'Etaples, Jacques. In hoc libro continetur. Introductorium astronomicum... adiecto commentario declaratum (by J. Clichtove). *Paris: H. Estienne, 9 December 1517*

folio (275 x 200mm.), ff. 56 (i.e. 66), ILLUSTRATION: woodcut title border, numerous woodcut illustrations in text, woodcut criblé initials in various sizes, BINDING: eighteenth-century vellum-backed boards, *a few paper repairs*

The work was originally published in 1503. This is the first edition with Clichtove's commentary.

References: Renouard, *Estienne,* p.20; Schreiber 27; Houzeau & Lancaster 2290

£700-1,000
€1,050-1,450

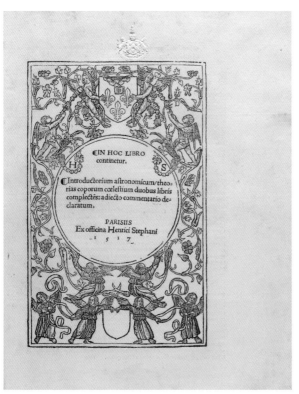

1224

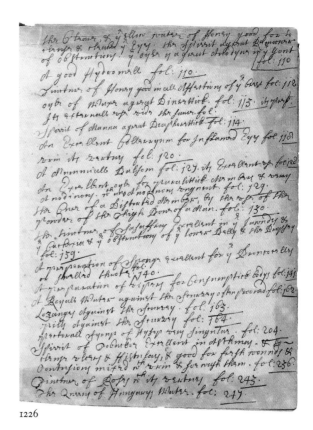

1226

1225 Le Fèvre, Jacques *and* **Josse van Clichtove (*c.* 1473-1543).** In hoc libro contenta. Epitome, compendiosaque introductio in libros arithmeticos divi Severini Boetij adiecto familiari commentario delucidata. Praxis numerandi... Editio secunda. *Paris: S. de Colines, (June 12) 1522*

folio (285 x 200mm.), ff. 48, BINDING: nineteenth-century half calf by Hatton, sixteenth-century manuscript annotations, *occasional foxing*

References: Renouard, *Colines,* pp. 38-39

£600-800
€900-1,200

1226 Le Fevre, Nicolas (d. 1674). A compleat body of chymistry: wherein is contained whatsoever is necessary for the attaining to the curious knowledge of this art; comprehending in general the whole practice thereof: and teaching the most exact preparation of animals, vegetables and minerals, so as to preserve their essential vertues. Laid open in two books, and dedicated to the use of all apothecaries, &c... Rendred into English by P[ierre] D[e] C[ardonnel]. *London: O. Pulleyn for John Wright, 1670*

4to (195 x 152mm.), [12], 286, [6]; 320, [8]pp., ILLUSTRATION: woodcut initials and headpieces, 5 folding engraved plates, folding engraved table, 2 full-page engraved illustrations, BINDING: contemporary calf, annotated on the front endpapers with contemporary jottings about various sections in the book, *A4 loose, paper flaw in Nn3, binding rubbed*

Le Fevre was professor of botany and chemistry at the Jardin du Roi, and this work (first published in French in 1660) is a collection of lectures given there by him. In 1664 he arrived in London at the invitation of Charles II and became a Fellow of the Royal Society (this 1670 English edition appears with two different title-pages, of which only one, the present one, mentions that he was a Fellow of the Royal Society).

References: Wing L926; Duveen p.346; Wellcome III, p.479

£500-700
€750-1,050

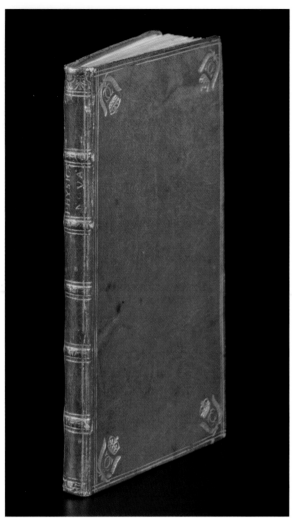

1227

1227 [Leibnitz, Gottfried Wilhelm von (1646-1716)] Hypothesis physica nova, quae phaenomenorum naturae plerorumque causae ab unico quodam universali motu, in globo nostro supposito, neque Tychonicis, neque Copernicanis aspernando, repetuntur. Nec non theoria motus abstracti. Autore G.G. L.L. *London: J. Martyn, 1671*

8vo (140 x 80mm.), 74 (C1 (pp. 49-50) folding with table on p. 49); 30pp., BINDING: bound for Charles II by Samuel Mearne, contemporary English red Turkey leather, double gilt fillet on covers, with crowned cross feathers and monogram C at corners, spine in 6 compartments with raised bands outlined by gilt fillets, lettered PHYSICA NOVA

BOUND FOR CHARLES II BY SAMUEL MEARNE. The second edition of this celebrated work in which Leibnitz first adumbrated his idea of *Monadalogie*. It was first printed in Mainz in 1671 and Leibnitz sent a copy to Oldenburg in London in March of that year. Oldenburg wrote a notice in *Philosophical Transactions* 73 (17 July 1671). Newton had a copy of the English reprint (Harrison 826).

For a discussion of Mearne's bindings with the royal cipher, see H.M. Nixon, *English Restoration bookbindings: Samuel Mearne and his contemporaries* (London, 1974).

References: Ravier 15

£4,000-6,000
€5,800-8,700

1228 Le Grand, Antoine (d. 1699).

Institutio philosophiae, secundum principia D. Renati Descartes. Nova methodo adornata, & explicata. In usum juventutis academicae. Editio quarta, prioribus editionibus multo auctior. *London: M. Clark for J. Martyn, 1680*

4to (208 x 150mm.), [4], xvi, [18], 731, [1 (blank)] pp., ILLUSTRATION: engraved frontispiece portrait of Le Grand, woodcut initials, woodcut and engraved illustrations, BINDING: contemporary calf with blind fillets and corner fleurons, *A2 & 3 partially stuck together, Hh2 torn without loss, extremities slightly rubbed*

Originally published in London in 1672, Le Grand's exposition of Descartes' theories proved a popular work. It was translated into English in 1694.

1228

References: Wing L957; Wellcome IV, p.480

Provenance: Thomas Parker of the Inner Temple (the first Earl of Macclesfield), armorial bookplate pasted to verso of title dated 1704

£250-300
€400-450

1229 Leipzig—Acta eruditorum. Opuscula omnia actis eruditorum lipsiensibus inserta, quae ad universam mathesim, physicam, medicinam, anatomiam, chirurgiam, et philologiam pertinent... Ab anno 1682 (ad annum 1710). *Venice: Giovanni Battista Pasquali, 1740-1743*

volumes 1-4 (of 7), 4to (236 x 165mm.), [8], 596; [8], 515, [5]; [8], 547; [4], 523pp., first title printed in red and black, one folding printed table in volume 4, ILLUSTRATION: 127 folding engraved plates, woodcut head-pieces and initials, BINDING: contemporary mottled calf, spines gilt in compartments

This reprint of selections was published in seven volumes between 1740 and 1746.

£300-400
€450-600

1230 Lemery, Nicolas (1645-1715). A course of chymistry: containing an easie method of preparing those chymical medicines which are used in physick. With curious remarks upon each preparation, for the benefit of such as desire to be instructed in the knowledge of this art. The fourth edition. Translated [by James Keill] from the eleventh edition in the French... *London: A. Bell, D. Midwinter, W. Taylor and John Osborn, 1720*

8vo (196 x 121mm.), xvi, 543, [1 (advertisement)] pp., ILLUSTRATION: engraved frontispiece, woodcut initials, head- and tailpieces, full-page woodcut illustrations, BINDING: contemporary calf gilt, spine gilt in compartments, morocco lettering-piece, *joints splitting, binding slightly rubbed*

References: Wellcome III, p.487

£300-400
€450-600

1231

1231 Le Monnier, Pierre Charles (1715-1799). Histoire celeste, ou recueil de toutes les observations astronomiques faites par ordre du Roy... *Paris: Briasson, 1741*

4to (254 x 187mm.), [12 (including frontispiece)], xcii, 368, [2]pp., ILLUSTRATION: engraved frontispiece, woodcut vignette on title-page, woodcut initials, head- and tailpieces, 6 folding engraved plates, BINDING: contemporary mottled calf gilt, spine gilt in compartments, morocco lettering-piece, red speckled edges

FIRST EDITION. Le Monnier was a well-respected astronomer, being admitted to the Académie royale at the age of twenty and becoming a favourite of the king, who then procured for him the best astronomical equipment available.

References: Norman 1330

£500-700
€750-1,050

1232 Le Monnier, Pierre Charles. La theorie des cometes, où l'on traite du progrès de cette partie d'astronomie; avec les tables pour calculer les mouvements des cometes, du soleil, & des principales etoiles fixes. *Paris: Gab. Martin, J.B. Coignard & les freres Guerin, 1743*

8vo (200 x 119mm.), [6], xlvi, 192, [8]pp., ILLUSTRATION: woodcut vignette on title-page, woodcut initials, head- and tailpieces, folding letterpress table, 4 folding engraved plates, BINDING: contemporary calf gilt, spine gilt in compartments, morocco lettering-piece, red speckled edges

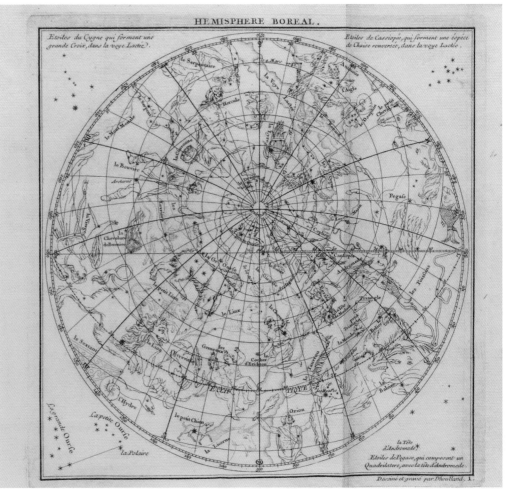

1232

FIRST EDITION. This work demonstrates Le Monnier's regard for developments in English astronomy, taking much of its material from Halley's *Cometographia* of 1726.

References: Houzeau & Lancaster 11947

£400-600
€600-900

1233 Le Monnier, Pierre Charles. Astronomie nautique lunaire où l'on traite de la latitude & de la longitude en mer, de la période ou saros, des parallaxes de la lune avec des tables du nonagésime sous l'équateur & sous les tropiques, suivies d'autres tables des mouvemens du soleil & des étoiles fixes, auxquelles la lune sera comparée dans les voyages de long cours. *Paris: Imprimerie Royale, 1771*

8vo (196 x 120mm.), [6], xxiv, 112, [4]pp., ILLUSTRATION: woodcut device on title-page, woodcut initials and headpieces, BINDING: contemporary speckled calf, red morocco lettering-piece, *occasional slight spotting*

FIRST EDITION. "Le Monnier supported the view of Edmond Halley that the irregularities of the moon's motion could be discovered by observing the moon regularly through an entire cycle of 223 lunations (the saros cycle of approximately eighteen years and eleven days), with the assumption that the irregularities would repeat themselves throughout each cycle" (*DSB*).

References: Houzeau & Lancaster 10757

£200-300
€300-450

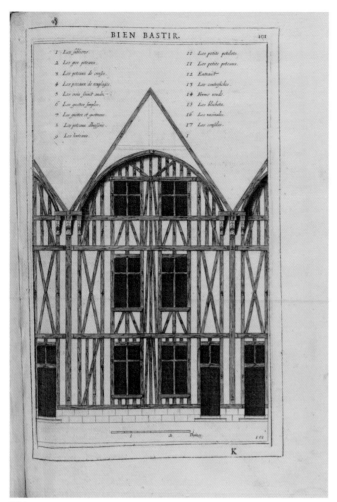

1234

1235

1234 Le Muet, Pierre (1591-1669). Maniere de bien bastir pour toutes sortes de personnes... Revue, augmentee et enrichie en cette seconde edition de plusieurs figures, de beaux bastimens & edifices, de l'invention & conduitte dudit sieur le Muet, & autres (Augmentations de nouveaux bastimens faits en France). *Paris: François Langlois, 1647*

2 parts in one volume, folio (354 x 242mm.), [8 (including engraved title)], 113, [1 (blank)]; [2]pp., ILLUSTRATION: additional engraved title-page, woodcut device on printed titles, woodcut initials and headpieces, full-page engraved illustrations (one double-page), replacement plate pasted onto p.63, 31 engraved plates (22 folding), BINDING: eighteenth-century mottled calf, spine gilt in compartments, red morocco lettering-piece, *a few plates torn and repaired or shaved, extremities rubbed, joints weak*

This, the second edition of Muet's treatise, contains an extra suite of plates not present in the first edition of 1623, with views and plans of various chateaux. The plates in the first section depict elevations and plans of town houses of varying sizes.

References: Fowler 177; Cicognara 574

£1,000-1,500
€1,450-2,200

1235 Lencker, Hans (*c.* 1550-1590). Hansen Lenckers... Perspectiva in welcher ein leichter Weg allerley Ding es seyen Corpora Gebew. *Ulm: Johann Meder for Stephan Michelspacher, 1617*

folio (297 x 192mm.), [20], 43, [1]pp., ILLUSTRATION: engraved border on title-page, engraved portrait of Lencker by Kilian, dated 1616, on)(6 verso, woodcut illustrations and diagrams (one double-page), BINDING: eighteenth-century vellum-backed boards, *A1 misbound after D2*

Lencker was, together with Stoer, Jamnitzer and Hirschvogel, one of a group of Nuremberg perspectivists who specialised in portraying geometrical bodies, inspired both by Dürer and Pacioli. Lencker's *Perspectiva* was first published in 1571.

References: Berlin Catalogue 4698; cf. M. Kemp, *The Science of Art* (London, 1990), pp.62-63

£2,000-3,000
€2,900-4,350

1236 Leonardo da Vinci (1452-1519). A Treatise of painting... translated from the original Italian, and adorn'd with a great number of cuts. To which is prefix'd, the author's life; done from the last edition of the French. *London: for J. Senex and W. Taylor, 1721*

8vo (195 x 121mm.), [16], 189, [19]pp., title printed in red and black, ILLUSTRATION: engraved frontispiece and 35 plates, woodcut initials, head- and tail-pieces, BINDING: eighteenth-century mottled calf

FIRST EDITION IN ENGLISH. The *Trattato* was first published in Paris in 1651, with the life of Leonardo by Raphael Du Fresne.

£900-1,200
€1,350-1,750

1236

1237 Le Poivre, Jacques-François. Traité des sections du cylindre et du cône, considerées dans le solide & dans le plan, avec des démonstrations simples & nouvelles. *Paris: Barthelemy Girin, 1704*

8vo (193 x 118mm.), [10], 5, [1], 61, [2]pp., ILLUSTRATION: woodcut vignette on title, woodcut headpieces and initials, 8 folding engraved plates, BINDING: contemporary speckled calf, spine gilt in compartments, *some light spotting, spine worn*

The only published work by Le Poivre, about whom little is known. This treatise was reviewed in both the *Acta Eruditorum* (1707) and the *Journal des Sçavans* (1704).

References: Conlon 12308

£300-500
€450-750

1238   1240

1238 Leunenschloss, Johann von (b. 1620). Thesaurus mathematum reseratus per algebram novam tam speciebus quam numeris declaratam et demonstratam. Cui praefixa universae philosophiae mathematicarum in primis disciplinarum synopsis. *Padua: Crivellari, 1646*

folio (324 x 222mm.), [48 (including frontispiece)], 311, [21]pp., ILLUSTRATION: engraved frontispiece, engraved coat-of-arms of the dedicatee (Ludovicus de Geer) on verso of title-page, 3 folding letterpress tables, woodcut initials and tailpieces, engraved and woodcut diagrams, engraved plate, BINDING: contemporary vellum, *binding a little soiled and warped*

FIRST EDITION, RARE. This book has appeared once at auction in the last thirty years (the Honeyman copy, in 1980) and ICCU records only one copy, in Padua. Leunenschloss (or Luneschlos) was professor of mathematics and rector at the University of Heidelberg.

£2,000-3,000
€2,900-4,350

1239 Leunenschloss, Johann von. Tractatus de corpore. Figuris aeneis elegantissimis illustratus. *Heidelberg: Adrian Wyngaerde, 1658*

FIRST EDITION, 4to (195 x 150mm.), [18], [128]pp., ILLUSTRATION: engraved device on title-page, 20 engraved plates, BINDING: contemporary calf, flat spine gilt, *binding rubbed*

£400-500
€600-750

1240 Leupold, Jakob (1674-1727). Theatrum machinarum generale. Schau-Platz des Grundes mechanische Wissenschaften. *Leipzig: C. Zunkel, for the author and son of J.F. Gleditsch, 1724,* [20], 240, [4]pp., title printed in red and black, ILLUSTRATION: woodcut initials, head- and tailpieces, 71 engraved plates

Ibid. Theatrum machinarum hydrotechnicarum... *Leipzig: C. Zunkel, for the author and son of J.F. Gleditsch, 1724,* [12], 184, [4]pp., title printed in red and black, ILLUSTRATION: woodcut initials, head- and tailpieces, 51 engraved plates, *half-title detached*

Ibid. Theatrum machinarium... *Leipzig: C. Zunkel, for the author and son of J.F. Gleditsch, 1725,* [16], 162, [4]pp., title printed in red and black, ILLUSTRATION: woodcut initials, head- and tailpieces, 56 engraved plates (one double-page), *folding plate detached*

3 works in one volume, folio (382 x 235mm.), BINDING: contemporary mottled calf gilt, spine gilt in compartments, morocco lettering-pieces, red and speckled edges, *some light browning, calf detaching from boards at edges*

FIRST EDITIONS of these three treatises by Leupold which form part of a nine-volume set, published between 1724 and 1739. Leupold was director of mines to the Elector of Saxony and his *Theatrum machinarum* was an early enyclopedic work on technology with extensive illustrations.

£2,000-3,000
€2,900-4,350

1241 Leupold, Jakob. Theatrum machinarum hydraulicarum. Tomus I (-II). Oder, Schau-Platz der Wasser-Künste. Erste (-Anderer) theil. *Leipzig: C. Zunkel, for the author and son of J.F. Gleditsch, 1724,* [14], 172, [2]; [20], 165, [3]pp., titles printed in red and black, ILLUSTRATION: woodcut initials, head- and tailpieces, 53+52 engraved plates (2 folding)

Ibid. Pars I (-IV) theatri statici universalis... *Leipzig: C. Zunkel, for the author and son of J.F. Gleditsch, 1726,* [12], 92; [4], 197-236; [4], 241-308; [4], 313-332, [4]pp., title printed in red and black, ILLUSTRATION: woodcut initials, head- and tailpieces, 57 engraved plates

FIRST EDITIONS, 2 works in one volume, folio (381 x 237mm.), BINDING: contemporary mottled calf gilt, spine gilt in compartments, morocco lettering-pieces, red and speckled edges, *calf detaching from boards at edges*

£2,500-3,000
€3,650-4,350

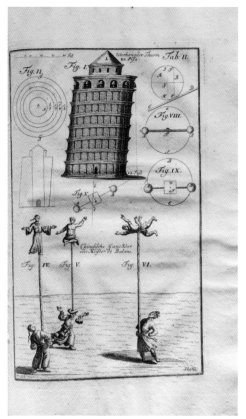

1241

1242 Leupold, Jakob. Theatrum arithmetico-geometricum, das ist: Schau-Platz der Rechen- und Mess-Kunst. *Leipzig: C. Zunkel, for the author and son of J.F. Gleditsch, 1727*

folio (375 x 240mm.), [12], 300[=200]pp., ILLUSTRATION: 45 engraved plates, numbered I-XLIII, with XXb & XXIb, BINDING: contemporary German mottled calf, spine gilt, red morocco lettering-piece, red edges

A large copy on thick paper. Various calculating machines are illustrated.

£2,000-3,000
€2,900-4,350

1243 Leutmann, Johann Georg (1667-1736). Instrumenta meteorognosiae inservientia I. Thermoscopia, II. Baroscopia, III. Hygroscopium, IV. Anemometrum, V. Plagoscopium, VI. Hyetometrum... *Wittenberg: widow of B. Godofrid Zimmermann, 1725*

8vo (174 x 102mm.), [26], 175, [1]pp., title printed in red and black, ILLUSTRATION: woodcut headpieces, 19 engraved plates (1 folding), BINDING: contemporary mottled calf gilt, spine gilt in compartments, morocco lettering-piece, red edges, *extremities slightly rubbed*

FIRST EDITION. Leutmann studied theology and mathematics in Wittenberg and became professor of mechanics and optics at the Academy of Sciences in St Petersburg, where he died.

£500-700
€750-1,050

1244 Lewis, William (1708-1781). A course of practical chemistry. In which are contained all the operations described in Wilson's Complete course of chemistry... *London: for J. Nourse, 1746*

8vo (202 x 121mm.), [20], 368, 379-432, [42]pp., final unnumbered section containing index, 2 advertisement leaves and explanations of plates, ILLUSTRATION: 9 engraved plates, BINDING: contemporary polished calf, morocco lettering-piece, speckled edges

FIRST EDITION. Lewis was elected to the Royal Society in 1745 and pursued pharmaceutical as well as chemical research.

£150-200
€250-300

1245 Lewis, William. Commercium philosophico-technicum; or, the philosophical commerce of arts: designed as an attempt to improve arts, trades, and manufactures. *London: H. Baldwin for the author, to be sold by R. Willock, 1763*

4to (258 x 198mm.), [8], xviii, x, 646, [14]pp., ILLUSTRATION: woodcut head- and tailpieces, 6 engraved plates (1 folding), BINDING: contemporary calf, morocco lettering-piece, *extremities slightly rubbed, lettering-piece chipped, joints cracking at head*

FIRST EDITION. Some copies are recorded with an extra title-page between pp.314 and 315, dated 1765, not present in this copy. Lewis printed a proposal for a journal called *Commercium philosophico-technicum* in 1748, but it never came to fruition. This work covers a wide range of chemical subjects.

References: Kress 6114; Goldsmiths 9846

£300-400
€450-600

1246

1246 Levera, Francesco (*fl.* 1650-1670). Prodromus universae astronomiae restitutae de anni solaris, & siderei, ac dierum magnitudine [etc.]. *Rome: A. Bernabo, 1663*, [8], 417, [15]pp., ILLUSTRATION: additional engraved title, dedicated to Queen Christina of Sweden

Ibid. De inerrantium stellarum viribus, & excellentia [etc.]. *Rome: A. Bernabo, 1664*, 105, [7]pp., dedicated to Queen Christina of Sweden

Muti, Savinio. Dialogus contra duas hic transcriptas epistolas [by Riccioli & Cassini] nuper editas in Prodromum F. Leverae. *Rome: A. Bernabo, 1664*, [2], 63, [1]pp.

Palazzi, Pietro. Novae ephemerides motuum solis ab anno 1664. usque ad annnum 1670 completum [etc.]. *Rome: A. Bernabo, 1664*, [12], 60, [4]pp.

4 works in one volume, folio (335 x 210mm.), BINDING: contemporary English calf, spine gilt

A collection of rare and unusual pieces. The British Library has a similar volume.

References: Riccardi ii, 36-37 (Levera), 190 (Muti), 258 (Palazzi)

£2,000-3,000
€2,900-4,350

1247 Leybourn, William (1626-1716). A platform for purchasers, a guide for builders, a mate for measurers, in three books. *London: Thomas Ratcliffe and Thomas Daniel for Nathanial Brooks, 1668*

8vo (155 x 88mm.), [12], 160, [8], 161-200pp., ILLUSTRATION: woodcut initials, 2 folding engraved plates, BINDING: eighteenth-century calf, spine gilt in compartments, red morocco lettering-piece, *lacking A1 (with woodcut arms) and A8 (blank?), some leaves shaved*

FIRST EDITION. "The *Platform* just missed being the first book to deal with the economics of the ownership of land and the erection of houses on it" (Harris, p.292).

References: BAL RIBA 1892; Harris 510; Wing L1930

£400-600
€600-900

1248 Leybourn, William. Arithmetick: vulgar, decimal, instrumental, algebraical... The third edition, corrected and inlarged. *London: J. Streeter for George Sawbridge, (parts 2 & 3 dated 1668)*

4 parts in one volume, 8vo (164 x 99mm.), [14], 436, [2 (advertisement)] pp., ILLUSTRATION: engraved portrait, one folding engraved plate, BINDING: contemporary calf, flat spine gilt, *some browning and spotting, small burn-hole in text of Bb6, binding rubbed at edges, upper joint split*

References: Wing L1893B (one copy only); cf. Taylor, *Tudor and Stuart* 227 (first edition)

Provenance: James Hardres, inscription on flyleaf dated 10 December 1669

£200-300
€300-450

1249 Leybourn, William. Panorganon: or, a universal instrument, performing all such conclusions geometrical and astronomical as are usually wrought by the globes, spheres, sectors, quadrants, planispheres, or other like instruments. *London: for William Birch, 1672*

FIRST EDITION, 2 parts in one volume, 4to (188 x 141mm.), [6], 140; [8], 119pp. ILLUSTRATION: engraved portrait, 2 folding engraved plates, BINDING: contemporary calf, *some light browning and spotting*

References: Wing L1928; Taylor, *Tudor and Stuart* 346

£500-700
€750-1,050

1250 Leybourn, William. The line of proportion or numbers, commonly called Gunter's Line, made easie. *London: J.S. for G. Sawbridge, 1673*

12mo (125 x 72mm.), [6], 153, [3]pp., ILLUSTRATION: one folding engraved plate, BINDING: contemporary red morocco gilt, crowned cypher of Charles II at corners and in spine compartments (see lot 1227), gilt edges, *small paper flaw in upper margin of G6*

References: Wing L1917; cf. Taylor, *Tudor and Stuart* 304

£300-400
€450-600

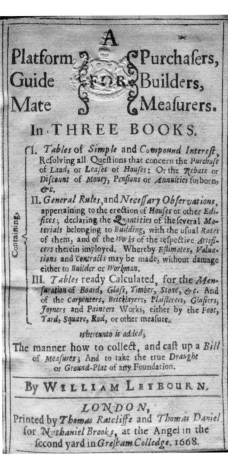

A

Platform Purchasers,
Guide FOR Builders,
Mate Measurers.

In·THREE BOOKS.

Containing,

I. *Tables* of *Simple* and *Compound Interest,*
Resolving all Questions that concern the *Purchase*
of *Land,* or *Leases* of *Houses:* Or the *Rebate* or
Discount of *Money, Pensions* or *Annuities* forborn,
&c.

II. *General Rules,* and *Necessary Observations,*
appertaining to the erection of *Houses* or other *Edifices;* declaring the *Quantities* of the several *Materials* belonging to *Building,* with the usual *Rates*
of them, and of the *Works* of the respective *Artificers* therein imployed. Whereby *Estimates, Valuations* and *Contracts* may be made, without damage
either to *Builder* or *Workman.*

III. *Tables* ready Calculated, for the *Men-
suration* of *Board, Glass, Timber, Stone, &c.* And
of the *Carpenters, Bricklayers, Plaisterers, Glasiers,
Joyners* and *Painters* Works, either by the *Foot,
Yard, Square, Rod,* or other measure.

whereunto is added;

The manner how to collect, and cast up a *Bill*
of *Measures;* And to take the true *Draught*
or *Ground-Plat* of any Foundation.

By WILLIAM LEYBOURN.

LONDON,
Printed by *Thomas Ratcliffe* and *Thomas Daniel*
for *Nathaniel Brooks,* at the Angel in the
second yard in *Gresham Colledge.* 1668.

1247

EFFIGIES AVTHORIS.

1249

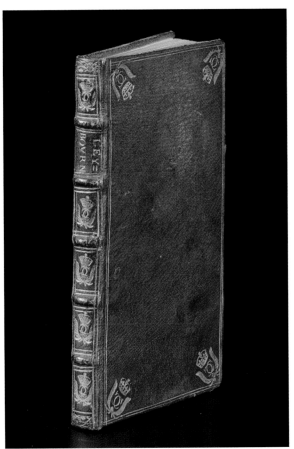

1250

printed for John Williamson 1677. T: Cross sculpsit

1251

1251 Leybourn, William. The art of measuring, containing the description and explanation of the carpenters new rule... The third edition... To which is added a supplement [by John Wiblin]. *London: for Richard Northcott, 1681 (1677)*

2 parts in one volume, 8vo (145 x 90mm.), [14], 39, 1-32, [33-144], 145-162; [2], 44, [4]pp., ILLUSTRATION: engraved frontispiece, one folding engraved plate, woodcut diagrams in text, BINDING: contemporary speckled calf, *joints partly split*

A reissue of the 1677 edition.

References: Wing L1903A

Provenance: "Scarce & valuable book Anno 1709, Dan King", inscription at head of title

£200-250
€300-400
For illustration see previous page

1252 Leybourn, William. Cursus mathematicus. Mathematical sciences, in nine books. *London: for Thomas Basset, Benjamin Tooke, Thomas Sawbridge, Awnsham and John Churchill, 1690*

FIRST EDITION, folio (323 x 197mm.), [16], 904 [i.e. 1044], [92]pp., title printed in red and black, ILLUSTRATION: engraved portrait, 44 engraved plates (most folding), engraved illustrations in text, BINDING: contemporary calf, *short tear in Æ1 without loss, small ink-stain in lower margin of last few leaves, binding rubbed*

References: Wing L1911; Taylor, *Tudor and Stuart* 480; Houzeau & Lancaster 9333

Provenance: James King, Harwich, September 3rd 1715, inscription on flyleaf

£500-700
€750-1,050

1253 Leybourn, William. Pleasure with profit: consisting of recreations of divers kinds, viz. numerical, geometrical, mechanical... To this work is also annext, a treatise of algebra... by R. Sault. *London: for Nathaniel Rolls, 1695*

12 parts in one volume, folio (305 x 186mm.), [4], vi, [2], 56; 86; 31; 24; 63; 28; 13; 2-10; 10; 11; 26; [4], 52pp. ILLUSTRATION: 2 folding engraved plates, woodcut and engraved diagrams in text, BINDING: contemporary mottled calf, *some light paper browning, binding rubbed*

This work was first printed in the previous year.

References: Wing L1932; Wellcome III, p.513

£250-300
€400-450

1252

1254 Leybourn, William. Arithmetical recreations: or, enchiridion of arithmetical questions: both delightful and profitable. All of them performed without algebra... The third edition... *London: for Ch. Brome, 1699*

12mo (140 x 85mm.), [8], 163, [1 (blank)] pp., BINDING: contemporary speckled calf, spine gilt in compartments, *boards detached*

Originally published in 1667 and again in 1676.

References: Wing L1899

£200-300
€300-450

1255 Leybourn, William. The art of dialling, performed geometrically.. arithmetically... instrumentally... The fourth edition with copper plates. To which is added a supplement. *London: George Sawbridge, 1702*

2 parts in one volume, 4to (199 x 155mm.), [6], 166; 3-24pp., ILLUSTRATION: 7 engraved plates (some loosely inserted), woodcut diagrams in text, BINDING: contemporary panelled calf, *lacking final advertisement of part 1 and title-page to part 2 (as in British Library copy), binding slightly rubbed, spine chipped at head and foot*

This edition is a reissue, with a cancel title-page, of the second edition of *The art of dialling* (1681) and the *Supplement* of 1689.

£200-250
€300-400

1256 L'Hospital, Guillaume François Antoine (1661-1704), *marquis de.* Analyse des infiniment petits, pour l'intelligence des lignes courbes... Seconde édition. *Paris: François Montalant, 1716*

4to (256 x 192mm.), xvi, 182pp., ILLUSTRATION: 11 folding engraved plates, BINDING: contemporary speckled calf gilt, *some light spotting*

Second edition of L'Hospital's *Analyse des infiniment petits*, the first text-book of the differential calculus. The work was first published in 1696. Some copies appear to contain an engraved portrait of the author, which is not present here.

£200-300
€300-450

1257 L'Hospital, Guillaume François Antoine, *marquis de.* An analytick treatise of conick sections, and their use for resolving of equations in determinate and indeterminate problems... made English by E[dmund] Stone. *London: for J. Senex, W. Taylor, W. & J. Innys and J. Osborn, 1723*

4to (227 x 170mm.), viii, 352pp., title printed in red and black, ILLUSTRATION: 33 folding engraved plates, woodcut vignette on title, woodcut head- and tail-pieces, BINDING: contemporary calf gilt, *lacking spine-label*

FIRST EDITION IN ENGLISH of L'Hospital's *Traité analytique des sections coniques*, first published posthumously in 1720. The mathematician Edmund Stone (1700-1768) also published a translation of L'Hospital's *Analyse des infiniment petits* (see lot 1256).

£200-300
€300-450

1258 L'Hospital, Guillaume François Antoine, *marquis de.* The Method of fluxions both direct and inverse. The former being a translation from... L'Hospital's Analyse des infiniments petits: and the latter supply'd by the translator, E[dmund] Stone, F.R.S. *London: for William Innys, 1730*

2 parts in one volume, 8vo (203 x 118mm.), xx, iv, 238; [2], 212, [2 (errata)] pp., ILLUSTRATION: 15 folding engraved plates, woodcut head- and tail-pieces, BINDING: contemporary calf gilt, *short tear in E2 without loss*

FIRST EDITION IN ENGLISH of L'Hospital's *Analyse des infiniment petits*, translated by Edmund Stone, who, according to the title-page, also supplied the second part of this work, about the integral calculus. This was itself translated into French in 1735.

£300-400
€450-600

1259

1259 Liceti, Fortunio (1577-1657). De monstris, ex recensione Gerardi Blasii... qui monstra quaedam nova & rariora ex recentiorum scriptis addidit. Editio novissima, iconibus illustrata. *Amsterdam: Andreas Frisius, 1665*

4to (195 x 147mm.), [18 (including frontispiece], 1-262, [2], 335-347, [1], 277, 350-351, 280-316, [26]pp., ILLUSTRATION: engraved frontispiece, engraved device on title-page, woodcut initials, engraved illustrations (some repeated), 3 engraved plates, BINDING: contemporary panelled calf, *binding rubbed*

Originally published in 1616, without illustrations, Liceti's treatise contains both genuine and imaginary cases of human and animal deformities, and was still in use by medical professionals in the nineteenth century.

References: Krivatsy 6959; Wellcome III, p.514; cf. Garrison-Morton 534.52

£600-800
€900-1,200

1260 Liebknecht, Johann Georg (1679-1749). Elementa geographiae generalis triplici sectione exposita... *Frankfurt: Dominicus a Sande, 1712*

FIRST EDITION, 8vo (172 x 94mm.), [16], 476, [34]pp., ILLUSTRATION: woodcut device on title-page, woodcut initials, engraved and woodcut head- and tailpieces, 25 engraved plates, BINDING: contemporary calf with roll-tooled panels with corner fleurons, spine gilt in compartments, *binding rubbed, joints weak*

£100-150
€150-250

1261 Limning and Perspective—Sanderson, *Sir* **William (1586?-1676).** Graphice: the use of the pen and pencil. Or, the most excellent art of painting: in two parts. *London: for Robert Crofts, 1658,* FIRST EDITION, [16], 87, [1 (blank)] pp., ILLUSTRATION: 2 engraved portraits (of Charles I and Mary Ruthven, wife of Antony van Dyck), woodcut initials and headpieces, [Wing S648], *lacking portrait of the author, occasional browning*

Serlio, Sebastiano (1475-1554). A book of perspective & geometry, being the ABC, and first degree of all good art... This second book of architecture... translated out of Italian into Dutch, and out of Dutch into English, for the benifit of our English nation. *London: M.S. for Thomas Jenner, 1657,* [2], 30pp., ILLUSTRATION: woodcut initials and headpieces, 22 engraved plates, [Harris 818, calling for 24 plates; Wing S2623], *?lacking 2 plates, upper corner of C2 torn (affecting 2 words), a few page numerals shaved*

[Ibid.] A new-naturalised work of a learned stranger. Or, an exquisite tutor powerfull to benefit the publick, and convey unto English men, especially architects & artificers of all sorts... Necessary certaine and most ready helps of geometrie, which is the first degree of all good art... *London: M.S. for Thomas Jenner, 1657,* [2], 11 (i.e. 12)pp., ILLUSTRATION: woodcut initials, head- and tailpieces, engraved illustrations, [Harris 819; Wing N680A], *a few leaves shaved at foot*

Gaultier, René, *sieur de Maignannes.* Invention nouvelle et brieve, pour reduire en perspective, par le moien de quarré, toutes sortes de plans, & corps, comme edifices, meubles, &c. Composé par R.G.S.D.M. Angevin. *La Flèche: George Griveau, 1648,* FIRST EDITION, [20], 98, 97-110, [2]pp. (pages 97-98 repeated but with different text, the first probably being the cancellandum), ILLUSTRATION: woodcut device on title-page, woodcut initials, head- and tailpieces, woodcut coat-of-arms (repeated), 7 folding engraved plates, engraved illustrations, other engravings cut out and pasted to edge of relevant leaves, [*Rép. bibl. xviie siècle,* La Flèche 214bis], *a few leaves and plates shaved at foot*

4 works in one volume, folio (260 x 168mm.), BINDING: eighteenth-century mottled calf, spine gilt in compartments, red morocco lettering-piece, red edges

£2,000-3,000
€2,900-4,350

1261

In hoe grootten Pervickel het gansche Jaar door, ens geheele Lande, so mies het Ondeugender worden vandeZyeken, als het verswaaren eer waatteren, sig overnat, is maar

En tot Blyck van welcke Ruineusheyt en seer slegte Toestandt, van ese aloeroudste en euderwetste Zee-Dyk, den Heer H. de selve seer wel en Pertinent, sedanig Maniere ende de Middelen, onse op't sterckste en fuyngste weder te herstellen. Als voor eerst, dat mend'er bevooren van soude moeten wegruymen en afbreecken, all Ende ten derden hier, niet alleen, nog plaatsen de see onneste ende meest beswaarende Riet-Voeten, met see veele Aarde-Graaf en andere Wercken meer, daar op en Buyten daar door heen te maken w. Van alle 't welk, de kosten niet uyt te spreecken, veel min te betaalen; en nogtans, alle geheel nodeloos, onnut en te vergeefs souden

1262

1262 [Listingh, Nicolaas (1630-1702)] Incitamentum & adiumentum. Dat is opweckinge ende aanleydinge tot het uytvinden van bequaame Middelen en gronden om de zee-dycken in Hollandt en West-Vrieslandt, tegens het soo dickwils doorbreecken en geduyrig afspoelen beter, als tot nog toe te beschermen en te bevreyden (Incitamentum... secundum, dat is een tweede opwecking en aanleiding, so tot het vereischte beeter versorgen en meerder verstercken van de oude magteloose Muyder-Zee-Dyk... nu ontdeckt en wederlegt door N. L[istingh] j[uris] c[onsultum]. *Amsterdam: P. Matthysz, 1702 (-1705)*

4to (195 x 150mm.), [5], 51, [1 (blank)], 1-5, [1 (blank)], 57-86, plus 2 blank leaves; 40, 4pp., ILLUSTRATION: 9 large folding engraved plates, BINDING: eighteenth-century English calf, gilt spine, morocco label lettered "Dutch Sea Dyckes"

£1,500-2,000
€2,200-2,900

1263 Loehneyss, Georg Engelhard von (1552-1622). Gründlicher und auszführlicher Bericht von Bergwercken... *Stockholm and Hamburg: Gottfried Liebezeit; Leipzig: Christopff Günther, 1690*

folio (330 x 195mm.), [10], 76pp., ff. 76-80, 81-82pp., ff. 83-84, 85-320pp., ff. 321-328, 329-343, [1 (blank)] pp., ILLUSTRATION: additional engraved title-page, woodcut initials, 16 folding engraved plates, BINDING: contemporary mottled calf, spine gilt in compartments, morocco lettering-piece, *some browning, extremities rubbed*

This treatise on mining and metallurgy was first published in 1617. Loehneyss was a courtier and statesman in Wolffenbüttel, and also wrote works on political science and horsemanship.

References: Ferguson II, p.43; VD17 3:623071T

£1,000-1,500
€1,450-2,200

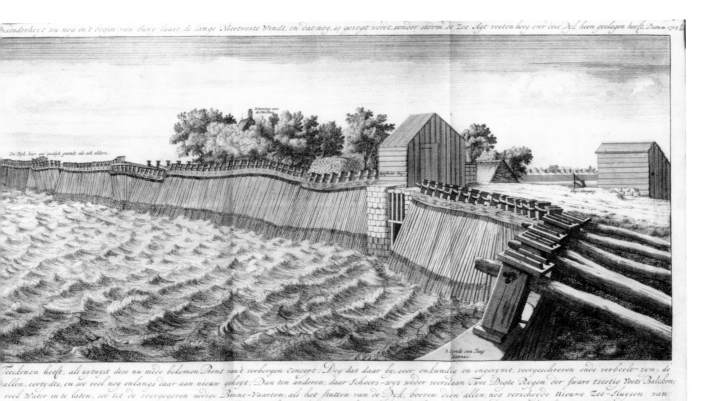

1264 Loir, Alexis (1630-1713). Nouveaux desseins d'ornemens de paneaux, lambris, carosse &c. Inventez et gravez par A. Loire (Frises et ornemens de paneaux...). *Paris: N. Langlois, [1680]*, ILLUSTRATION: 2 engraved title-pages, 10 engraved plates, [Berlin Catalogue 338 (item 1) & 340], *stain affecting 5 leaves*

Marot, Daniel (*c.* 1663-1752). Nouveaux livre de boites de pendulles de coqs et etuys de montres et autres necessaire au orlogeurs (Second livre d'orlogeries). *[The Hague, c. 1690]*, ILLUSTRATION: 12 engraved plates, [cf. BAL RIBA 2041 (items 14-15); Berlin Catalogue 356 (items 16-17)]

2 works in one volume, folio (305 x 195mm.), both works engraved throughout, BINDING: eighteenth-century calf-backed marbled paper boards, spine gilt in compartments, red morocco lettering-piece

Marot, a French architect and designer, fled France in 1685 after the revocation of the Edict of Nantes. He went to Holland where he became architect to William of Orange, and followed him to England when he became William III.

Each of these works was part of a series of architectural and ornamental details and plans, issued separately but often bound with others from the series.

£800-1,000
€1,200-1,450

1264

1265 Lomazzo, Giovanni Paolo (1538-1600). Trattato de l'arte e de la pittura... diviso in sette libri. Ne' quali si contiene tutta la theorica, & la prattica d'essa pittura. *Milan: Paolo Gottardo da Ponte, 1584*

4to (205 x 146mm.), [40], 692, 695-700, [6]pp., last three leaves containing errata and an additional chapter 17 for book 6, ILLUSTRATION: woodcut arms on title-page of the dedicatee (Carlo Emanuele, grand duke of Savoy), woodcut initials, woodcut medallion portrait of the author after Annibale Fontana, BINDING: eighteenth-century speckled calf gilt, spine gilt in compartments, morocco lettering-piece, red speckled edges, *binding a little rubbed*

Lomazzo, a painter by trade, was a pupil of Gaudenzio Ferrari. The onset of blindness at the age of 33 turned him to the theory and philosophy of art. Strongly Neoplatonist in his views, he believed that beauty was something divine infused into man, independent of sense impressions, a spiritual grace ("una certa grazia vivace & spirituale"). He was much influenced by astrology, and in his attitude towards mathematics and its relationship with painting, he turned away from the geometrical attitude of the early humanists towards one that relied more on the individual eye.

References: Censimento 16 CNCE 24452; Cicognara 159; A. Blunt, *Artistic theory in Italy 1450-1600*, chapter IX, "The later Mannerists"

£2,000-3,000
€2,900-4,350

1266 Lomazzo, Giovanni Paolo. A tracte containing the artes of curious paintinge, carvinge & buildinge... Englished by R. H[aydock]. *[Oxford: Joseph Barnes for R. H[aydock], 1598]*

folio (278 x 195mm.), [24 (including engraved title-page)], 119, [1], 218pp., ILLUSTRATION: engraved title-page, woodcut initials, head- and tailpieces, full-page engraved illustrations, BINDING: eighteenth-century vellum-backed blue boards, *lacking final leaf (containing colophon), title-leaf slightly soiled, C6 frayed at edge (affecting illustration) and remounted, D6 remounted, paper flaw on Aa1, occasional slight damp-staining, boards a little soiled*

First English translation of books 1-5 of Lomazzo's *Trattato* (see lot 1265). "It was the first book on the arts to be translated and the reason for its choice must have been its thorough treatment of painting, which was not to be found in any earlier treatises, rather than its exhaustive exposition of later Mannerist theory imbued with the religious principles of the Counter Reformation" (Harris, p.297).

The original text was unillustrated; the images here were supplied by Haydock and are his earliest extant engravings.

References: STC 16698; Harris 519

£1,000-1,500
€1,450-2,200

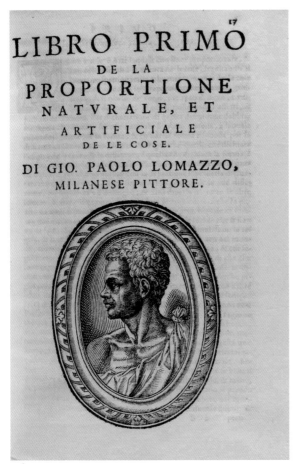

1265

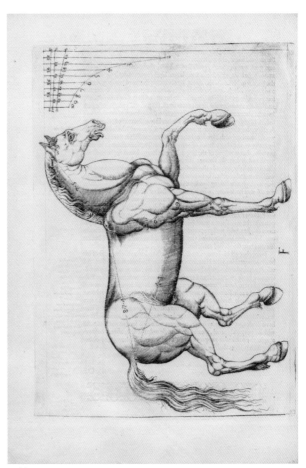

1266

1267 Lomazzo, Giovanni Paolo. Idea del tempio della
pittura... nella quale egli discorre dell'origine, &
fondamento delle cose contenute nel suo trattato
dell'arte della pittura. *Milan: Paolo Gottardo da
Ponte, (1590)*

FIRST EDITION, 4to (201 x 146mm.), [32], 168pp.,
ILLUSTRATION: woodcut portrait medallion of the
author after Annibale Fontana on title-page,
woodcut initials, BINDING: eighteenth-century
speckled calf gilt, spine gilt in compartments,
morocco lettering-piece, red speckled edges, *small
water-stain towards end, binding very slightly rubbed*

References: Censimento 16 CNCE 24458;
Cicognara 162

£1,500-2,000
€2,200-2,900

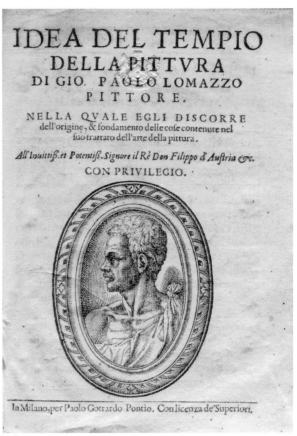

1267

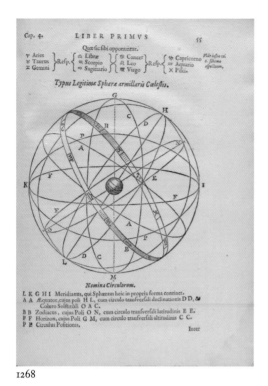

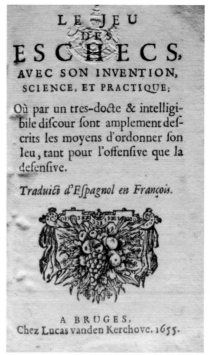

1268   1269

1268 Longomontanus, Christian Sørenson (1562-1647). Astronomia Danica... cum appendice de asscititiis coeli phaenomenis, nempe stellis novis et cometis. *Amsterdam: Guillielmus I. Caesius, 1622*

2 parts in one volume, 4to (240 x 176mm.), [16], 159 (i.e. 163), [1 (blank)], 342 (i.e. 344); [8], 44pp., ILLUSTRATION: woodcut device on title-pages, woodcut initials, woodcut and engraved diagrams, BINDING: contemporary calf, spine gilt in compartments, morocco lettering-piece, *small inkstain on Ttt4, extremities rubbed*

FIRST EDITION. Longomontanus was Tycho's disciple and this work is a great summary of Tycho's astronomical researches, based on his data, and denying Copernicus's heliocentrism and Kepler's elliptical orbits. It was twice reprinted. For other works by Longomontanus, see Macclesfield Science A-C, lots 207, 233 and 261, and lot 1406 in the present catalogue.

References: Houzeau & Lancaster 2926; J.R. Christianson, *On Tycho's island* (2000), *passim*

£2,000-3,000
€2,900-4,350

1269 Lopez de Sigura, Ruy. Le jeu des eschecs, avec son invention, science, et practique; où par un tres-docte & intelligibile discour sont amplement descrits les moyens d'ordonner son Jeu, tant pour l'offensive que la defensive. Traduict d'Espagnol en François. *Bruges: Lucas vanden Kerchove, 1655*

8vo (145 x 85mm.), 83, [5]pp., ILLUSTRATION: woodcut vignette on title-page, BINDING: eighteenth-century mottled calf gilt, spine gilt in compartments, red edges

This popular work on chess first appeared in Spanish in 1561; this translation was first published in Paris in 1609.

References: Linde, *Schachlitteratur* 1612; Palau 141995

£500-700
€750-1,050

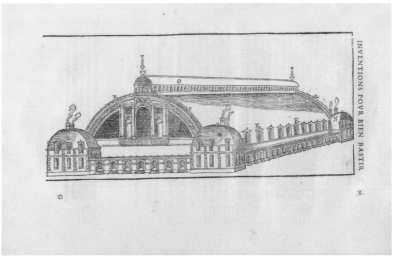

1270

1270 L'Orme, Philibert de (c. 1515-1570). Nouvelles inventions pour bien bastir et à petits fraiz. *Paris: Federic Morel, 1561*

folio (335 x 215mm.), ff. [6], 57, [5], ILLUSTRATION: woodcut device on title, woodcut headpieces and initials, woodcut illustrations in text (many full-page), woodcut allegorical scene on recto of final leaf, BINDING: later vellum-backed boards, *a few leaves spotted*

FIRST EDITION. Philibert de L'Orme was one of the most important architectural theorists of the sixteenth century and the *Nouvelles inventions*, a treatise on carpentry, roofs and building details, was his first published work. He was in Rome between 1533 and 1536 and this work illustrates his application of the principles of Renaissance architecture to a French tradition of building. In his address to the reader, L'Orme mentions plans for his major work, which was published in 1567 entitled *Le premier tome de l'architecture*. This and the *Nouvelles inventions* were amalgamated in 1626.

The woodcut allegorical scene at the end of this copy is not present in all copies: it is not mentioned by either Millard or Fowler, while Mortimer describes the last leaf as blank. An explanation of this scene is provided by L'Orme in the prologue to book 3 of *Le premier tome de l'architecture*.

References: Mortimer, *Harvard French* 354; Fowler 98; Millard 104; BAL RIBA 1954; see V. Hart & P. Hicks, *Paper Palaces* (1998), chapter 12

£5,000-7,000
€7,300-10,200

1271 Lorenzini, Lorenzo (1652-1721). Exercitatio geometrica in qua agitur de dimensione omnium conicarum sectionum, curvae parabolicae, curvae superficiei conoidis parabolici... *Florence: Giovanni Gaetano Tartini and Santi Franchi, 1721*

4to (242 x 173mm.), xxxxiv, 122, [2]pp., ILLUSTRATION: engraved portrait frontispiece, woodcut initials, head- and tailpieces, 14 folding engraved plates, BINDING: contemporary speckled calf, spine gilt in compartments, red speckled edges

FIRST EDITION of the only published work by Lorenzini, a pupil of Viviani, who spent twenty years in prison in Volterra for political reasons. He died while this work was in the press.

References: Riccardi i, 45

£300-400
€450-600

1271

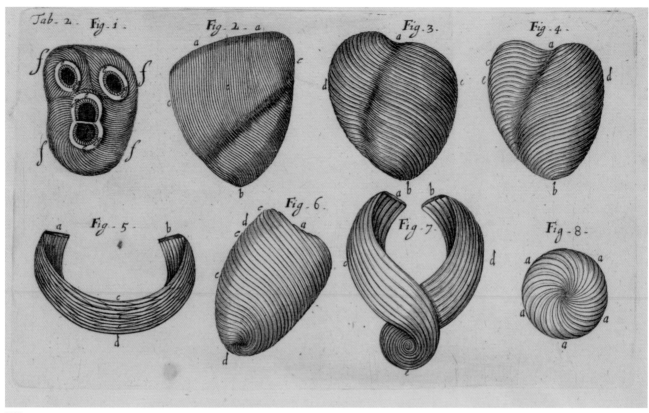

1272

1272 Lower, Richard (1631-1691). Tractatus de corde. Item de motu & colore sanguinis et chyli in eum transitu. *London: John Redmayne for James Allestry, 1669*

8vo (167 x 108mm.), [14], 220, [20]pp., A6 a cancel, ILLUSTRATION: 7 folding engraved plates, BINDING: contemporary calf, a few pencil markings in margins and text, *some leaves lightly spotted, binding rubbed, small wormhole on upper cover*

FIRST EDITION, second issue. The first important work on cardiac physiology to appear after the work of Harvey. Lower was one of the foremost English physiologists of the seventeenth century and was the first to perform a successful artery to vein transfusion from animal to animal. The present work contains the most accurate description of the structure of the heart to date, including his concept of the heart's musculature. Lower also showed that the difference in colour between venous and arterial blood was caused by the blood's absorption of air through the lungs.

Fulton recorded only 14 copies of the first edition, of which ten were the second issue, with the cancel leaf A6. An Amsterdam edition of the same year is generally considered to be the second.

References: Wing L3310; Fulton 5; Garrison-Morton 761; Wellcome III, p.552; Krivatsy 7157; Waller 6046; *PMM* 149

£8,000-10,000
€11,600-14,500

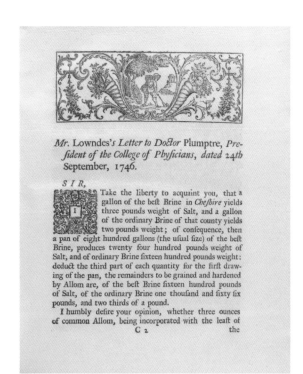

Mr. Lowndes's *Letter to Doctor* Plumptre, *President of the College of Physicians, dated 24th* September, 1746.

SIR,

I Take the liberty to acquaint you, that a gallon of the best Brine in *Cheshire* yields three pounds weight of Salt, and a gallon of the ordinary Brine of that county yields two pounds weight; of consequence, then a pan of eight hundred gallons (the usual size) of the best Brine, produces twenty four hundred pounds weight of Salt, and of ordinary Brine sixteen hundred pounds weight: deduct the third part of each quantity for the first drawing of the pan, the remainders to be grained and hardened by Allom are, of the best Brine sixteen hundred pounds of Salt, of the ordinary Brine one thousand and sixty six pounds, and two thirds of a pound.

I humbly desire your opinion, whether three ounces of common Allom, being incorporated with the least of
C 2   the

1273

1273 Lowndes, Thomas (1692-1748). Brine-salt improved: or, the method of making salt from brine, that shall be as good or better than French bay-salt. In a letter to the Right Honourable the Lords Commissioners of the Admiralty. *London: S. Austen, 1746*, 38, [2]pp., ILLUSTRATION: woodcut head-pieces and initials, *lacking a leaf of plates (as often, e.g. both Kress and Goldsmiths copies)*

Ibid. A seasonable hint for our pilchard and coast fishery: or, a letter of advice to the brine-salt proprietors of Great-Britain and Ireland. *London: for W. Sandby, 1748*, 31, [1 (blank)] pp.

2 works in one volume, 4to (247 x 199mm.), BINDING: contemporary vellum-backed boards

Thomas Lowndes spent, in his own words, "ten of the best years of [my] life, and no inconsiderable sum of money" on a method to improve the bad quality of English salt. Although his specimens were approved by the Royal College of Physicians, the admiralty refused his terms. In June 1746 the House of Commons petitioned the King to instruct the admiralty to accept his terms and in September of the same year he published the first pamphlet in this volume. He died only a few weeks after the publication of the second work, on 12 May 1748, and in his will left all his property for the founding of a chair of astronomy at Cambridge University, the Lowndean chair.

References: Goldsmiths 8214 & 8331; Kress 4817 & 4917

£700-900
€1,050-1,350

1274 [Loys de Cheseaux, Jean Philippe (1718-1751)] Essais de physique. *Paris: Durand, 1743*

FIRST EDITION, 12mo (161 x 87mm.), [4], 317, [5]pp., ILLUSTRATION: woodcut vignette on title-page, woodcut initials and headpieces, 10 folding engraved plates, BINDING: contemporary calf gilt, spine gilt in compartments, red morocco lettering-piece, red speckled edges, *joints cracked at head and foot*

£200-300
€300-450

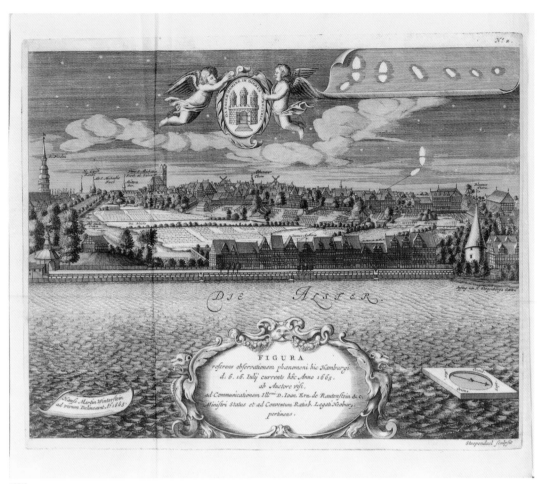

1275

1275 Lubieniecki, Stanislaw (1623-1675). Theatrum cometicum, duabus partibus constans. 1. Quarum prior continet epistolas & communicationes variorum per Europam clarissimorum virorum, cum quibus auctor de hoc argumento contulit... 2. Posterior exhibet historiam universalem omnium cometarum a tempore Diluvii ad Ann. 1665... *Leiden: Petrus vander Meersche, 1681*

2 volumes, folio (318 x 205mm.), [26], 888, [2], 889-966, [4]; [10], 464, [4 (including third frontispiece)], 78, [4]pp., title-pages printed in red and black, ILLUSTRATION: woodcut device on title-pages, engraved portraits of the author and Joannes Ernestus of Rautenstein, 3 engraved frontispieces, 84 engraved plates (31 folding), woodcut initials and tailpieces, BINDING: contemporary calf, spines gilt in compartments, morocco lettering-pieces, red speckled edges, *bindings slightly rubbed*

Originally published in Amsterdam in 1666-1668, this compendium of comets contains information about recent comets in volume 1, notified by contemporary astronomers across Europe with whom Lubieniecki corresponded, and those recorded in historical sources in volume 2. Those letters that were originally sent in the vernacular have been translated into Latin. Lubieniecki, a Polish aristocrat, was a Socinian who also wrote a history of the Reformation in Poland. His religious beliefs led to his expulsion from Poland and he died in Hamburg, probably poisoned by one of his enemies.

References: not in Houzeau & Lancaster

£5,000-7,000
€7,300-10,200

1276

1276 Lucar, Cyprian (b. 1544). A treatise named Lucarsolace devided into fouuer bookes, which in part are collected out of diverse authors in diverse languages, and in part devised by Cyprian Lucar Gentleman. *London: Richard Field for John Harrison, 1590*

4to (205 x 156mm.), [6], 167, [1]pp., ILLUSTRATION: woodcut device on title-page, woodcut coats-of-arms on verso of title and on final verso, woodcut initials, head- and tailpieces, woodcut illustrations, 4 folding woodcut plates, BINDING: contemporary vellum, *without final blank, one plate crudely repaired, plates shaved, hinges partly broken, binding soiled*

FIRST EDITION of Lucar's treatise on surveying, which includes detailed descriptions of the instruments used in surveying. He was educated at New College Oxford and also translated Tartaglia's work on gunnery.

References: STC 16890; Taylor, *Tudor & Stuart* 74

£1,500-2,000
€2,200-2,900

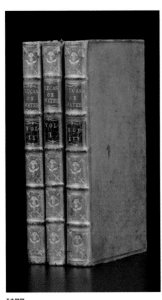

1277 Lucas, Charles (1713-1771). An essay on waters. In three parts. Treating, I. Of simple waters. II. Of cold, medicated waters. III. Of natural baths. *London: for A. Millar, 1756*

3 volumes, 8vo (210 x 125mm.), xxxv, [5], 232; xiv, [2], 274; xiii, [3], 368pp., ILLUSTRATION: 2 folding engraved plates, BINDING: contemporary calf gilt, spine gilt in compartments, red and brown morocco lettering-pieces, red speckled edges, *?lacking B1 in vol.3, R2 of vol.2 torn in corner*

FIRST EDITION. Lucas was an apothecary in Dublin and was active in Irish political life, coming into conflict with the authorities for his political pamphlets. After being imprisoned by the House of Commons in London, he journeyed to the Continent to study medicine, where he visited the natural spas he describes in this book. In 1759 he was admitted to the Royal College of Physicians.

References: Wellcome III, p.554

£300-400
€450-600

1277

1278 Ludolff, Johann Hiob (1649-1711). Tetragonometria tabularia, qua per tabulas quadratorum a radice quadrata 1 usque ad 100000 simplici additionis, subtractionis & dimidiationis beneficio. *Frankfurt & Leipzig: typis Groschianis for the author, 1690*

4to (198 x 155mm.), [6], 150, [418]pp., title and second p.[2] printed in red and black, ILLUSTRATION: woodcut diagrams, BINDING: later vellum-backed blue boards, red speckled edges, *some quires browned, binding slightly soiled*

One of at least three editions printed in 1690, all with different imprints. Ludolff was Professor of Mathematics at the University of Erfurt from 1683.

References: VD17 39:121085L

£400-600
€600-900

1279 Luminarium atque planetarum motuum tabulae octoginta quinque: omnium ex his quae Alphonsum sequuntur quam faciles auctoribus Ioanne Blanchino, Nicolao Prugnero, Georgio Peurbachio; nunc primum collectae, auctae & emendate. *Basel: Joannes Hervagius, 1553*

folio (318 x 205mm.), ff. [354], ILLUSTRATION: woodcut printer's devices on title-page and final verso, woodcut initials, head- and tailpieces, woodcut illustrations, woodcut portraits of Bianchini and Prugner on A1, BINDING: contemporary calf over wooden boards with two blind-tooled borders of renaissance ornament, two clasps, spine gilt in compartments, later morocco lettering-piece, *title-leaf repaired at foot (not affecting text, but obscuring some manuscript on verso), A1 slightly torn in gutter, final leaf slightly torn in gutter and rebacked, spine rubbed and chipped at head*

Bianchini composed his astronomical tables, based on those of Alfonso X of Castile with the corrections of Ptolemy, in Ferrara in the middle of the fifteenth century, and they were first published in Venice in 1495. He corresponded with both Peurbach and Regiomontanus.

References: IA 118.965 (under Bianchini); Houzeau & Lancaster 12595; Zinner 2056

£1,500-2,000
€2,200-2,900

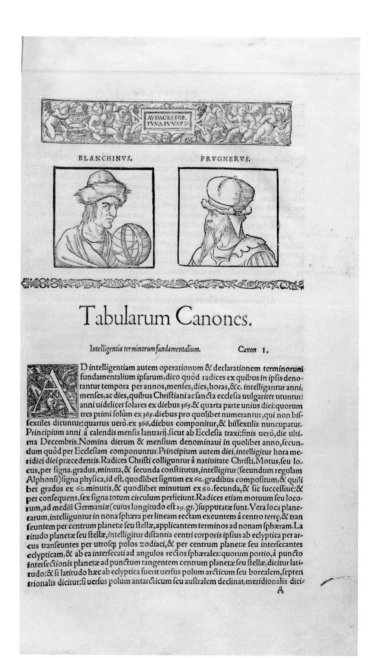

1279

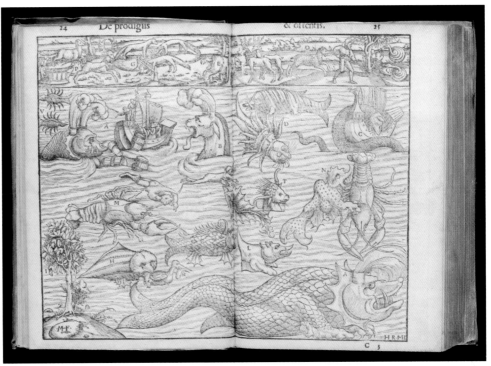

1280

1280 Lycosthenes [Wollfhart], Conrad (1518-1561). Prodigiorum ac ostentorum chronicon, quae praeter naturae ordinem, motum, et operationem, et in superioribus & inferioribus mundi regionibus, ab exordio mundi usque ad haec nostra tempora, acciderunt. *Basel: Henric Petri, (August 1557)*

folio (275 x 192mm.), ff. [12], 670, [2], ILLUSTRATION: woodcut illustration on title-page, woodcut device on final verso, woodcut initials, numerous woodcut illustrations throughout text (including one double-page), some repeated, BINDING: later vellum, yapp edges, *headlines on double-page woodcut shaved, occasional light browning, slightly damp-stained at end, boards slightly soiled and warped*

FIRST EDITION. In 1552 Conrad Lycosthenes had published the first separate edition of Julius Obsequens, a Latin writer on prodigies (*c.* 400 AD) who arranged his material chronologically, drawing in large part on Livy. This work had proved popular and had been translated and, building on this foundation, Lycosthenes undertook the present work. Believing, as he did, that prodigies or portents had a religious significance, he states in his preface that these portents are not purely fortuitous, but show "God's anger and severity towards crimes, and fortell great changes ("vicissitudines") in the world". Such happenings often have natural causes, but it is God who is nature's master and who uses it when he wishes to show his favour or disfavour towards mankind (such as the eclipse at the hour of Christ's death).

Lycosthenes begins with the serpent talking to Eve and carries his narrative up to 1557, some sixty pages being devoted to the years 1550-1557 (in his edition of Julius Obsequens he had left blank pages at the end for the recording of further prodigies). He was not alone in collecting such things: there are many in the pages of the Nuremberg Chronicle (1493), and in Polydore Virgil and Joachim Camerarius, not to mention Belleforest, Boistuau, Belon and others. Lycosthenes's work, in an abbreviated form and translated by Johann Heroldt into German, also issued from the same press in 1557.

References: Caillet 11470; VD16 W4314; see J. Céard, *La nature et les prodiges* (Geneva: Droz, 1996)

£2,500-3,000
€3,650-4,350

1281 [**Machin, John (1680-1751)**] The laws of the moon's motion according to gravity [extracted from Newton's *The mathematical principles of natural philosophy*]. *[London: for Benjamin Motte, 1729]*, 71, [1]pp., ILLUSTRATION: woodcut initial and headpiece, 3 folding engraved plates, [Wallis 23], *last page (containing errata for the rest of "The mathematical principles") pasted to following blank leaf*

An account of a tract, entitled, The laws of the moon's motion according to gravity... taken from the Literary Journal for the months of April, May, and June, 1731. *[London, 1731]*, 19, [1 (blank)] pp.

Jones, William (1675-1749). Manuscript copy, in a neat scribal hand, of a letter by Jones, to Maupertuis, referring to Machin (see below), 7 pages, 3/14 June 1729

loosely inserted:

Machin, John. Manuscript copy of "A correction of the Hypothesis of Bullialdus [Ismael Boulliau] for the motions of the planets, by the Quadratine of certain portions of the Ellipsis", in a contemporary hand, WITH AUTOGRAPH SUBSCRIPTION SIGNED BY WILLIAM JONES ("This is a Copy of a paper communicated by M^r. Machin to S^r. Is. Newton, & to D^r. Halley. W^m: Jones") , 4 pages, 4to, [early eighteenth-century]

1281

3 works in one volume (and inserted letter), 8vo (200 x 116mm.), BINDING: contemporary calf gilt, spine gilt in compartments, morocco lettering-piece

For Maupertuis's treatise on the moon, *Parallaxe de la lune*, see lot 1340. Lot 1335 is a presentation copy to William Jones of one of Maupertuis's works.

Jones sends Maupertuis "a little piece just published here [a copy of Machin's pamphlet]; composed by a particular friend of mine, got from him much against his will... and tack'd by the Bookseller to an English Edition of Sir Is. Newtons principia [*sic*]... 'Tis needless to tell you... that this Tract contains the principal laws of the Lunar motions: which taken altogether, do, I think, make a tolerable Theory of the Moon... But it is not proposed as a perfect Theory... But the chief end was to establish such principles, as will, when rightly applied, prove a point in Philosophy... and that is, that the motions of the moon are such, and no other, that what do arrive from its gravity to the Sun and Earth. The force which Sir Is. Newton supposes to be the immediate cause of the motion of the Apogee and Node, does not appear sufficient to produce much more than half the motions...". Jones continues to give a further account of the views of the author and where they differ from Newton and writes that the author had communicated many things to Newton "as particularly the substance of what is delivered here on the Keplerian problem" before the publication of the second edition of *Principia*, but the author despaired of attracting any attention and abandoned the study of mathematics. But in the 1726 edition his proposition was inserted and "another person mentioned as a sharer with him in the invention of it", and this has made him publish. The communication to Newton concerned the annual equation of the Node.

The author in question is Machin (see Cohen, *Introduction*, pp.282-284: "Newton and Pemberton: the reference (in book III) to Machin"). In the 1726 edition Machin and Pemberton are both named (hence the plaint above): "alia ratione motum nodorum J. Machin... & Hen. Pemberton M.D. seorsum invenerunt" (see Koyré & Cohen, *Principia* ii, 648, which is p.451 of the original).

£1,000-1,500
€1,450-2,200

1282 MacLaurin, Colin (1698-1746). Geometria organica: sive descriptio linearum curvarum universalis. *London: for William and John Innys, 1720*

4to (248 x 187mm.), [10], 139, [1]pp., ILLUSTRATION: 12 folding engraved plates, woodcut initials, head- and tail-pieces, BINDING: contemporary mottled calf

FIRST EDITION. Dedicated to Newton, whom MacLaurin, a Scot and professor at Aberdeen, had met in London in 1719, *Geometrica organica* is concerned with conics and the higher plane curves. It provides proofs for important theorems described by Newton, without proof, as well as some of MacLaurin's own theorems.

£800-1,000
€1,200-1,450

1283 MacLaurin, Colin. A Treatise of fluxions. In two books. *Edinburgh: T.W. and T. Ruddimans, 1742*

2 volumes, 4to (234 x 175mm.), [6], vi, 412; [411]-763, [1 (errata)] pp., half-title in volume 1 only, ILLUSTRATION: 41 folding engraved plates, BINDING: contemporary calf, spines gilt in compartments, *slight worming in lower margins of first few leaves of volume 2*

FIRST EDITION. Written as a staunch defence of Newton, and described as "the earliest logical and systematic publication of the Newtonian methods", this work was written in reply to Bishop George Berkeley's *The Analyst. A letter addressed to an infidel mathematician* of 1734. This latter work, which derided Newton's conception of "prime and ultimate ratios", was addressed to Halley who had steered the first edition of the *Principia* through the press. In his preface to the *Treatise*, MacLaurin lays out his reasons for defending Newton and his methods. This work also provides solutions for a large number of problems in geometry, statics and the theory of attractions, and elaborations of many of the principles described by Newton in the *Principia* (DSB).

References: Norman 1408

Provenance: William Jones, manuscript note on p. 621 signed

£1,000-1,500
€1,450-2,200

1284 MacLaurin, Colin. A treatise of algebra in three parts, containing I. The fundamental rules and operations. II. The composition and resolution of equations of all degrees; and the different affections of their roots. III. The application of algebra and geometry to each other. To which is added an appendix, concerning the general properties of geometrical lines. *London: for A. Millar and J. Nourse, 1748*

8vo (209 x 126mm.), xiv, 366, [2], 65, [1]pp., ILLUSTRATION: woodcut diagrams, 12 folding engraved plates, BINDING: contemporary sheep gilt, spine gilt in compartments, *covers rubbed*

FIRST EDITION. MacLaurin was professor of mathematics at Edinburgh University and part of this treatise, published posthumously, was originally written for his lectures in Edinburgh. The Latin appendix derives from Newton's work on cubic curves (*De quadratura*), first published in Newton's *Opticks* (1704).

£400-600
€600-900

1285 MacLaurin, Colin. An account of Sir Isaac Newton's philosophical discoveries... Published... by Patrick Murdoch. *London: for the author's children, sold by A. Millar, and J. Nourse etc., 1748*

FIRST EDITION, 4to (285 x 222mm.), LARGE PAPER COPY, [8], xx, 392pp., ILLUSTRATION: 6 folding engraved plates with 71 figures, BINDING: contemporary black morocco, gilt fillet on covers, spine handsomely gilt with crowned dolphins, red edges

References: Wallis 112; Babson 85

£6,000-8,000
€8,700-11,600

1286 Macquer, Pierre-Joseph (1718-1784). Elements of the theory and practice of chymistry. Translated from the French... The second edition [by Andrew Reid]. *London: A. Millar and J. Nourse, 1764*

2 volumes, 8vo (206 x 123mm.), xix, [1], 419, [1 (blank)]; viii, 434pp., ILLUSTRATION: 6 engraved plates, BINDING: contemporary speckled calf, spines gilt in compartments, *bindings slightly rubbed, spine of volume 2 discoloured at head*

References: Cole, *Chemical Literature* 887

£200-300
€300-450

1287 Macquer, Pierre-Joseph. A dictionary of chemistry, containing the theory and practice of that science... Translated from the French, with notes and additions by the translator [James Keir]. *London: S. Bladon, 1771*

2 volumes in one, 4to (264 x 201mm.), [4], vi, [2], xii, 888pp., ILLUSTRATION: 3 engraved plates, one letterpress table, BINDING: contemporary calf gilt, spine gilt in compartments, red morocco lettering-piece, *without half-title and title to volume 2, extremities slightly rubbed, upper joint cracking at foot*

References: Cole, *Chemical Literature* 874

£300-400
€450-600

1288 Magini, Giovanni Antonio (1555-1617). Novae coelestium orbium theoricae congruentes cum observationibus Nicolai Copernici. *Venice: Damiano Zenaro, 1589*

4to (237 x 164mm.), ff. [14 (including engraved title)], 115, ILLUSTRATION: engraved title-page, woodcut initials and headpieces, woodcut illustrations, BINDING: contemporary calf with two sets of blind fillets with corner fleurons and blind-stamped centrepieces, *L4 torn at head with loss of a few words, a few light inkstains, binding rubbed, head of spine torn*

FIRST EDITION. Magini was appointed to a chair of mathematics at the University of Bologna in 1588, beating Galileo to the post. As a result of Magini's dismissal of the Copernican system contained within this treatise, he came into regular conflict with Galileo.

References: Censimento 16 CNCE 46659; Houzeau & Lancaster 12741; Riccardi ii, 65-66

£1,500-2,000
€2,200-2,900

1285

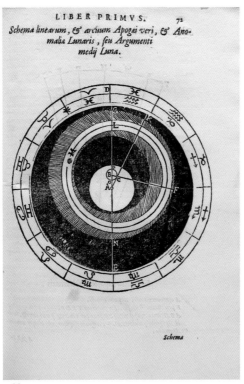

LIBER PRIMVS.   72

Schema linearum, & arcuum Apogæi veri, & Ano-
malia Lunaris, seu Argumenti
medij Lunæ.

Schema

1288

1289 Mairan, Jean-Jacques Dortous de (1678-1771). Dissertation sur l'estimation et la
mesure des forces motrices des corps. Nouvelle edition. *Paris: Charles-Antoine
Jombert, 1741*, iv, 5-107, [1 (blank)] pp., ILLUSTRATION: woodcut initials, head-
and tailpieces, folding engraved plate

Ibid. Lettre de M. Mairan... a Madame *** [la marquise de Châtelet]. Sur le
question des forces vives, en réponse aux objections qu'elle lui fait sur ce sujet dans
ses Institutions de physique. *Paris: Charles-Antoine Jombert, 1741*, [2], 52pp.

2 works in one volume, 12mo (173 x 94mm.), BINDING: contemporary mottled
calf gilt, spine gilt in compartments, red morocco lettering-piece, red speckled
edges

The first work was originally published in the *Mémoires* of the Académie royale in
1728. Mairan was admitted to the Académie in 1718 and was its secretary from
1741 to 1743.

The marquise de Châtelet was the lover and collaborator of Voltaire on his
Elémens de la philosophie de Newton, and herself the translator of Newton.

£150-200
€250-300

1290 Malcolm, Alexander (1685-1763). A new system of arithmetick, theorical and
practical. Wherein the science of numbers is demonstrated in a regular course...
London: J. Osborn, T. Longman, F. Fayram and E. Symon, 1730

4to (232 x 171mm.), xx, 144, *145-*160, 137-296, *293-*296, 297-440, [437]-
[440], 441-623, [1]pp., BINDING: contemporary mottled calf gilt, spine gilt in
compartments, morocco lettering-piece, *binding rubbed*

FIRST EDITION. Malcolm, a "teacher of the mathematicks at Aberdeen", also wrote
a *Treatise of music* in 1721. He emigrated to America in the early 1730s where he
continued teaching in Maryland.

£300-400
€450-600

1291 Malconet, Jacob. Selbst-Lehrende Geometrie oder neue und kurtze Institutiones mechanicae, stereometriae et geodesiae... *Frankfurt: Johann Adolph and Philipp Wilhelm Stock, 1700*

FIRST EDITION, 4to (199 x 170mm.), [2], 490, [2]pp., title printed in red and black, ILLUSTRATION: engraved frontispiece, woodcut device on title-page, woodcut headpieces and illustrations, 23 woodcut plates, folding engraved plate, BINDING: contemporary vellum-backed boards, blue edges, *one plate detached*

£600-800
€900-1,200

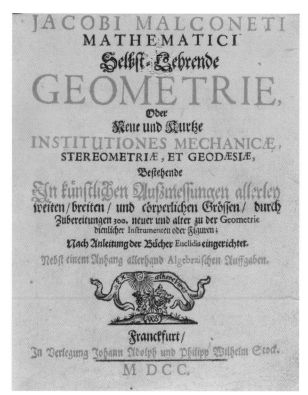

1291

1292

1293

1292 Malvasia, Cornelio (1603-1664), *marchese.* Ephemerides novissimae motuum coelestium... ad longitudinem urbis Mutinae gr.34.5. Ex Philippi Lansbergii hypothesibus... supputatae... Additis ephemeridibus solis, & tabulis refractionum, ex novissimis hypothesibus doctoris Ioannis Dominici Cassini. *Modena: A. Cassiani, impensis authoris, 1662*

folio (380 x 260mm.), [24 (including engraved frontispiece)], 220pp., ILLUSTRATION: engraved frontispiece and large folding plate of the moon at end, full-page engraved illustrations in text, BINDING: eighteenth-century English vellum-backed blue boards, uncut, *slight damage in middle of volume to gutter caused by crude sewing*

FIRST EDITION. Cornelio Malvasia, from Bologna, made his astronomical observations in the private observatory he built over his villa in Panzano, near Modena. Amongst his collaborators was Geminiano Montanari. Malvasia was also interested in astrology. He was deeply interested in Montanari's astronomical activity and did much to foster the talent of the young Cassini, whom he recommended for the chair of astronomy at Bologna University.

The allegorical frontispiece shows a young woman observing Jupiter with a telescope while she paints a coat of arms, which contains the stripes of the planet. In the dedicatory epistle to cardinal Giulio Sacchetti (whose portrait appears on the top of the frontispiece) the author explains that, during his observations, he had observed that the Sacchetti coat of arms is striped like Jupiter, whence a supposed origin of the family from the planet, in honour of the cardinal. In the frontispiece the young woman eventually depicts a coat of arms, with three stripes that go in the reverse direction from those of planet Jupiter, visible in the sky. The engraving is by Francesco Stringa (Modena, 1635-1708), a portrait painter from the school of Guercino, who was the favourite artist at the Este court. He was part of the circle known to the anatomist Malpighi.

References: Riccardi ii, 77

£5,000-6,000
€7,300-8,700

1293 Malvasia, Carlo Cesare (1616-1693). Felsina pittrice, vite de pittori bolognesi... divisa in duoi tomi, con indici copiosissimi. *Bologna: heirs of Domenico Barbieri for Gio. Francesco Davico, 1678*

2 volumes, 4to (233 x 160mm.), [16], 581, [1]; 606, [2]pp., ILLUSTRATION: woodcut initials, head- and tailpieces, woodcut illustrations and portraits of artists, BINDING: contemporary mottled calf, spines gilt in compartments, speckled edges, *lacking 2 leaves of preliminaries in vol.2, extremities slightly rubbed*

FIRST EDITION. A third volume was produced by Luigi Crespi in 1769.

References: Cicognara 2310

Provenance: Nicolas-Joseph Foucault, bookplate

£300-400
€450-600

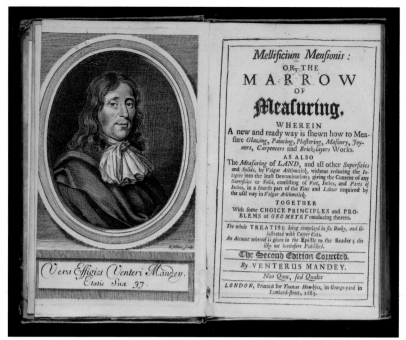

1294

1294 Mandey, Venterus (d. 1709). Mellificium mensionis, or, the marrow of measuring, wherein a new and ready way is shewn how to measure glazing, painting, plastering, masonry, joyners, carpenters, and bricklayers works. As also the measuring of land and all other superfices and solids, by vulgar arithmetick, without reducing the intergers into the least denomination... the like not heretofore published. The second edition corrected. *London: for Thomas Howkins, 1685*

8vo (164 x 99mm.), [26], 376, [2]pp., ILLUSTRATION: engraved frontispiece portrait of the author, 11 folding engraved and woodcut plates (3 pasted to a page edge), engraved diagrams, BINDING: contemporary speckled calf, spine gilt in compartments, red morocco lettering-piece, *portrait, some plates and a few headlines shaved, binding rubbed*

Venterus Mandey was, like Jones, a teacher of mathematics. His library, from which a number of volumes made their way into Jones's collection, was sold in February/March 1714 (cf. note to lot 877, Macclesfield Science, D-H).

References: Wing M420B

£300-400
€450-600

1295 Mandey, Venterus *and* **James Moxon.** Mechanick powers: or, the mistery of nature and art unvail'd. Shewing what great things may be perform'd by mechanick engines. *London: for the authors, [1696?]*

4to (198 x 149mm.), [12], 315, [5]pp., title ruled in red, ILLUSTRATION: 17 folding engraved plates, BINDING: contemporary calf, occasional notes in pencil or ink, *short tear in margin of E4, binding worn, upper cover detached*

A dated edition of 1696 bears the same imprint, with the addition of R. Clavel (Wing M418).

References: Wing M419

£300-400
€450-600

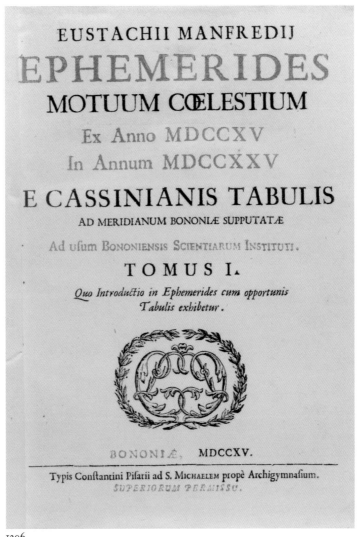

1296

1296 Manfredi, Eustachio (1674-1759). Ephemerides motuum coelestium ex anno MDCCXV in annum MDCCXXV e Cassinianis tabulis ad meridianum bononiae supputatae. Tomus I (-II). *Bologna: Costantino Pisarro, 1715*, 2 volumes, 4to (269 x 186mm.), [16], 143, [1], 179, [1 (blank)]; [4], 373, [1 (blank)] pp., title and some tables printed in red and black, ILLUSTRATION: woodcut device on title-pages, woodcut initials, head- and tailpieces, woodcut diagrams, 15 folding engraved plates, BINDING: nineteenth-century half calf by Hatton of Manchester, morocco lettering-pieces, red speckled edges

Ibid. Novissimae ephemerides... tomus I (-II). Ex anno 1726 in annum 1737 (ex anno 1738 in anno 1750). *Bologna: Costantino Pisarro, 1725*, 2 volumes in one, 4to (270 x 189mm.), [20], 383, [1 (blank)]; [2], 415, [1]pp., ILLUSTRATION: woodcut device on title-pages, woodcut initials, head- and tailpieces, woodcut diagrams, 15 folding engraved plates, BINDING: contemporary calf, spine gilt in compartments, morocco lettering-piece, *a few plate edges creased, binding rubbed and stained on lower cover*

together 3 volumes

FIRST EDITIONS. Manfredi succeeded Cassini as professor of astronomy at Bologna.

References: Houzeau & Lancaster 15461; Riccardi ii, 80 & 83

£1,000-1,500
€1,450-2,200

1297 Manfredi, Eustachio. De annuis inerrantium stellarum aberrationibus. *Bologna: Costantino Pisarri, 1729*

4to (240 x 170mm.), [4], 80pp., ILLUSTRATION: 6 folding engraved plates numbered I-VI with figures 1-50, BINDING: contemporary sprinkled calf, gilt spine, morocco lettering-piece

References: Riccardi ii, 83

£500-600
€750-900

1298 Manfredi, Eustachio. De gnomone meridiano bononiensi ad divi Petronii deque observationibus astronomicis eo instrumento ad ejus constructione ad hoc tempus peractis. *Bologna: Lelio da Volpe, 1736*

4to (250 x 180mm.), [4], 397, [1]pp., ILLUSTRATION: 2 engraved plates at p. 96, engraved device on title and engraved head and tail-piece, BINDING: contemporary English smooth calf, gilt spine, specked edges, *upper hinge weak*

For another work on the meridian of San Petronio, see lot 491 (Cassini) in Macclesfield Science A-C.

References: Riccardi ii, 85

£750-1,000
€1,100-1,450

1299 Manfredi, Eustachio. Novissimae ephemerides motuum coelestium e Cassinianis tabulis ad meridianum bononiae supputatae... ex anno 1741 in annum 1750. Editio altera. *Bologna: Costantino Pisarro, 1739*

4to (270 x 178mm.), [4], 319, [1 (blank)] pp., ILLUSTRATION: woodcut device on title-page, woodcut initials, head- and tailpieces, woodcut diagrams, 3 folding engraved plates, BINDING: nineteenth-century half calf by Hatton of Manchester, morocco lettering-pieces, red speckled edges

£200-300
€300-450

1300 Manilius, Marcus (late 1st century BC-early 1st century AD). Astronomicon a Iosepho Scaligero ex vetusto codice Gemblacensi infinitis mendis repurgatum. Eusdem Iosephi Scaligeri notae... *Leiden: Christopher Raphaelengius, in officina Plantiniana, 1600*

4to (190 x 133mm.), [32], 131, [5]; [20], 510, [2]pp., ILLUSTRATION: woodcut device on title-pages, woodcut initials and diagrams, BINDING: near-contemporary mottled calf gilt, spine gilt in compartments, *paper flaw on C1 with loss of a few letters, a few diagrams shaved, binding rubbed*

First published in 1579, Scaliger completely revised the work. "The second Manilius marked a culmination, perhaps the highest point on the arc of his humanistic scholarship" (Grafton, *Scaliger II*, p.458).

References: Houzeau & Lancaster 1037

£300-400
€450-600

1301

1301 Manilius, Marcus. The Sphere... made an English poem, with annotations and an astronomical appendix, by Edward Sherburne. *London: Nathanael Brooke, 1675*

folio (412 x 258mm.), [10], 68, [2], 221, [9]pp., title in red and black, ILLUSTRATION: engraved allegorical frontispiece by W. Hollar dated 1673, engraved initials and headpieces, 11 engraved plates (6 folding), engraved diagrams, woodcut initials, BINDING: contemporary speckled calf, spine gilt in compartments, *worn*

This is a translation into English of the first book of Manilius's poem *Astronomicon*, which discusses the sphere, zodiacal and other constellations, great circles and comets, and is written under the influence of Aratus. The complete work is in five books, is strongly Stoic in character, and is largely political and religious in its driving force. The translator Sir Edward Sherborne (1618-1702) was a cousin of the poet and scholar Thomas Stanley, of a recusant family, and the author of a number of short poems, and translations of Theocritus, Coluthus, the Polish Jesuit Sarbiewski and others.

References: Wing M432; Pennington 2678

£1,000-1,500
€1,450-2,200

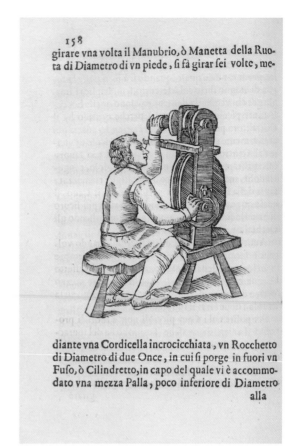

158

girare vna volta il Manubrio, ò Manetta della Ruo-
ta di Diametro di vn piede, si fà girar sei volte, me-

diante vna Cordicella incrocicchiata, vn Rocchetto
di Diametro di due Once, in cui si porge in fuori vn
Fuso, ò Cilindretto, in capo del quale vi è accommo-
dato vna mezza Palla, poco inferiore di Diametro
alla

1302

1303

1302 Manilius, Marcus. Astronomicon ex recensione et cum notis Richardi Bentleii.
London: Henry Woodfall for Paul and Isaac Vaillant, 1739

4to (265 x 195mm.), xvi, 307, [5]pp., ILLUSTRATION: engraved frontispiece portrait of
Bentley, engraved headpiece, folding engraved plate of the marble globe in the Palazzo
Farnese in Rome, BINDING: contemporary mottled calf, spine gilt in compartments, red
morocco lettering-piece, red speckled edges

The last work edited by Bentley who died three years later aged eighty. Like Scaliger's
edition, this was greatly praised by Housman.

References: Houzeau & Lancaster 1037

£500-700
€750-1,050

1303 Manzini, Carlo Antonio (d. 1677?), *conte.* L'Occhiale all'occhio, dioptrica pratica.
Bologna: heirs of Benacci, 1660

4to (207 x 143mm.), [12], 268, [4]pp., ILLUSTRATION: engraved portrait of Eustachio
Divini, woodcut vignette on title, woodcut illustrations and diagrams in text, woodcut
head-pieces, BINDING: eighteenth-century mottled calf, *portrait trimmed at fore-edge,
binding rubbed*

FIRST EDITION. Dedicated to St Lucia, the patron saint of the blind, this practical work
deals with light, refraction, vision, the eye and the making of spectacles and telescopes.

References: Riccardi ii, 96; Krivatsy 7389; Wellcome IV, p.48; British Optical
Association 137

£1,500-2,000
€2,200-2,900

1304

1304 Maraldi, Giovanni Domenico (1709-1788). Connoissance des temps pour l'année 1751, au mérdien de Paris, publiée par l'ordre de l'Académie Royale des Sciences. *Paris: Imprimerie Royale, 1750*

8vo (180 x 107mm.), 228pp., quire B (pp. 13-24) repeated, ILLUSTRATION: engraved frontispiece, woodcut device on title-page, title within decorative border, 3 folding engraved plates, BINDING: contemporary vellum-backed boards, red speckled edges, *binding slightly rubbed*

These ephemerides were published annually from 1679 to the middle of the nineteenth century. Maraldi produced them for the years 1735 to 1758.

Maraldi was the nephew of the astronomer Giacomo Filippo Maraldi and was related to the Cassini dynasty of astronomers. He went to Paris in 1728, where his uncle worked with the Cassini, and stayed there until 1771. This series of ephemerides is his only published work.

References: Houzeau & Lancaster 15332

£300-400
€450-600

1305

1305 Marci a Kronland, Jan Marcus (1595-1662). De caussis naturalibus pluviae purpureae Bruxellensis (6 Oct. 1646). *Prague: typis academicis, 1647*, [3], 21pp., ILLUSTRATION: small view of Prague on title-page

Piccolomini, Alessandro (1508-1578), *archbishop of Patras.* [In mechanicas quaestiones Aristotelis paraphrasis [with the text]. Commentarium de certitudine mathematicarum scientiarum disciplinarum. *Venice: Traiano Curzio, 1565*], ff. 108, ILLUSTRATION: woodcut illustrations in text, [Censimento 16 CNCE 31566; Riccardi ii, 271], *lacking title-page*

2 works in one volume, 8vo (141 x 83mm.), BINDING: eighteenth-century mottled calf, spine gilt in compartments, red morocco lettering-piece

For other works by Marci a Kronland see Macclesfield Science, lots 202, 871, 877.

References: R.J.W. Evans, *The Making of the Habsburg Monarchy 1550-1700* (Oxford, 2002), for Marci a Kronland

£1,500-2,000
€2,200-2,900

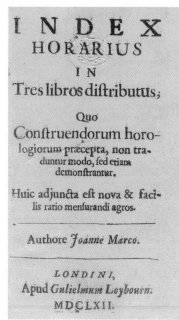

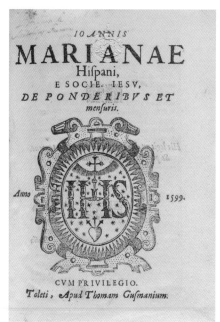

1306   1307

1306 Marcus, Joannes. Index horarius in tres libros distributus, quo construendorum horologiorum praecepta, non traduntur modo, sed etiam demonstrantur. *London: William Leybourn, 1662*

8vo (140 x 84mm.), [6], 277, [11]pp., first and last leaves blank, ILLUSTRATION: woodcut initials and diagrams, BINDING: contemporary speckled calf, spine gilt in compartments, speckled edges, *possibly lacking one leaf of prefatory material, a few lines of p.55 pasted over, binding rubbed*

FIRST EDITION. The British Library ascribes the authorship to Jan Marcus Marci a Kronland. Taylor (*Tudor & Stuart*, p.252) records a John Marke (*fl.* 1665-1679) who made mathematical instruments. This copy is a variant, with the author's name on the title-page; Wing records a variant with just the author's initials.

References: Wing M588A

£200-300
€300-450

1307 Mariana, Juan de (1536-1623?), *S.J.* De ponderibus et mensuris. *Toledo: Thomas de Guzman, 1599*

4to (203 x 142mm.), [8], 192pp., ILLUSTRATION: large woodcut Jesuit device on title-page, woodcut initials and headpieces, BINDING: eighteenth-century black morocco gilt, spine gilt in compartments with crowned monogram, morocco lettering-piece, red edges

FIRST EDITION. Mariana, a Spanish Jesuit, taught at the Jesuit college in Messina and in Rome before retiring to his native Toledo, and is important early economic and political theorist. His writings brought him into conflict with the royal authorities, particularly for his treatise justifying tyrannicide, which was publicly burned in Paris. He also wrote on the debasement of coinage, for which he was imprisoned for life. The present work treats of the comparative values of Roman, Greek, Hebrew and Spanish weights and measures against those of Toledo.

References: Palau 151724; Adams M580A; Goldsmiths 290; Kress 214

£1,000-1,500
€1,450-2,200

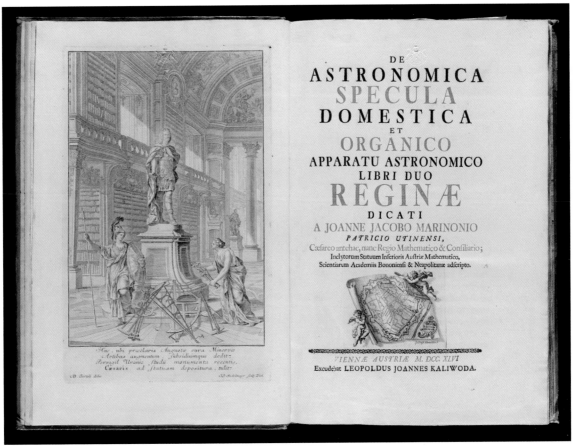

1308

1308 Marinoni, Giovanni Jacopo de (1676-1755). De astronomica specula domestica et organico apparatu astronomico libri duo. *Vienna: L.J. Kaliwoda, 1746*

folio (348 x 233mm.), [24 (including frontispiece)], 210, [2]pp., title printed in red and black, last leaf with errata and instructions to binder (in Latin and German), ILLUSTRATION: engraved frontispiece, 43 large folding plates (numbered I-IV, I-II, I-IX, I-III, I-IV, I-IX, I-IX, I and those at pp.191 and 194), illustrations in text (some full-page), head-pieces and initials, woodcut ornaments, BINDING: contemporary smooth calf, gilt spine, speckled edges, *one plate with small paper repair*

FIRST EDITION of this luxuriously printed and illustrated work, which describes and illustrates the astronomical instruments in the private observatory of G.J. Marinoni, mathematician and astronomer to the Imperial Court of Austria and geodetic surveyor. Like the private observatories of Tycho Brahe and Hevelius in the two preceding centuries, Marinoni's observatory was one of the most beautiful and best equipped in Europe in his time. He built his own instruments and those illustrated here include quadrants, telescopes, micrometers, an improved Graham pendulum, and a camera obscura. Marinoni left all the instruments to the Empress Maria Theresa, to whom he dedicated this work. "In 1755... in connection with a general reform of the University of Vienna, the Hapsburgs decided to establish a great central astronomical observatory. Its basic equipment was to be the instruments of the late imperial mathematician and geodetic survey, J.J. de Marinoni, who had made his house, on a relatively favorable site at the edge of Vienna, into an astronomical observatory" (*DSB* VI, p.223).

References: Riccardi ii, 119

£6,000-8,000
€8,700-11,600

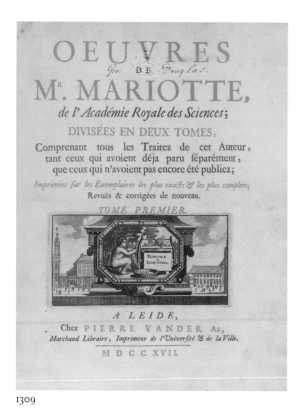

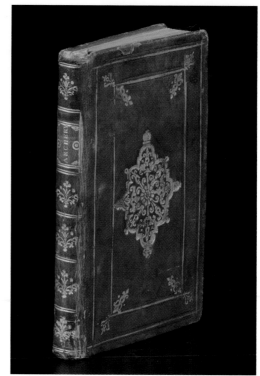

1309   1311

1309 Mariotte, Edmé (*c.* 1620-1684). Oeuvres... divisées en deux tomes... revuës & corrigées de nouveau. *Leiden: Pierre Vander Aa, 1717*

2 volumes in one, 4to (246 x 190mm.), [12], 320; [4], 321-701 (pages 567 to 600 omitted in pagination), [35]pp., titles printed in red and black, ILLUSTRATION: engraved device on title-pages, woodcut initials and tailpieces, 25 folding engraved plates, engraved illustrations, BINDING; contemporary speckled calf, spine gilt in compartments, *occasional slight browning of plates, binding rubbed*

First collected edition of the works of Mariotte. "Honored as the man who introduced experimental physics into France, Mariotte played a central role in the work of the Paris Academy of Sciences from shortly after its formation in 1666 until his death in 1684" (*DSB* IX, p.114). He was above all an empiricist and his wide-ranging experiments show this, as does his lack of scientific dogmatism.

Provenance: George Douglas, inscription on title-page

£500-700
€750-1,050

1310 Mariotte, Edmé (*c.* 1620-1684). A treatise of the motion of water, and other fluids: with the origin of fountains of springs, and the cause of winds... Written originally in French... And translated into English, with several annotations for explaining the doubtful places, by J. T. Desaguliers. *London: for J. Senex and W. Taylor, 1718*

8vo (194 x 116mm.), xiii, [1], 290pp., ILLUSTRATION: woodcut initials, typographical headpieces, 7 folding engraved plates, BINDING: contemporary panelled calf, spine gilt in compartments, morocco lettering-piece, *without final advertisement leaf, binding rubbed, spine chipped at head, upper joint cracking*

A translation of Mariotte's *Traité du mouvement des eaux* (Paris, 1686).

£300-400
€450-600

1311 Markham, Gervase (1568?-1637). The art of archerie, [etc.]. *London: B. A[lsop] and T. F[awcet] for Ben Fisher, 1634*

8vo (138 x 80mm.), [24], 172pp., BINDING: contemporary English binding of Turkey leather, covers gilt with a central cartouche within a single gilt fillet, spine gilt

FIRST EDITION AND A MOST HANDSOME COPY.

"Whatsoever I have formerly spoken in praise of the Bowe... yet I would not have the curious to mistake me, and thinke in it I derogate from other Weapons, and so call me a King *Harry* Captaine, or a man of an old edition, out of date in these refined times, where nothing is excellent, but that which is least excellent, *Folly* and *Selfe-opinion*'" (p.17).

References: STC 17333; F.N.L. Poynter, *A Bibliography of Gervase Markham* (Oxford: OBS, 1962) 40.1; Cockle 129

£2,500-3,500
€3,650-5,100

1312 Marolois, Samuel (1572?-1627/8). [Oeuvres mathématiques] Géometrie, contenant la théorie et practique d'icelle, nécessaire à la fortification... Corrigée & augmentée par Théodore Verbeeck mathématicien. *Amsterdam: Guillaume Iansson Caesius, 1628*

part 1 only (of 2), 4to (247 x 180mm.), [6], 219pp., ILLUSTRATION: one double-page engraved plate, woodcut illustrations and diagrams in text, woodcut initials, BINDING: eighteenth-century vellum-backed boards

This edition of the *Oeuvres mathématiques* contains two parts, each with a separate title-page. The second part relating to fortification, absent here, was edited by François van Schoten.

£300-400
€450-600

1313 Marolois, Samuel. Opticae, sive perspectivae, pars prima (-quarta). *Amsterdam: Jan Jansson, 1647*

folio (300 x 193mm.), [4 (including additional engraved title-page from another edition)], 50pp., ILLUSTRATION: 80 double-page engraved plates, BINDING: eighteenth-century mottled calf, spine gilt in compartments

Marolois's treatise on perspective first appeared in his *Opera mathematica* of 1614. It was then published separately in several editions throughout the seventeenth century. This copy contains an additional engraved title-page from the French edition of 1662.

£600-800
€900-1,200

1314 Marolois, Samuel. Geometria theoretica ac practica... Studio atque opera Alberti Girardi. *Amsterdam: J. Jansson, 1647*

folio (301 x 194mm.), [2], 51pp., ILLUSTRATION: additional engraved title from 1662 edition, 47 engraved plates, BINDING: eighteenth-century mottled calf, *additional engraved title cut down and mounted*

£400-500
€600-750

1315 Martin, Benjamin (1704-1782). A new compleat and universal system of body of decimal arithmetick. *London: for J. Noon, 1735*

8vo (196 x 120mm.), [8], 403, [5]pp., title printed in red and black, ILLUSTRATION: woodcut illustrations in text, BINDING: contemporary panelled calf

FIRST EDITION. One of Martin's earliest works, published in the same year as his first work *The philosophical grammar*. One of the great popularisers of science in the mid-eighteenth century, Martin was at this time running his own boarding-school in Chichester. He later became a travelling lecturer in experimental philosophy before settling in London by 1755. Here he set up shop and established a monthly journal, *The General Magazine of Arts and Sciences*, which ran from January 1755 until 1765.

£300-400
€450-600

1316 Martin, Benjamin. The young student's memorial book, or pocket library. *London: for J. Noon, 1736*, 12mo (168 x 97mm.), viii, 210pp., ILLUSTRATION: 2 engraved plates, woodcut diagrams, BINDING: contemporary panelled calf

Ibid. The philosophical grammar; being a view of the present state of experimented physiology, or natural philosophy... The second edition, with alterations, corrections, and very large additions. *London: for John Noon, 1738*, 8vo (200 x 125mm.), viii, 362 (161/162 omitted, 177/178 repeated), [6]pp., 2 folding printed tables (one after p.160, one after p.264), ILLUSTRATION: 26 folding engraved plates, BINDING: contemporary mottled calf, [Blake p. 289; Taylor, *Hanoverian* 289], *fol. 4 pasted down to an additional blank leaf obscuring advertisement on verso, some plates slightly trimmed*

together 2 volumes

First published in 1735, *The Philosophical grammar* was Martin's earliest published work. The present second edition contains a description of a pocket microscope. In 1740 he is credited with having supplied a microscope fitted with a micrometer, and in 1759 he produced a microscope with two lenses set one inch apart.

£300-400
€450-600

1314

1317 Martin, Benjamin. The young trigonometer's compleat guide. Being the mystery and rationale of plain trigonometry made clear and easy. *London: for J. Noon, 1736*

2 volumes in one, 8vo (196 x 119mm.), xvi, 328, [2 (blank)]; xii, 370pp., 2 folding tables, ILLUSTRATION: 9 folding engraved plates, engraved and woodcut illustrations and diagrams in text, BINDING: contemporary mottled calf

FIRST EDITION. This work includes sections on the application of trigonometry to subjects such as astronomy, surveying, optics and navigation.

References: Wellcome IV, p.64

£300-400
€450-600

1318 Martin, Benjamin. Logarithmologia: or the whole doctrine of logarithms, common and logistical, in theory and practice. *London: for J. Hodges, 1740-1739*

2 parts in one volume, 8vo (199 x 123mm.), xii, 246; *62, [2]pp., ILLUSTRATION: one folding engraved plate, BINDING: contemporary mottled calf, *lacking advertisement leaf after p. 246, final leaf pasted down obscuring advertisement on verso*

References: Wellcome IV, p.64

£200-300
€300-450

1319 Martin, Benjamin. A new and compendious system of optics. *London: for James Hodges, 1740*

8vo (202 x 116mm.), xxiv, 295pp., ILLUSTRATION: 35 folding engraved plates, BINDING: contemporary mottled calf

FIRST EDITION. The third part contains *A practical description of a great number of optical instruments.*

References: Wellcome IV, p.64; Blake p. 289; Taylor, *Hanoverian* 289

£250-300
€400-450

1320 Martin, Benjamin. Philosophia Britannica: or a new and comprehensive system of the Newtonian philosophy, astronomy and geography, in a course of twelve lectures. *Reading: C. Micklewright and Co. for the author [etc.], 1747*

2 volumes, 8vo (208 x 126mm.), [40], 343; [24], 526, [10]pp., titles printed in red and black, ILLUSTRATION: 73 folding engraved plates (numbered I-XIII, XV-XXXVII, XXXIX-LXIV, [LXIVb], LXV-LXXIV), BINDING: contemporary black morocco, *some light browning, several plates trimmed at head with slightly loss of numbering, bindings worn and rubbed*

FIRST EDITION. Published at a time when Martin worked as a peripatetic lecturer, these lectures, covering subjects such as electricity, mechanics, hydrostatics, hydraulics, optics, pneumatics and astronomy, were presumably delivered in Reading, where this first edition was printed. The prefatory material includes a *Catalogue of the principal books made use of in compiling the following work*, which lists 42 works and in most cases the particular edition used, including: Newton's *Principia* (3rd edition), his *Optics* and *Chronology of Ancient Kingdoms amended*; Galileo's *Sidereus nuncius* (London, 1653); as well as works by s' Gravesande, van Musschenbroek, MacLaurin, Muller, Desaguliers, Keill, Rohault, Simpson, Maupertuis and others. Later editions were published in London in 1759 and 1771.

Although the title-page calls for 75 plates, the copy at Imperial College, London, also contains only 73 plates.

References: Taylor, *Hanoverian* 289

£1,000-1,500
€1,450-2,200

1321 Martindale, Adam (1623-1686). The country-survey-book: or, land-meters vade-mecum. Wherein the principles and practical rules for surveying of land, are so plainly (though briefly) delivered... with an appendix, containing twelve problems touching compound interest and annuities... *London: R. Clavel and G. Sawbridge, 1702*

12mo (155 x 87mm.), [12], 120, 191-226, 229-234pp., ILLUSTRATION: 3 folding engraved plates, BINDING: contemporary panelled calf, spine gilt in compartments, *some browning, binding rubbed, upper joint cracked*

Originally published in 1682, this reached an eighth edition in 1711.

References: cf. Taylor, *Tudor & Stuart* 418 (1st edition)

£100-150
€150-250

1322 Martine, George (1702-1741). Essays medical and philosophical. *London: A. Millar, 1740*

8vo (206 x 124mm.), [14], 376pp., ILLUSTRATION: folding engraved plate showing comparative thermometric scales, BINDING: contemporary calf gilt, spine gilt in compartments, morocco lettering-piece, *without initial advertisement leaf, lower joint cracking at head*

FIRST EDITION. "First important work on clinical thermometry, and the only scientific treatment of the subject before Wunderlich [published in 1868]" (Garrison-Morton, p.430).

References: Garrison-Morton 2671; Wellcome IV, p.67

£300-400
€450-600

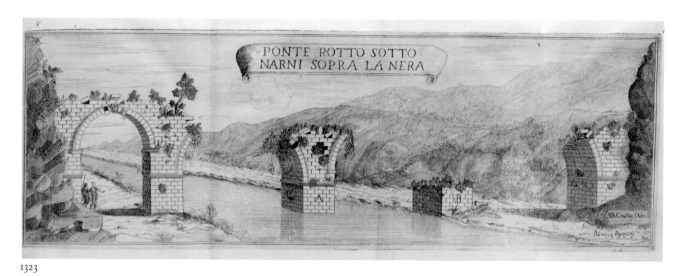

1323

1323 Martinelli, Agostino. Descrittione di diversi ponti esistenti sopra li fiumi Nera, e Tevere con una discorso particolare della navigazione da Perugia a Roma. *Rome: Nicolò Angelo Tinassi, 1676*

4to (201 x 142mm.), [8 (including engraved arms)], 58pp., ILLUSTRATION: woodcut vignette on title-page, engraved plate containing arms of Innocent XI, the dedicatee, woodcut initials, 21 engraved and woodcut plates (19 folding), BINDING: contemporary mottled calf gilt, spine gilt in compartments, morocco lettering-piece, red edges

FIRST EDITION, containing plates of various bridges along the course of the Nera and the Tiber, including those within Rome itself.

References: Cicognara 940; Rossetti 6710; Riccardi ii, 122-123

£400-600
€600-900

1324 Martinelli, Domenico (1650-1718). Horologi elementari divisi in quattro parti. Nella prima parte fatti con l'acqua. Nella seconda con la terra. Nella terza con l'aria. Nella quarta con fuoco... *Venice: Bortolo Tramontino, 1669*

4to (220 x 155mm.), 155, [5]pp., ILLUSTRATION: title printed within a border of typographical fleurons, woodcut initials, head- and tailpieces, 16 full-page engravings in text numbered I-XVI, BINDING: contemporary gilt panelled vellum with coronets at corners of panels

FIRST EDITION, and a handsome copy. The work was translated into French by Ozanam.

Provenance: Charles Lord Halifax, engraved armorial bookplate dated 1702

£2,000-3,000
€2,900-4,350

1325 Martinez Siliceo, Juan (1486-1557), *cardinal.* [Liber arithmetice practice astrologis phisicis et calculatoribus admodum utilis]. *(Paris: Thomas Kees for Jean Petit and Jean Lambert, 23 June 1513)*

folio (269 x 194mm.), ff. [25], ILLUSTRATION: woodcut initials and diagrams, BINDING: later vellum-backed blue boards, *lacking A1 (title-leaf), very slight soiling*

FIRST EDITION. Martinez Siliceo was a Spanish priest and mathematician with a strong interest in astrology, who studied in Seville and Paris. In 1534 he became tutor and later confessor to the future Philip II.

References: Moreau 664; Smith pp.95-96; Palau 156382

£1,000-1,500
€1,450-2,200

1326 Martinez Siliceo, Juan, *cardinal.* Arithmetica. *Paris: Simon de Colines, September 1526*

folio (270 x 200mm.), ff. 63, [1 (blank, here lacking)], ILLUSTRATION: woodcut marginal diagrams, title within a border, woodcut initials etc., BINDING: nineteenth-century half calf by Hatton, contemporary manuscript marginalia, *title soiled and some leaves slightly browned, small worm holes at end (mostly marginal)*

References: Mortimer, *Harvard French* 368; Renouard, *Colines*, pp. 89-91; Palau 156384

£800-1,200
€1,200-1,750

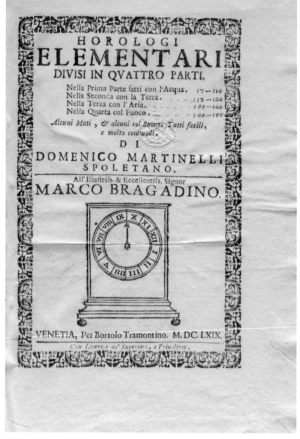

1324

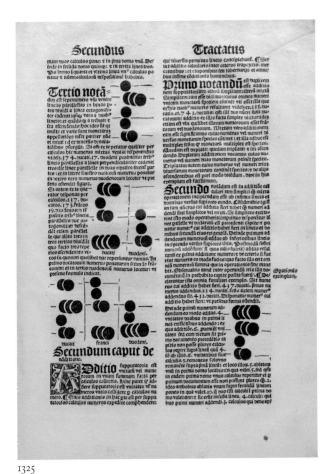

1325

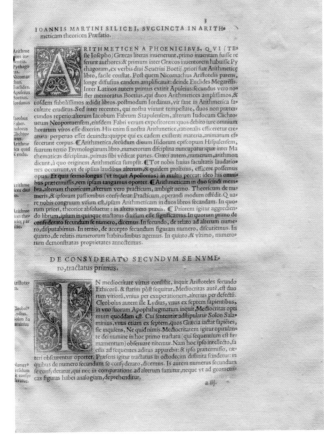

1326

1327 Martino, Niccolò di (1701-1769). Elementa algebrae pro novis tyronibus tumultario studio concinnata. *Naples: Felix Mosca for Bernardino Gessari, 1725*, 2 volumes, 8vo (174 x 104mm.), [24 (including half-title)], lxxx, 448; [4 (including half-title)], lxiv, 480pp., ILLUSTRATION: engraved frontispiece, 4 engraved plates, BINDING: contemporary mottled calf

Ibid. Elementa sectionum conicarum conscripta ad usum Faustinae Pignatelli. *Naples: Felix Mosca for Gaetano Elia, 1734*, 2 volumes, 8vo (204 x 124mm.), [16 (including half-title)], 312; 352pp., ILLUSTRATION: 16 folding engraved plates, BINDING: contemporary calf

together 4 volumes, *occasional light browning in all volumes*

Niccolò de Martino was a prolific author of mathematical textbooks and professor of mathematics at the Spanish Bourbon academy in Naples. He also held a number of other posts connected with military and marine engineering.

Amongst his pupils was Faustina Pignatelli (d. 1785), princess of Colubrano, herself a distinguished figure in astronomy, who was elected in 1732 to the Accademia delle Scienze at Bologna, and it was for her that this little treatise on conics was written. She was one of a number of Italian ladies, such as Laura Bassi (1717-1778) and, most famously, Maria Gaetana Agnesi (1718-1799), who had a strong interest in mathematics and the physical sciences; see Paula Findlen, "Translating the new science: women and the circulation of knowledge in Enlightenment Italy" in *Configurations* 2: 167-206, and her piece on Laura Bassi in *Isis* 84 (1993).

References: Riccardi ii, 127 & 128

£500-700
€750-1,050

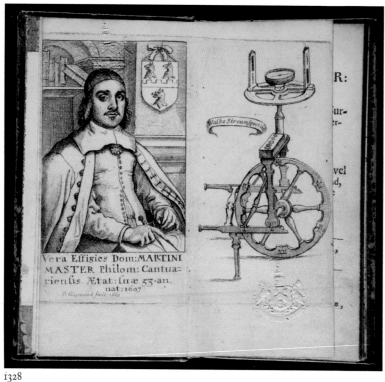

1328

1330

1328 Master, Martin (b. 1607). The surveyours perambulator: or, an engine, wherewith the surveyour may with much more perfectness, speed, and ease measure land then either with chain or pole. And wherewith he may travel a whole day, and at his journeys end, he shall have the length of the ground given him at an instant unto the hundreth part of a pole. *London: Robert and William Leybourn, to be sold by Will. Gilbertson, 1661*

12mo (133 x 68mm.), [16], 71, [1 (blank)] pp., ILLUSTRATION: double-page engraved frontispiece containing portrait of the author by R. Gaywood, woodcut headpiece and initial, folding table with engraved diagram, BINDING: eighteenth-century mottled calf gilt, spine gilt in compartments, red morocco lettering-piece, contemporary manuscript additions to list of errata on p.[16] and errata in text corrected, *frontispiece shaved at edges, binding very slightly rubbed*

VERY RARE, POSSIBLY UNIQUE. We have not been able to trace another copy of this work.

Master describes himself as a "student in mathematics" from Canterbury, and at the time of publication he was living in Epping. His perambulator, depicted in the frontispiece, is a wheel attached to a frame that can measure up to 125 miles in one go.

£1,500-2,000
€2,200-2,900

1329 **Massaria, Domenico** (*fl. c. 1500*). De ponderibus & mensuris medicinalibus libri tres. Ex Graecis, Arabicis, et Latinis rei medicae scriptoribus diligentissime conscriptus... nunc vero ab innumeris mendis Conradi Gesneri opera repurgatus. Huic accedunt etiam alia quaedam eiusdem argumenti, quorum titulos post epistolas positos reperies: omnia studio Caspari Wolphii... in lucem data. *Zurich: Froschauer, 1584*, ff. [8], 107, ILLUSTRATION: woodcut initials, *without final blank, lacking folding table*

Elvius, Petrus (1660-1718), *praeses.* Pes suethicus eiusque usus breviter expositus disputatione academica... praeses Petrus Elvius... respondens Petrus Schultsberg... 13 Maii anni 1696. *Uppsala: Henricus Keyser, [1696]*, [2], 22pp., ILLUSTRATION: woodcut initials and headpiece, folding engraved plate, *many leaves cropped at head (including title-page)*

2 works in one volume, 8vo (147 x 88mm.), BINDING: eighteenth-century half calf, spine gilt in compartments, red morocco lettering-piece, red edges

References: 1st work: Krivatsy 3004; Vischer C1032

£400-600
€600-900

1330 **Mathematical Tracts—Gregory, James (1638-1675).** Exercitationes geometricae... *London: W. Godbid for Moses Pitt, 1688*, [8], 27pp., ILLUSTRATION: folding engraved plate, manuscript table pasted to final recto, [Wing G1909]

Mercator, Nicolaus (?1620-1687). Logarithmo-technia: sive methodus construendi logarithmos... Michaelis Angeli Riccii exercitatio geometrica de maximis & minimis... *London: W. Godbid for M. Pitt, 1688*, [4], 34, [4], 13 [i.e. 14]pp., ILLUSTRATION: folding engraved plate, [Wing M1730]

Boulenger, Jean. La géometrie ou mesure des lignes droittes esloignées, par le quarré géometrique... Seconde edition. *Paris: J. Moreau, 1628*, [8 (including engraved title)], 174 (i.e. 172), [4]pp., ILLUSTRATION: engraved title-page, 71 engraved trigonometrical illustrations in text, a few woodcut diagrams, *engraved title cut down and remounted*

Eckhard, Arnoldus, *praeses.* Positionum mathematicarum sylloge quam... sub praesidio Arnoldi Eckhardi... publice tuebitur Phillipus Henricus Eulalius... ad diem vi Martii horis locoque solitis. *Rinteln: G.C. Wächter, 1676*, [2], 86pp., ILLUSTRATION: 4 engraved plates, manuscript notes on title-page, *some slight worming affecting text at beginning*

Hanbury, Nathaniel (1658/9-1715). Supplementum analyticum ad aequationes cartesianas. *Cambridge: J. Hayes, for the author, to be sold by E. Hall, 1691*, [4], 19pp., dedicated to Dr Busby, [Wing H638; BL copy has 3 preliminary leaves not here present], *title soiled*

3 works in one volume, 4to (187 x 130mm.), BINDING: eighteenth-century mottled calf, spine gilt in compartments, morocco lettering-piece, red edges

Gregory's work was partly written in response to the controversy with Huygens, generated by Gregory's *Vera circuli et hyperbolae quadratura.* In 1670 Gregory, on reading the present work of Mercator, became interested in series expansions, and through Collins became aware of what Newton and others were working on. In *Logarithmo-technia*, Mercator "constructed logarithms from first principles based on rational operations only, and expressed the area under the segment of a hyperbola by a logarithm. Most important, this book was the first to publish a function in the form of an infinite series - obviously independent of similar revolutionary results obtained by Jan Hudde and Newton. Mercator accepted such series as a new type of function in mathematical anaysis" (C.J. Scriba, in *ODNB*). For Mercator see also Macclesfield Science A-C, lots 248 and 257.

£6,000-8,000
€8,700-11,600

1331 Mathematical Tracts—Viviani, Vincenzio (1622-1703). Enodatio problematum universis geometris propositorum a... Claudio Comiers... praemissis, horum occasione, tentamentis variis ad solutionem illustris veterum problematis de anguli trisectione. *Florence: G. Gugliantini, 1677,* [10], 63pp., ILLUSTRATION: 4 engraved plates with 63 figures, [Riccardi ii, 627]

Jode, Cornelis de (1568-1600). De quadrante geometrico libellus. In quo quidquid ad linearum et superficierum, utpote altitudinum et latitudinum, dimensiones facit lucidissime demonstratur. *Nuremberg: C. Lochner, 1594,* [8], 63pp., ILLUSTRATION: folding engraved plate (printed on both sides) at p. 1, engraved illustrations (some full-page) in text, *a few engravings shaved*

[Frénicle de Bessy, Bernard (1605-1675)] Solutio duorum problematum circa numeros cubos & quadratos, quae tanquam insolubilia universis Europae mathematicis a... D. Fermat sunt proposita... a D.B.F.D.B. datis. *Paris: J. Langlois, 1657,* [4], 31pp., errata corrected (by V. Mandey?)

Biancani, Giuseppe (1566-1624), *S.J.* De mathematicarum natura dissertatio una cum clarorum mathematicorum chronologia... [with an index, part of 'Aristotelis loca mathematica... explicate', but sometimes found separately]. *Bologna: G. Tamburini, 1615,* 65, [5]pp., without the final blank, [Riccardi i, 127]

Calender historicall. Wherein is contained an easie declaration of the golden nombre... *[Geneva]: J. Crespin, 1569,* ff. [8], ILLUSTRATION: woodcut border on title-page, small woodcut illustrations, a few contemporary annotations, [part of STC 2106 (Bible, *English*); Gilmont, *Bibl. de J. Crespin* (1981), no. 69/3.4]

Machin, John (1680-1751). The solution of Kepler's problem. *(London: for T. Woodward & C. Davis, printers to the Royal Society, 1739),* pp.205-230

6 works in one volume, 4to (215 x 150mm.), BINDING: eighteenth-century mottled calf, gilt spine, red morocco lettering-piece, red edges

Claude Comiers came from Embrun and was variously a military engineer, priest, teacher of mathematics and author. In 1677 he published *La duplication de cube, la trisection de l'angle, etc.*, to which this work is a response.

Jode's book is extremely rare, and has appeared twice at auction in the last 25 years, in the Honeyman sale and in 1998 in a selection of books from the library of M. de Vitry.

"M. Frénicle de Bessy que vous connoissez par reputation pour ester extremement scavant dans les nombres" (Huygens, *Oeuvres* xi, 2). A number of the letters from early 1657 deal with the problem of cubes set by Fermat. In a letter to Claude Mylon, Fermat mentions that "M. Defréicle [*sic*] a resolu des questions, et M. Marin qui en a les solutions les fait imprimer a ce qu'on m'a dit" (Huygens, *Oeuvres* ii, 13).

£3,000-4,000
€4,350-5,800

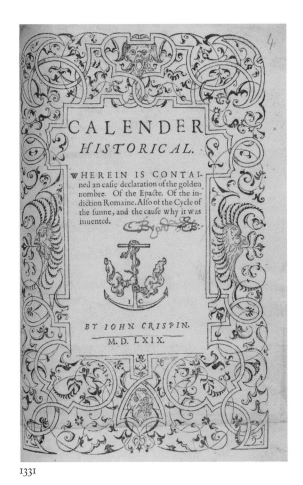

CALENDER HISTORICAL.

WHEREIN IS CONTAI-
ned an easie declaration of the golden
nombre. Of the Epacte. Of the in-
diction Romaine. Also of the Cycle of
the sunne, and the cause why it was
inuented.

BY IOHN CRISPIN.

M. D. LXIX.

1331

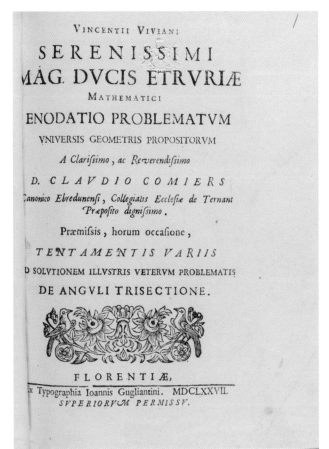

VINCENTII VIVIANI

SERENISSIMI
MAG. DVCIS ETRVRIÆ
MATHEMATICI

ENODATIO PROBLEMATVM

VNIVERSIS GEOMETRIS PROPOSITORVM

A Clarissimo, ac Reverendissimo

D. CLAVDIO COMIERS

Canonico Ebredunensi, Collegialis Ecclesiæ de Ternant
Præposito dignissimo.

Præmissis, horum occasione,

TENTAMENTIS VARIIS

AD SOLVTIONEM ILLVSTRIS VETERVM PROBLEMATIS

DE ANGVLI TRISECTIONE.

FLORENTIÆ,

Ex Typographia Ioannis Gugliantini. MDCLXXVII.
SVPERIORVM PERMISSV.

1331

GEOMETRICA.
CAPVT XXXII.
COPIOSIOR DECLARATIO IMMINV-
TAE ET FICTAE MENSVRAE, QVA PRO VERA
in delineandis rebus vtimur.

Schema.

Sicut se habet centumpeda ficta ad rei ima-
ginem; ita se habet centumpeda vera, ad rem
ipsam.

Mensura

1331

DE
MATHEMATICARVM
NATVRA DISSERTATIO.
VNA CVM CLARORVM
MATHEMATICORVM
CHRONOLOGIA.
AD ILLVSTRISSIMVM AC NOBILISSIMVM
PETRVMFRANCISCVM MALASPINAM
ÆDIFICIORVM MARCHIONEM.
Authore eodem Iosepho Blancano è Societate IESV,
Mathematicarum in Parmensi Academia professore.

BONONIÆ M. DC. XV.
Apud Bartholomæum Cochium. Superiorum permissu.

Sumptibus Hieronymi Tamburini.

1331

145

6 Van de Scheppinge des

afreyfen/ tot dat de Son met al zijn Planeten niet meer dan
vafte Sterre foude gelijcken. Waerom en hebbe ick alhier n
meer dan de wegen der Planeten met den aertkloot in defe g
gure gestelt / alwaer de Sonne omtrent het midden heel on
weeglijck stil gestelt is / en naest de Sonne doet Mercurius

1332

*Vulva marina, aculeis
inftar pubis horrida.*

1332

Num.
XXVII

Solanum   Furiosum.

M. H. fc.

1332

THE
Natural Hiftory
OF
COFFEE.

SECT. I.

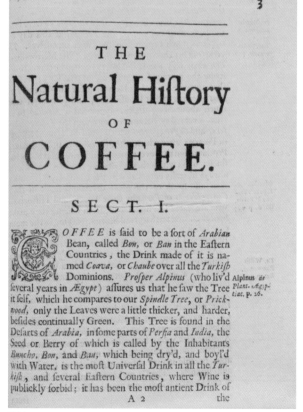

COFFEE is faid to be a fort of *Arabian* Bean, called *Bon*, or *Ban* in the Eaftern Countries, the Drink made of it is na-med *Coava*, or *Chaube* over all the *Turkifh* Dominions. *Profper Alpinus* (who liv'd Alpinus *de* feveral years in *Ægypt*) affures us that he faw the Tree Plant. Ægyp-it felf, which he compares to our *Spindle Tree*, or *Prick-* tiac. p. 26. *wood*, only the Leaves were a little thicker, and harder, befides continually Green. This Tree is found in the Deferts of *Arabia*, in fome parts of *Perfia* and *India*, the Seed or Berry of which is called by the Inhabitants *Buncho, Bon,* and *Bau,* which being dry'd, and boyl'd with Water, is the moft Univerfal Drink in all the *Tur-kifh*, and feveral Eaftern Countries, where Wine is publickly forbid; it has been the moft antient Drink of

A 2   the

1332

146

1332 Mathematics and Natural History—Nierop, Dirck Rembrantsz van. Eenige Oefeningen in god-lijcke, wis-konstige, en natuerlijcke dingen. Waer in dat gehandelt wordt. Ten eerstyen, van des werelsts scheppinge. Ten tweeden, een meetkonstige beschryvinge des geheelen aertkloots. Ten derden, het maecksel van alderhande kaerten. Ten vierden, van de cometen of staert-starren haer verschijninge. *Amsterdam: Gerrit van Goedesberge, 1669*, [8], 84pp., ILLUSTRATION: woodcut figures

Ibid. Tweede deel van enige oefeninghen... Ten tweden, enige aenmerkingen op de raise benoorden om na Oost-India. Ten derden van Abel Tasmans ontdekking nah et onbekende Suid-lant. Ten vierden, van de letterspelling... *Amsterdam: Abel Symonsz van der Storck, 1674*, 68pp., ILLUSTRATION: woodcut figures

Ibid. By-voeghsel op eenige oefeningen welcke sijn eenige aenteyckeningen, dienende tot verbeteringh en vermeerderingh, en dat so wel op 't eerste als het tweede deel des zelfden... Also oock van de overtoght der menschen en schadelijke beesten, na Amerika of West-India. *Amsterdam: A. van Storck, 1678*, 47pp., ILLUSTRATION: woodcut figures

Brückmann, Franz Ernest (1697-1753). Relatio brevis physica de curiosissimis duabus conchis marinis quarum una vulva marina et altera concha venerea nominantur in chartam coniecta et cum orbe erudito communicata. *Brunswick, 1722*, 24pp., ILLUSTRATION: engraved plate with 2 figures

Faber, Johann Matthaeus (1626-1702). Strychnomania explicans strychni manici antiquorum, vel solani furiosi recentiorum, historiae monumentum, indolis nocumentum, antidoti documentum... *Augsburg: J. Schönigk for T. Goebel, 1677*, [8], 109, [21]pp., ILLUSTRATION: engraved frontispiece, 12 engraved plates by Melchior Haffner, [Pritzel 2788], *frontispiece mounted*

The natural history of coffee, thee, chocolate, tobacco... with a tract on elder and juniper-berries, shewing how useful they may be in our coffee-houses: and also the way of making mum... *London: C. Wilkinson, 1682*, 36, [4]pp., [Wing C1859, under Chamberlayne, to whom this is sometimes attributed]

Asp, Matthias, *praeses.* Q.F.S. dissertatio gradualis de Wikia ostrogothica; quam... publico examini sistit Wilhelmus Andreas Wennerdahl... ad diem 28 novemb. anni 1733. *Uppsala: literis Wernerianis, [1733]*, [4], 54, [2]pp.

7 works in one volume, 4to, (186 x 140mm.), BINDING: eighteenth-century half calf, spine gilt in compartments, morocco lettering-piece, red edges

For Nierop, see lots 1451 and 1452. These works which contain secondary accounts of voyages and travels based on larger travel works, and dealing with America and Tasmania as well as the West Indies, seem to be unnoticed in the geographical literature (JCB etc).

£3,000-5,000
€4,350-7,300

1333

1333 Mathematical Tracts—Torricelli, Evangelista (1608-1647). Lezioni accademiche. *Florence: for Jacopo Guiducci and Santi Franchi, 1715*, xlix, [1], 96pp., ILLUSTRATION: engraved frontispiece portrait of the author, engraved device on title-page, woodcut initials, head- and tailpieces, woodcut diagrams

Aleaume, Jacques (1562-1657). La perspective speculative et pratique... mise au jour par Estienne Migon. *Paris: Melchior Tavernier and François Langlois, 1643*, [6], 155, [5]pp., title-page ruled in red, ILLUSTRATION: woodcut and engraved initials and headpieces, engraved illustrations, *without initial blank*

2 works in one volume, 4to (232 x 169mm.), BINDING: contemporary mottled calf, spine gilt in compartments, red morocco lettering-piece, red edges

BOTH FIRST EDITIONS. Only one work of Torricelli's was published during his lifetime.

References: 1st work: Norman 2088; Riccardi ii, 544; *2nd work:* BAL RIBA 70

Provenance: William Jones, signature on title-page of second work

£1,500-2,000
€2,200-2,900

1334 Matlock, John (*fl.* 1685-1710?). Fax nova artis scribendi: or, an introduction (by way of dialogue) to the best forms and proportions of all letters, in each hand most useful; and excellent for all business both in clerkship and trade. To which is added, rules for spelling and pointing. As also, a table of abbreviations, so large that it will facilitate both the writing and reading of any business at common or civil law. Together, with some directions which may be beneficial for a clerk in the progress of his whole clerkship. *London: John Leake for the author, to be sold by Luke Meredith, 1685*

4to (210 x 160mm.), [10], 37, [1 (advertisement)] pp., BINDING: later vellum-backed blue boards, *first and last leaves browned, slight spotting*

FIRST EDITION, RARE. A second edition was printed the following year, in which Matlock defended his way of teaching lettering. Matlock is mentioned by Samuel Pepys, appropriately enough, as Pepys was a clerk himself.

References: Bonacini 1143; Heal, p.158; Wing M1292A

£3,000-4,000
€4,350-5,800

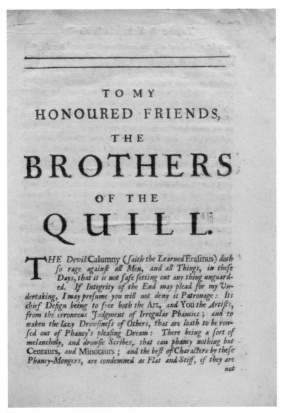

TO MY
HONOURED FRIENDS,
THE
BROTHERS
OF THE
QUILL.

THE Devil Calumny (*faith the Learned Eralmus*) *doth
so rage against all Men, and all Things, in these
Days, that it is not safe setting out any thing unguard-
ed. If Integrity of the End may plead for my Undertaking, I may presume you will not deny it Patronage: Its
chief Design being to free both the Art, and You the Artists,
from the erroneous Judgment of Irregular Phancies; and to
waken the lazy Drowsiness of Others, that are loath to be rous-
sed out of Phancy's pleasing Dream: There being a sort of
melancholy, and drowsie Scribes, that can phancy nothing but
Centaurs, and Minotaurs; and the best of Characters by these
Phancy-Mongers, are condemned as Flat and Stiff, if they are
not*

1334

1335 Maupertuis, Pierre Louis Moreau de (1698-1759). Discours sur les différentes figures des astres; d'où l'on tire des conjectures sur les étoiles qui paroissent changer de grandeur; & sur l'anneau de Saturne. Avec une exposition abbrégée des systèmes de M. Descartes & de M. Newton. *Paris: Imprimerie Royale, 1732*

8vo (193 x 124mm.), [4], 83pp., ILLUSTRATION: woodcut diagrams in text, woodcut head-piece, BINDING: contemporary calf, spine gilt in compartments

FIRST EDITION. PRESENTATION COPY, inscribed by Maupertuis to William Jones (cf lot 1281 for a letter from Jones to Maupertuis). In this work Maupertuis "controverted the prevailing opinion in France that universal gravitation was an 'absurd principle', insisting that it was metaphysically viable and mathematically superior to vortices as an explanation of celestial mechanics". Maupertuis and Voltaire corresponded and the *Lettres philosophiques* was published in 1733, followed by Voltaire's *Elémens*.

References: Wallis 122

Provenance: William Jones, presentation inscription

£2,000-3,000
€2,900-4,350

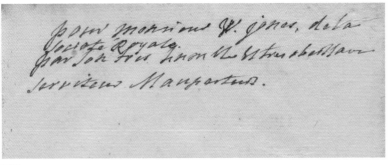

1335

1336

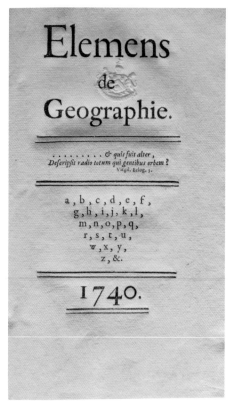

1339

1336 Maupertuis, Pierre Louis Moreau de. Discours sur les différentes figures des astres... Seconde édition augmentée. *Paris: G. Martin, J.-B. Coignard & les frères Guerin, 1742*

8vo (199 x 117mm.), [16 (including half-title)], 176pp., ILLUSTRATION: engraved frontispiece printed in blue, woodcut diagrams in text, BINDING: contemporary calf gilt

Second, augmented edition of a work first published in 1732 (see lot 1335).

References: Wallis 122.002

£300-400
€450-600

1337 Maupertuis, Pierre Louis Moreau de. La figure de la terre, déterminée par les observations de Messieurs de Maupertuis, Clairaut, Camus, Le Monnier... de M. l'abbé Outhier... de M. Celsius... faites par ordre du roy au cercle polaire. *Paris: Imprimerie royale, 1738*

8vo (194 x 120mm.), xxiv, [4], 184pp., ILLUSTRATION: engraved map, 9 folding engraved plates, one engraved head-piece and initial, BINDING: contemporary calf, spine gilt in compartments

FIRST EDITION. In 1735 France sent an expedition, headed by Maupertuis, to Lapland to measure a degree of meridian at the polar circle. The results, which supported Newton's theory that the earth is flattened by gravity towards the poles, were corroborated by the findings of a similar mission to Peru led by La Condamine. See also Macclesfield Science A-C, lot 253.

References: Babson 94; Norman 1458

£600-900
€900-1,350

1338 Maupertuis, Pierre Louis Moreau de. The figure of the earth, determined from observations... at the polar circle... Translated from the French. *London: for T. Cox, C. Davis, J. & P. Knapton and A. Millar, 1738*

8vo (203 x 127mm.), viii, 232pp., ILLUSTRATION: one engraved map, 9 folding engraved plates, one engraved head-piece, BINDING: contemporary mottled calf gilt

FIRST EDITION IN ENGLISH, published in the same year as the first edition (see lot 1337).

References: Babson 95

£500-700
€750-1,050

1339 [Maupertuis, Pierre Louis Moreau de] Elemens de geographie. *[Paris: chez G. Martin etc.], 1740*

8vo (203 x 123mm.), [4], 141, [3]pp., BINDING: contemporary French mottled calf, gilt fillet on covers, gilt spine, red edges, THICK PAPER COPY

The work sets out for the lay reader the results of Maupertuis's geodetic work, and in particular its importance for navigation. Published anonymously because of the sentence in which Maupertuis remarks that governments support scientific research not out of altruism but because (article XVIII) "the state can derive from them more substantial advantages. And though savants give their time to frivolous things whilst they are in their studies, they are not permitted to cross oceans and to risk their lives and those of others, except for discoveries whose utility justifies their perils and pains" (see Mary Terrall, *The man who flattened the earth: Maupertuis and the sciences in the Enlightenment*, Chicago, 2002).

£500-600
€750-900

1340 Maupertuis, Pierre Louis Moreau de. Discours sur la parallaxe de la lune, pour perfectionner la théorie de la lune et celle de la terre. *Paris: Imprimerie royale, 1741*

8vo (201 x 120mm.), xxxii, 133pp., ILLUSTRATION: woodcut diagrams in text, BINDING: contemporary calf gilt

£500-700
€750-1,050

1341 Maupertuis, Pierre Louis Moreau de. Astronomie nautique: ou élémens d'astronomie, tant pour observatoire fixe, que pour un observatoire mobile. *Paris: Imprimerie royale, 1743*

FIRST EDITION, 8vo (199 x 120mm.), xl, [8], 98pp., ILLUSTRATION: woodcut diagrams, BINDING: contemporary calf, spine gilt in compartments

References: Houzeau & Lancaster 10737

£250-300
€400-450

1342 [Maurisse, Jean] Introduction familière en la science d'astronomie, contre Copernic. En laquelle on void les principes & les choses plus essencielles qui concernent cette science. *Paris: Louis Vendosme, 1672*

4to (247 x 180mm.), [12], 272, [2]pp., ILLUSTRATION: engraved device on title-page, engraved illustrations, replacement plate pasted to p.215, 5 folding plates pasted to page edges, BINDING: contemporary calf, spine gilt in compartments, *binding rubbed*

The anonymous author, identified as Maurisse or Meurisse, treats of the Copernican world system with contempt. Despite the widespread acceptance of Copernicus' hypothesis by this time (forty years after the trial of Galileo), Maurisse attempts to reinstate the universe as described in the Bible.

£300-400
€450-600

1343 Mauro, Fiorentino (1493-1556). Annotationi sopra la lettione della Spera del Sacro Bosco doue si dichiarono tutti e principii mathematici & naturali... Con le infrascritte cose, cio, e, [*sic*] Una nuova e fedele (ad verbum) traduttione di detta Spera. Una spera theologica diuina, & christiana. Una spera platonica... Una nuoua inuentione... per subitamente fare le dodici case celesti della figura astronomica. *(Florence: [L. Torrentino], 6 March 1550)*

4to (210 x 130mm.), 219, [1]pp., errata on pp. 215-219, with a lengthy addition on the doctrine of the real presence, sonnet in praise of author on p. 219, ILLUSTRATION: woodcuts of sphere etc., woodcut initials, BINDING: eighteenth-century English mottled calf, spine gilt

FIRST EDITION. The author was a Franciscan and published his translation of Sacro Bosco in 1537 in Venice. This is reprinted here most handsomely, together with other material commenting on the text in various ways.

References: Riccardi ii, 138; Shaaber 374

Provenance: Richard Brakenbury, inscription on title-page dated 1566

£1,500-2,000
€2,200-2,900

1343

1344 Maurolico, Francesco. Opuscula mathematica (Arithmeticorum libri duo). *Venice: Francesco Franceschi, 1575*

4to (220 x 155mm.), [20], 285, [8], 175, [21]pp., last leaf a blank, ILLUSTRATION: woodcut devices, diagrams in text, initials etc., BINDING: contemporary English centre-piece binding, large gilt centre-piece within blind-stamped fillet, gilt fleurons at corners, on either side of the centre-piece the initials T.H., gilt ornaments on spine, red morocco lettering-piece, *upper joints weak, small worm holes at head of spine*

FIRST EDITION. There was another edition in 1580.

References: Riccardi ii, 141

Provenance: T.H.; Thomas Moffet (or Muffet, 1553-1604) the celebrated doctor and naturalist; Henry San[d]ford, with inscription 'Henry Sanfordus possidet donatum a doctore Moffet, 15 September 1594'

£2,000-3,000
€2,900-4,350

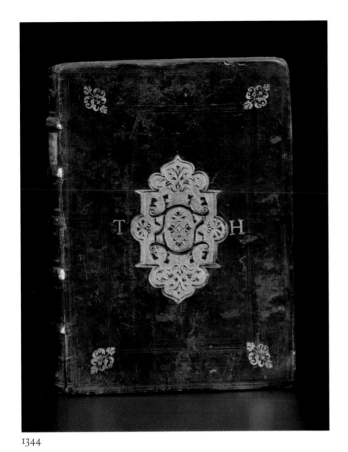

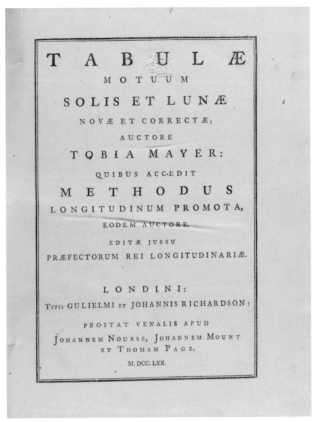

1344   1345

1345 Mayer, Tobias (1723-1762). Tabulae motuum solis et lunae: novae et correctae... quibus accedit methodus longitudinum promota, eodem autore; editae jussu praefectorum rei longitudinariae [edited by Nevil Maskelyne]. *London: William and John Richardson, for sale by John Nourse, John Mount and Thomas Page, 1770*

4to (262 x 203mm.), [8], 89, [6], 92-136, cxxx, [2]pp., ILLUSTRATION: 2 folding engraved plates, BINDING: contemporary calf, spine gilt in compartments, red morocco lettering-piece, *binding very slightly soiled*

FIRST EDITION. Mayer constructed his lunar tables according to Newton's principles on the motion of the moon. He also contributed to the debate on longitude, and while his tables could be used to determine longitude, they were deemed too complicated to be of practical use.

£1,500-2,000
€2,200-2,900

1346 Mayne, John (*fl.* 1673-1675). Socius mercatoris: or, the merchant's companion: in three parts. The first, being a plain and easie introduction to arithmetick... The second, a treatise of simple and compound interest and rebate... The third, a new and exact way of measuring solids in the form of a prismoid and cylindroid... *London: W.G. for N. Crouch, 1674 (1673)*

FIRST EDITION, 8vo (162 x 102mm.), [16], 206pp., ILLUSTRATION: engraved frontispiece portrait of the author, woodcut initials, typographical headpieces, woodcut diagrams, BINDING: contemporary sheep gilt, *without final leaf (containing errata), some slight foxing, binding worn*

References: Wing M1484

£800-1,000
€1,200-1,450

1346

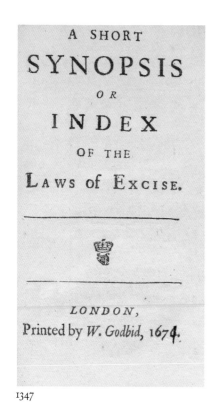

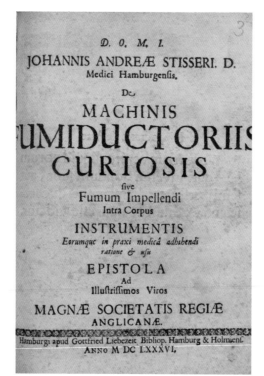

1347   1349

1347 Mayne, John. The practical gauger: being a plain and easie method of gauging all sorts of brewing vessels. Whereunto is added, a short synopsis of the laws of excise. *London: W[illiam] G[odbid] for N. Brooke, 1676*, [8], 59, [3], 59-77, [1 (blank)] pp., ILLUSTRATION: woodcut diagrams, *B7-8 torn in gutter with loss of a few letters*

Ibid. A short synopsis of the laws of excise. *London: W. Godbid, 1676*, [2], 12pp., *without final advertisement leaf, paper flaw in E3 affecting page number*

2 works in one volume, 12mo (131 x 74mm.), BINDING: contemporary sheep, marbled edges, *binding slightly rubbed*

FIRST EDITION. The date on all the title-pages has been altered in manuscript to 1674. The second work is in fact a separate issue of the final part of the first work, with a different woodcut on the title-page and separate pagination. It is not recorded separately in Wing but there is a copy on ESTC (Balliol College, Oxford).

References: Wing M1483 & ESTC R233442

£800-1,000
€1,200-1,450

1348 Mead, Richard (1673-1754). A mechanical account of the poisons in several essays...The third edition, with large additions. *London: J. Brindley, 1745*

8vo (220 x 130mm.), xlviii, 319pp., printed on thick paper, errata slip pasted on p. [320], ILLUSTRATION: 4 folding engraved plates each with several figures, engraved tail-piece on p.319, BINDING: contemporary polished calf, gilt double fillet on covers with corner ornament, edges mottled, *joints splitting at foot*

A handsome thick paper presentation copy from Mead, the fashionable society doctor and collector.

£400-500
€600-750

1349 Mechanical Tracts—Piccolomini, Alessandro (1508-1578). Parafrasi... sopra le Mecaniche d'Aristotile, tradotta da Oreste Vannocci Biringucci [with the text]. *Rome: Francesco Zanetti, 1582*, 127, [5]pp., title partly printed in red, ILLUSTRATION: woodcut figures and diagrams (that on Q3 possibly cropped at foot), [Censimento 16 CNCE 38670]

Baldi, Bernardino (1553-1617). In Mechanica Aristotelis problemata exercitationes: adiecta succincta narratione de autoris vita & scriptis. *Mainz: widow of J. Albinus, 1621*, [20], 194pp., title printed in red and black, ILLUSTRATION: woodcut figures, *lacking final leaf (blank?)*

Stisser, Johann Andreas (1657-1700). De machinis humiductoriis curiosis sive fumum impellendi intra corpus instrumentis... *Hamburg: G. Liebezeit, 1686*, ff. [8], ILLUSTRATION: 4 numbered engraved plates, the capital s of "humiductoriis" cropped at edges

Zannichelli, Gian Girolamo (1662-1726). De ferro eiusque nivis praeparatione dissertatio in qua varia de ipso metallo explicantur. *Venice, 1719*, [4], 46pp., ILLUSTRATION: frontispiece of Hercules and the Hydra, folding engraved plate at end, *printed marginalia shaved*

Jordan, Jean, *of Stuttgart*. [Deux machines] Explication des figures que l'on voit dans la taille douce ci-jointe. *[?Leiden, 1677]*, 3-8pp. (A2-4, A1 possibly a title, not present, but text complete), ILLUSTRATION: folding engraved plate with five figures

5 works in one volume, 4to (188 x 135mm.), BINDING: eighteenth-century half calf, spine gilt in compartments, red morocco lettering-piece, red edges

Mechanica is a work attributed to Aristotle, and is probably based on the teachings of the Peripatetics. Not printed in the fifteenth century (except as part of the Aldine edition of the Greek text), it was included in many sixteenth-century collected editions in a number of translations, and there were also some separate editions. The text, which discusses levers amongst other subjects, formed part of Galileo's reading and his *De motu*. Piccolomini's work was published in Latin in 1547 and again in 1575. Baldi's work appears here for the first time.

Stisser was a professor of medicine at Helmstädt, and the author of a number of works of a chemical and alchemical nature. He corresponded with Leibnitz in 1699.

Zannichelli was a pharmacist in Venice (born in Modena), known chiefly as a botanist who carried out extensive investigations and was a correspondent of many men of science. He put together a number of herbaria and a work on the plants of the Venetian *lidi* was published posthumously.

The last work describes some hydraulic machines invented by a certain Captain Jean Jordan of Stuttgart who has prepared the engravings. He is, we are informed (pp.7-8), happy to show his inventions to people, but as he has already expended a lot of time and money on them, he would like the money for any demonstration "up-front", money which he will not be able to touch until he has given visible demonstration and revealed everything about those machines. Anyone interested can apply in Leiden to Sieur Jean van Gelder, bookseller "à la Tortue", opposite the church of St Peter in the Cloksteech.

£800-1,000
€1,200-1,450

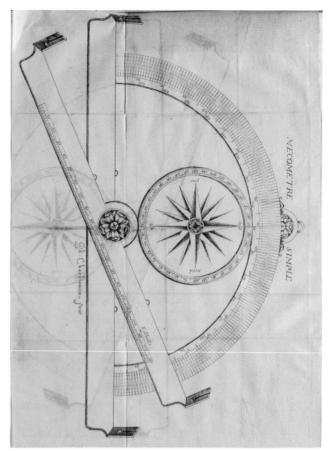

1350

1351

1350 Mechanics and Optics—Aristotle, *pseudo-*. Aristotelis Mechanica graeca
emendata, latina facta, et commentariis illustrata ab Henrico Monantholio. *Paris:
Jérôme Perier, 1599*, [32], 211, [9]pp., title printed in red and black, ILLUSTRATION:
woodcut device on title-page, woodcut initials and headpieces, woodcut diagrams
(1 full-page)

Damianus (4th century AD). Damiani philosophi Heliodori Larissaei de opticis
libri II. Nunc primum editi, et animadversionibus illustrati ab Erasmio Bartholino.
Paris: officina Cramoisiana, 1657, [24], 148pp., ILLUSTRATION: woodcut device on
title-page, woodcut diagrams

2 works in one volume, 4to (214 x 156mm.), BINDING: eighteenth-century mottled
calf, spine gilt in compartments, red morocco lettering-piece, red edges

For another copy of the Aristotle, see Macclesfield Science A-C, lot 196; and for
the Damianus, see Macclesfield Science D-H, lot 593, and the footnote there.

References: 1st work: IA 108.774

£2,000-3,000
€2,900-4,350

1351 Mecometry & Globes—Henrion, Didier (c. 1580-c. 1632). L'usage du mecometre qui est un instrument géometrique, avec lequel on peut... mésurer toutes sortes de longueurs et distances visibles... *Paris: Isaac Dedin for the author, to be sold by Samuel Thiboust, 1630*, [8], 191, [1]pp., ILLUSTRATION: woodcut initials and headpieces, woodcut diagrams, 2 folding engraved plates

Gigas, Johann Michael (c. 1582-1637?). Enchiridion sphaericum id est, systema cosmographicum, compendiosum: continens utriusque globi, caelestis & terrestris accuratam descriptionem, in gratiam eorum, qui ad solidam astronomiae & geographiae cognitionem aspirant: libris duobus adornatum. *Hanau: heirs of Wilhelm Antonius, 1615*, [32], 187, [1]pp., ILLUSTRATION: woodcut device on title-page and final verso, woodcut initials and headpieces, *a few quires browned*

2 works in one volume, 8vo (162 x 97mm.), BINDING: eighteenth-century polished calf, spine gilt in compartments, green morocco lettering-piece, red edges

BOTH FIRST EDITIONS. The word mecometry, deriving from the Greek μηκος (length), was coined by Henrion. Littré records it solely in an obstetrical context (an instrument for measuring the length of a foetus), but it seems to have disappeared from use.

References: 2nd work: Houzeau & Lancaster 2957; Zinner 4506

£1,000-1,500
€1,450-2,200

1352 Medical Tracts—Arbuthnot, John (1667-1735). [An essay concerning the nature of aliments] Practical rules of diet in the various constitutions and diseases of human bodies. *London: J. Tonson, 1732*, [8], [243]-430pp. only, errata pasted to p. 430, thick paper copy, *without pp. [20], 1-239*

Cocchi, Antonio (1695-1758). [Del vitto pitagorico] The Pythagorean diet of vegetables only... Translated from the Italian. *London: R. Dodsley, sold by M. Cooper, 1745*, [4], 91, [1 (blank)] pp.

Simon, Thomas (1696-1764). The system of the womb: with a particular account of the menses... *London: Harmen Noorthouck, 1730*, [4], 109, [1 (blank)] pp., dedicated to the Duke of Chandos with armorial headpiece

3 works in one volume, 8vo (189 x 117mm.), BINDING: contemporary mottled calf, spine gilt in compartments, red morocco lettering-piece, red edges

Arbuthnot is the well-known recipient of Pope's *Epistle* and an author himself; Cocchi too was a particular friend of Pope. Cocchi lived in England from 1723 to 1726, and after his return to Florence was often visited by English friends, particularly those that were Freemasons. A man of wide culture, he organised the Biblioteca Magliabechiana, and was behind the first edition of the *Life* of Benvenuto Cellini in 1730. The Duke of Chandos, to whom Simon's work is dedicated, was the patron of Handel and built Cannons Park at Stanmore.

£600-800
€900-1,200

1353 Medical Tracts—[Cadogan, William (1711-1797)] An essay upon nursing, and the management of children, from their birth to three years of age... *London: J. Roberts, 1748*, 34pp., [Wellcome II, p.285]

Morgan, Thomas (d. 1743). A letter to Dr Cheyne; occasioned by Dr Robinson's letter to him, in defence of his Treatise of the animal oeconomy, against Dr Morgan's objections, in his Mechanical Practice, &c. *London: Thomas Cox, 1738*, 55, [1 (blank)] pp., errata slip pasted to last page

[Pichatty de Croislainte] A brief journal of what passed in the city of Marseilles, while it was afflicted with the plague, in the year 1720... Translated from the original. *London: J. Roberts, 1721*, 68pp. [=76, last quire L mispaginated], [Wellcome IV, p.383]

Quincy, John (d. 1722). An essay upon the different causes of pestilential diseases, and how they become contagious. With remarks upon the infection now in France. The third edition, with large additions. *London: for E. Bell & J. Osborn, 1721*, [2], vi (=iv), 3-76pp., [Wellcome IV, p.458]

Hancocke, John (d. 1728). Febrifugum magnum: or, common water the best cure for fevers, and probably for the plague... The second edition. *London: R. Halsley; and sold by J. Roberts, 1723*, [4], 108pp., [Wellcome III, p.206]

5 works in one volume, 8vo (198 x 115mm.), BINDING: eighteenth-century polished calf, spine gilt in compartments, red morocco lettering-piece, yellow edges

£700-1,000
€1,050-1,450

1354 Medical Tracts—Experiments lately made by several eminent physicians [T. Atwood, J. Mackenzie, T. Cameron and J. Wall], on the surprising and terrible effects, of almond-water and black-cherry-water. With the cherry-planter's queries and objections... Likewise, a discourse on Ecclesiasticus 38.1. Honour the physician... because of necessity, for the Lord hath created him... *London: J. Huggonson, 1741*, [2], 62pp.

Mead, Richard (1673-1754). A discourse concerning the action of the sun and moon on animal bodies; and the influence which this may have in many diseases. *London, 1708*, 32pp., [Wellcome IV, p.95]

Hartley, David (1705-1757). A view of the present evidence for and against Mrs Stephens's medicines, as a solvent for the stone. Containing a hundred and fifty-five cases. With some experiments and observations. *London: S. Harding, J. Robinson and J. Roberts, 1739*, vi, [2], 204, [4]pp., [Wellcome III, p.215]

3 works in one volume, 8vo (195 x 113mm.), BINDING: eighteenth-century polished calf, spine gilt in compartments, red morocco lettering-piece, red edges

£800-1,000
€1,200-1,450

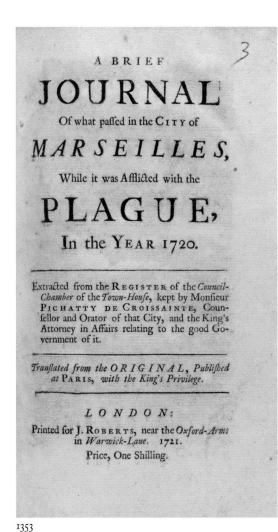

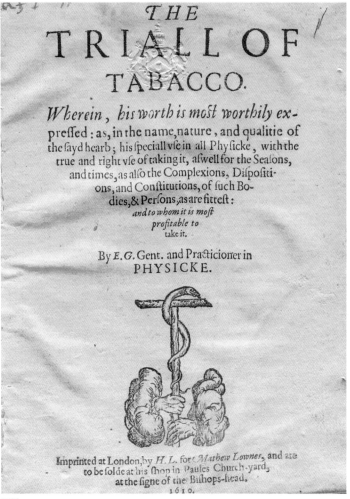

1353

1355

1355 Medical Tracts—G[ardiner], E[dmund] The triall of tabacco. Wherein, his worth is most worthily expressed... his speciall use in all physicke... *London: H. L[ownes] for Mathew Lownes, 1610*, ff. [6], 58, ILLUSTRATION: woodcut device on title-page, [STC 11564; Krivatsy 4547]

Olmo, Marco Antonio. Uterus muliebris hoc est de indiciis cognoscendi temperamenta uteri, vel partium genitalium ipsius mulieris. Liber unus... *Bologna: Giovanni Battista Bellagamba, 1601*, [50], 235pp., no leaf A1 in preliminaries, single line (verse) cancel slip pasted onto +4 recto, [Wellcome 6394; Krivatsy 8427], *first few leaves soiled, particularly the title-leaf*

2 works in one volume, 4to (177 x 132mm.), BINDING: eighteenth-century polished calf, spine gilt in compartments, red morocco lettering-piece, red edges

£1,500-2,000
€2,200-2,900

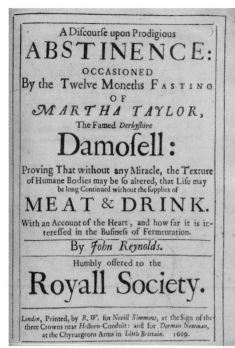

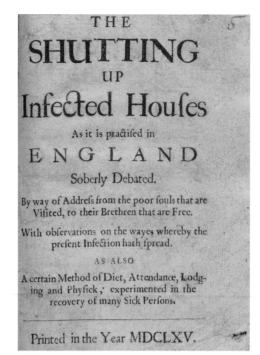

1356   1356

1356 Medical Tracts—Gatford, Lionel (d. 1665). Λογος αλεξιφαρμακος, or, hyperphysicall directions in time of plague... Disposed... according to the method of those physicall directions printed... at Oxford 1644... *Oxford: H. Hall, 1644*, [2], 35, [1 (blank)] pp., ILLUSTRATION: title within a woodcut frame, [Wing G335; Madan 1710; Krivatsy 4582]

Edwards, Edward. The cure of all sorts of fevers... with their definition, kindes, differences, causes, signes... and manner of cure... *London: Thomas Harper to be sold by William Sheeres, 1638*, [8], 53, [3]pp., [STC 7512; Krivatsy 3601], *3 leaves with small tears*

C[lark], R. Vermiculars destroyed, with an historical account of worms: collected from the best authors... and experiments proved by that admirable invention of the microscope... *London: J. Wilkins, for the author, [1691?]*, 30pp., ILLUSTRATION: woodcut on p.7, [Wing C4485], RARE, *A4 and title-page cropped at foot, small hole in last leaf not affecting text, title-leaf soiled*

Certain necessary directions as well for the cure of the plague, as for preventing infection... *London: John Bill and Christopher Barker, 1665*, [6], 35, [1 (blank)] pp., Black Letter, [Wing C1705], RARE, *last leaf damaged with loss of some text, some headlines shaved*

The shutting up infected houses as it is practised in England soberly debated... With observations on the wayes whereby the present infection hath spread. As also a certain method of diet, attendance, lodging and physick, experimented in the recovery of many sick persons. *[London], 1665*, 19 [1 (blank)] pp., [Wing S3717], RARE

Reynolds, John. A discourse upon prodigious abstinence: occasioned by the twelve moneths fasting of Martha Taylor, the famed Derbyshire damosell: proving that without any miracle, the texture of humane bodies may be so altered, that life may be long continued without the supplies of meat & drink... *London: R.W. for Nevill Simmons and Dorman Newman, 1669*, [6], 37, [1 (blank)] pp., [Wing R1314], RARE

6 works in one volume, 4to (171 x 130mm.), BINDING: eighteenth-century speckled calf, spine gilt in compartments, red morocco lettering-piece, red edges

The outbreak of plague during the Civil War was tiny compared with the mass outbreak in London in 1665 to which two of these tracts relate.

£2,500-3,000
€3,650-4,350

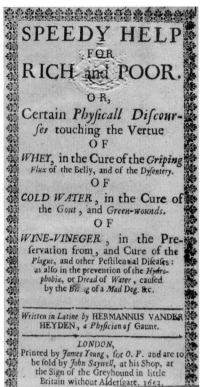

1357

1357 Medical Tracts—Heyden, Hermann van der (1572-c. 1650). Speedy help for rich and poor. Or, certain physicall discourses touching the vertue of whey, in the cure of the griping flux of the belly... of cold water, in the cure of the gout... of wine-vineger in the preservation from, and cure of the plague... *London: James Young for O.P., and are to be sold by John Saywell, 1653,* [36], 211, [5]pp., first and last leaves blank (here lacking), [Wing V63; Krivatsy 5595], *title-leaf shaved at foot, a few page numerals shaved*

Dufour, Philippe Sylvestre (1622-1687) *and* **Antonio Colmenero de Ledesma.** The manner of making of coffee, tea, and chocolate... with their vertues. Newly done out of French and Spanish [by John Chamberlayne of Merton College, Oxford]. *London: W. Crook, 1685,* [10], 116pp., separate title-pages for Tea and Chocolate, [Wing D2455; von Hünersdorff, *Coffee,* p.421], *title-border shaved at foot, some upper margins cut close*

2 works in one volume, 12mo (135 x 74mm.), BINDING: eighteenth-century polished calf, spine gilt in compartments, green morocco lettering-piece, red edges, *very slight worming on lower cover*

Heyden's work first appeared in French at Ghent in 1645 and then in Latin, the author being a physician in Ghent. The publisher of the English edition was Octavian Pulleyn, who also published Heyden's *Synopsis* in Latin, and other medical works.

£2,000-3,000
€2,900-4,350

1358 Medical Tracts—Jorden, Edward (1569-1632). A briefe discourse of a disease called the suffocation of the mother... Wherein is declared that divers strange actions and passions of the body of man... imputed to the Divell, have their true naturall causes, and do accompanie this disease. *London: John Windet, 1603,* ff. [4], 25, [STC 14790; Krivatsy 6275]

Pemell, Robert (d. 1653). De morbis puerorum, or, a treatise of the diseases of children... *London: J. Legatt for Philemon Stephens, 1653,* [4], 58, [2]pp., [Wing P1132; Krivatsy 8774]

Border, Daniel. Πολυφαρμακος και χυμιστης: or, the English unparalell'd physitian and chyrurgian: shewing the true use of all manner of plants and minerals... *London: B. Alsop, 1651,* [16], 144pp., [Wing B3751; Wellcome II, p.203; not in Krivatsy], *last headline cropped*

Helmont, Jean Baptiste van (1577-1644). A ternary of paradoxes. The magnetick cure of wounds. [The] nativity of tartar in wine. [The] image of God in man... translated... and ampliated by Walter Charleton. *London: James Flesher for William Lee, 1650,* [52], 144pp., [Wing H1401; Krivatsy 5449]

4 works in one volume, 4to (172 x 123mm.), BINDING: eighteenth-century speckled calf, spine gilt in compartments, red morocco lettering-piece, red edges

Edward Jorden, who was strongly influenced by Paracelsus, here explains supposed demonic possession in terms of hysteria. The collection of Helmontian tracts (the first to appear in English) contains three items, one of which is medical, one chemical and the last theological. The book circulated widely: Samuel Jeake, for example, owned it.

References: Jorden: M. Macdonald, ed., *Witchcraft & hysteria in Elizabethan London: Edward Jorden and the Mary Glover case* (1991); *Helmont:* Partington II, chapter 6; W.R. Newman, *Gehennical Fire* (2003)

£3,000-4,000
€4,350-5,800

A
DECLARATION
OF SVCH GREIVOVS
accidents as commonly follow
the biting of mad Dogges,
together with the cure
thereof,
BY
THOMAS SPACKMAN
Doctor of Phylick.

LONDON
Printed for John Bill 1612.

1359

CERTAIN
neceſſary Directions, aſ-
well for the Cure of the
Plague, as for preuenting
the Infection;

With many eaſie Medicines of ſmall charge, very profitable to his Maieſties Subiects.

Set downe by the Colledge of Phyſicians by the
Kings MAIESTIES ſpeciall command.

With ſundry Orders thought meet by his Maieſtie, and his
Priuie Councell, to be carefully executed for preuention
of the Plague.

Alſo certaine ſelect Statutes commanded
by His Maieſtie to be put in execution by all
Iuſtices, and other officers of the Peace
throughout the Realme;

Together with His Maieſties Proclamation for further
direction therein : and a Decree in Starre-Chamber, concerning buildings and In-mates.

⸿ Imprinted at London by ROBERT
BARKER, Printer to the Kings moſt Excellent
MAIESTIE : And by the Aſſignes of
IOHN BILL. 1636.

1359

1359 **Medical Tracts—Spackman, Thomas.** A declaration of such greivous accidents
as commonly follow the biting of mad dogges, together with the cure thereof.
London: [Eliot's Court Press for] J. Bill, 1612, [6], 83pp., ILLUSTRATION: woodcut on
title, [STC 22977; not in Krivatsy or Wellcome], *some leaves cropped, particularly at
top and running-title, title-leaf soiled*

Royal College of Physicians. Certain necessary directions, as well for the cure of
the plague, as for preventing the infection... *London: R. Barker, and the assigns of J.
Bill, 1636*, ff. [72], Black Letter, ILLLUSTRATION: large woodcut arms on verso of
title-page, woodcut initials and headpieces, [STC 16769.5; Krivatsy 9995],
without initial (blank?) leaf, a few leaves with slight browning at edges

Pemell, Robert (d. 1653). Tractatus de facultatibus simplicium, the second part of
the treatise of the nature and qualitie of such physical simples as are most
frequently used in medicines... *London: J. Legatt for Philemon Stephens, 1653*, ff.
[34], [Wing P1134; Krivatsy 8777 (here treated as part of a larger work, but all
classed separately by Wing)], *some leaves cropped with loss of catchwords, running-
titles etc.*

3 works in one volume, 4to (170 x 120mm.), BINDING: eighteenth-century
sprinkled calf, spine gilt in compartments, red morocco lettering-piece, red edges

Provenance: Edmund Pitt, early inscription on title-page of work by Spackman

£3,000-4,000
€4,350-5,800

1360

1360 Medical Tracts—Verle, Giovanni Battista. Anatomia artificialis oculi humani inventa & recens fabricata... ex italico in latinum sermonem conversa. *Amsterdam: H. Wetstein, 1680*, [6], 63pp., second and third leaves of preliminaries signed [?]3-4, ILLUSTRATION: 7 numbered full-page engravings, [Krivatsy 12301]

Grew, Nehemiah (1641-1712). A discourse... concerning the nature, causes, and power of mixture. *London: J. Martyn, 1675*, [16], 112pp., [Wing G1948]

2 works in one volume, 12mo (125 x 69mm.), BINDING: eighteenth-century polished calf, spine gilt in compartments, red morocco lettering-piece, red edges

The work by Verle was originally published in Florence in 1679 and rapidly translated into Latin. According to the preface to this Latin edition, it was Verle's father Giovanni, who worked in Florence for Cosimo III, who had originally made a false eye, and it was his father's work, encouraged by Magliabechi, that G.B. Verle continued.

Artificial eyes were known in the sixteenth century and are discussed by Ambroise Paré, who may have invented them.

£800-1,200
€1,200-1,750

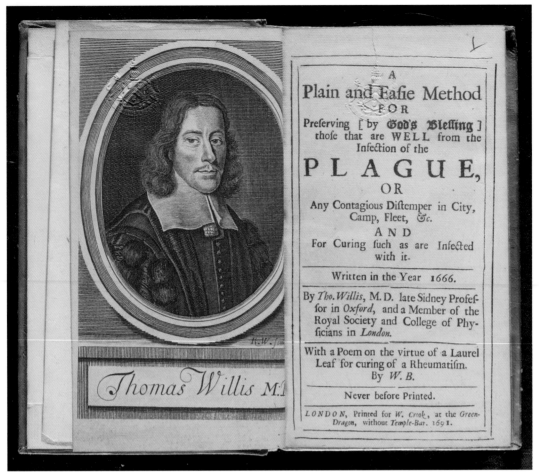

1361

1361 Medical Tracts—Willis, Thomas (1621-1675). A plain and easie method for preserving (by God's blessing) those that are well from the infection of the plague, or any contagious distemper in city, camp, fleet, &c... With a poem on the virtue of a laurel leaf for curing of a rheumatism by W[illiam] B[olton]. *London: W. Crook, 1691*, [12], 74pp., thick paper copy, π2 with errata list, ILLUSTRATION: engraved portrait of Willis, [Wing W2853; Krivatsy 13041], *without the poem on laurel*

Banyer, Henry. Pharmacopoeia pauperum: or, the hospital dispensatory: containing the chief medicines now used in the hospitals of London... The second edition much enlarged. *London: T. Warner, 1721*, iv, 128pp., thick paper copy, *G3 with a clean tear*

Sennert, Daniel (1572-1637). Practical physick: or, five distinct treatises of the most predominant diseases of these times... Written in Latine... in English, by H. Care, student in physick, and astrology. *London: William Whitwood, 1676*, [16], 151, [1 (blank)] pp. only, [Wing S2542], *without the second part*

3 works in one volume, 8vo (161 x 97mm.), BINDING: eighteenth-century speckled calf, spine gilt in compartments, red morocco lettering-piece, red edges

The poem on the medical virtues of laurel is called for by the title-page (thus Wing W2853), but there is also a variant title-page without these words (Wing W2852). This copy has clearly never had the extra 7 pages.

The work by Banyer went through several editions up to 1739.

£1,000-1,500
€1,450-2,200

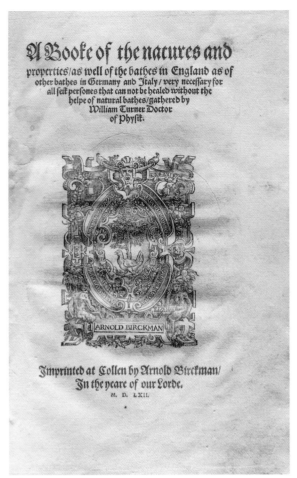

1362   1362

1362 Medicinal Tracts—Schurtz, Georg Niclaus. Neu-eingerichtete Material-
Kammer: das ist gründliche Beschreibung aller fürnemhmsten Materialien und
Specereyen... Samt einer Erklärung: der chimischen medicinischen
metallinischen... Characteren... Wobey angehängt ein ausführlicher Bericht des
Walfisch-sanges in den nordischen Landen... Aller Liebhabern der Handlungen
und Kauffmanschafften zum besten mit guten Nutz und Frommen eingerichtet.
Nuremberg: Christoff Gerhard und zu finden bey C. Endtern, 1673, [28], 112, [2]pp.,
ILLUSTRATION: additional engraved title (plate 1) and 3 engraved plates (2-4) of
'Nota vel signa metallorum', [BL STC German XVIIc. S1523 (dated 1672, as is
copy at HAB); not in Kress (but cf. Kress 683 for an earlier work)]

Turner, William (1509/10-1568). [The seconde part of W.T.'s herball] A booke
of the natures and properties, of the bathes in England. *Collen [Cologne]: A.
Birckman, 1562,* ff. [4], 17, [STC 24366 (part)], *slightly stained*

2 works in one volume, folio (290 x 185mm.), BINDING: eighteenth-century half
calf

£2,000-3,000
€2,900-4,350

END OF FIRST SESSION

The Library of the
Earls of Macclesfield
removed from Shirburn Castle

Part Five: Science I-O

Session Two   Lots 1363-1571
Thursday 14 April 2005 at 2.30 pm

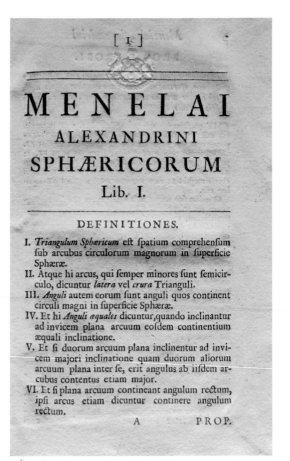

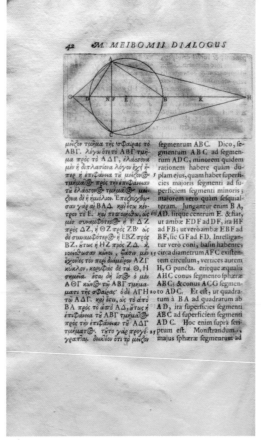

1363

1364

1363 **Menelaus of Alexandria (*c.* 100 AD).** [drop-title] Sphaericorum lib. I (-III) [translated into Latin and edited by Edmond Halley]. *[Oxford: at the Clarendon Press, 1713-14]*

8vo (198 x 125mm.), 112pp., ILLUSTRATION: woodcut diagrams, BINDING: eighteenth-century English polished calf, spine gilt

Menelaus' *Sphaerica* is a treatise on spherical trigonometry of some importance, which was first translated into Latin by Gerard of Cremona (second half 12th century). The text first appeared in print in 1558 edited by Maurolico (Messina, 1558), and it was included in Mersenne's *Synopsis* of 1644. This is the first separate edition.

Halley's edition is based on the Hebrew and Arabic versions of the work, of which two manuscripts in Hebrew and Arabic and one in Greek are to be found in the Bodleian Library. Halley's translation was set in type in Oxford in 1713-1714, but not published until in 1758. G. Costard added a preface, but some copies of the text (minus preliminaries) do seem to have been sold from the warehouse of the Press in the 1750s. The British Library and the Bodleian have copies like the present one, which was presumably acquired about this time.

In 1758 the Delegates "agreed that the copies of the Menelaus... be forthwith published, and that Mr. Costard be desir'd to prepare it for publication" (cited in Carter p. 291).

References: Carter, *OUP*, p.291; Sarton I, 253-254; Heath, *Greek mathematics* II, 260-273

£800-1,200
€1,200-1,750

1364 Meibom, Marcus (1630-1711). De proportionibus dialogus. *Copenhagen: Melchior Martzan, 1655*

folio (325 x 200mm.), [20], 204pp., title printed in red and black, ILLUSTRATION: engraved geometrical diagrams in text, BINDING: later seventeenth-century calf, vertical blind-stamped roll used twice on covers, *binding rubbed, joints cracking at head and foot*

A handsome copy with wide margins. The text contains (pp. 16-70) various extracts from Archimedes, Eutocius and Euclid in Greek with Latin versions.

References: Bruun ii, 13; Archimedes, *Opera omnia cum commentariis Eutocii*, 3 (1915), pp. 2-224

Provenance: Ia. Newton, inscription on flyleaf (i.e. James Newton?)

£700-1,000
€1,050-1,450

1365 Mengoli, Pietro. Geometriae speciosae elementa. *Bologna: Giovanni Battista Ferroni, 1659*, 80, 392pp., ILLUSTRATION: woodcut initials, head- and tailpieces, woodcut diagrams

Ibid. Novae quadraturae arithmeticae, seu de additione fractionum. *Bologna: Giacomo Monti, 1650*, [16], 130, [2]pp., ILLUSTRATION: woodcut arms of Bologna on title-page, woodcut initials, woodcut device on final recto

2 works in one volume, 4to (211 x 150mm.), BINDING: contemporary mottled calf, spine gilt in compartments, *binding rubbed, joints splitting at head*

BOTH FIRST EDITIONS. For other works by Mengoli, see Macclesfield Science A-C lot 250, D-H lot 860, and lot 1488 in the present catalogue.

References: Riccardi ii, 150

£300-400
€450-600

1366 Mengoli, Pietro. Anno di Pietro Mengoli. *Bologna: heir of V. Benacci, 1673*

4to (202 x 135mm.), [24], 280pp., BINDING: eighteenth-century sprinkled calf, spine gilt in compartments, green morocco lettering-piece, mottled edges

The short and charming "protesta dell'autore", printed in italic, gives us Mengoli's reasons for publishing: the first to vindicate his religious faith and the second local patriotism - "Bononia docet" - and not only this, he says, but just as Galileo wrote in the Florentine language, he has written in the Bolognese *lingua civile*. Too many books are printed, he says, but then asks who will read his book: "Gran fortuna sara la mia, se la decima delle cinquecento copie, ch'io stampo, sortirà il ricapito in buone mani". Mengoli's intention was thoroughly untenable, "to prove that the earth was made before the sun and all the other bodies of the universe... the earth is immobile, that the universe turns and that the sun moves". The "Anno" is, of course, the solar year. Malpighi wrote to Oldenburg that he was sending a copy of the book which was about to be published.

References: Riccardi ii, 151

£600-800
€900-1,200

ANNO
DI
PIETRO MENGOLI
Priore di Santa Maddalena,
Profeſſore di Mecaniche,
Filoſofo Collegiato,
Dottor di Leggi.

IN BOLOGNA,
Per l'Herede di Vittorio Benacci. 1673.
Con licenza de' Superiori.

1366

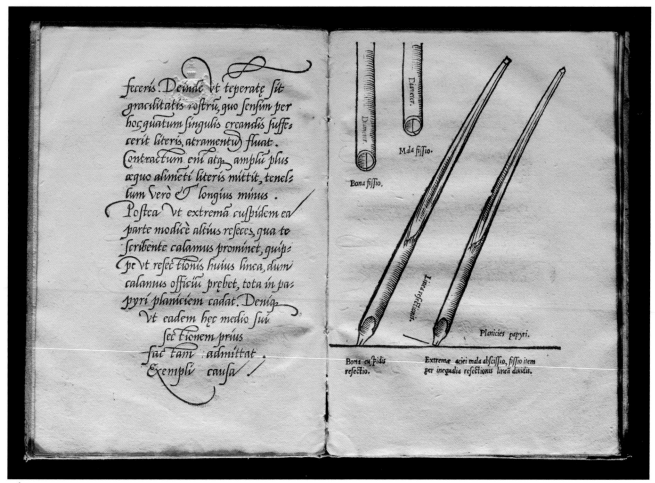

1367

1367 Mercator, Gerard (1512-1594). Literarum latinarum, quas italicas, cursoriasque vocat, scribendarum ratio. *Louvain: Rutger Rescius, March 1540*

4to (203 x 143mm.), ff. [27], ILLUSTRATION: all leaves with woodcut text and diagrams except imprint, errata and dedication, BINDING: later vellum-backed blue boards, *small stain on last few leaves, binding slightly soiled*

FIRST EDITION of this treatise on the penmanship of italic script, with diagrams demonstrating how to hold the pen correctly. Mercator provided mapmakers with a style of lettering "which could be worked harmoniously yet still legibly into the overall design of a map or chart, but without pointless flourishes or ornament" (J. Goss, *The mapmaker's art*, p.91).

Mercator studied philosophy and theology at the University of Louvain but later became more interested in mathematics and astronomy. While working with Gemma Frisius in Louvain he developed his skills in engraving and produced his first map in 1537.

This edition is rare; we have not been able to trace a copy sold at auction in the last thirty years.

References: Bonacini 1163; NK 3525

£10,000-15,000
€14,500-21,800

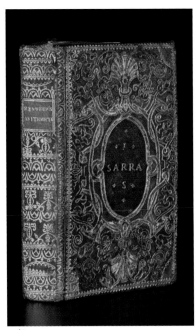

1368

1368 Menherr, Valentin. Arithmetique seconde. *(Antwerp: Jan Loë, 20 April 1556)*

8vo (154 x 100mm.), ff. [184], ILLUSTRATION: woodcut illustration on title-page, woodcut portrait on verso of title-page, woodcut illustrations, BINDING: contemporary Lyon calf gilt, sides decorated with leafy tendrils painted green, and a large white-painted palmette at top and bottom, central cartouche with a border of strapwork painted white, cartouche on upper cover lettered in gilt I / SARRA / S, that on the lower cover with a gilt ostrich, eighteenth-century flat spine gilt, red morocco lettering-piece, gilt edges, *rebacked and repaired at corners, cartouche on lower cover cracked and rubbed, colours rubbed*

FIRST EDITION, RARE. The letters on the upper cover, together with the Lyon binding, suggest that the book may be from the library of Jean-Antoine Sarrasin (1547-1598), a Protestant doctor from Lyon who wrote a treatise on the plague and edited the works of Dioscorides.

References: Machiels M409

£1,500-2,000
€2,200-2,900

1369 Mercator, Nicolaus (1620-1687). Cosmographia, sive descriptio coeli et terrae in circulos, qua fundamentum sternitur sequentibus ordine trigonometriae sphaericorum logarithmicae, astronomiae sphaericae, geographiae, histiodromiae, gnomonicae. Absoluto compendio pulcherrima... (Trigonometria sphaericorum logarithmica). *Gdansk: Andreas Hünefeldt, 1651*

8vo (192 x 94mm.), [4], 12; [4], 12; [96 (last 3 blank)]; [4], 24, [4]pp., ILLUSTRATION: woodcut initials, woodcut diagram, 4 folding engraved plates, BINDING: contemporary calf, spine gilt in compartments, *binding rubbed*

FIRST EDITION of this early textbook by Mercator, published two years before his *Rationes mathematicae* (Macclesfield Science A-C, lot 257). For other works by him, see Macclesfield Science A-C, lot 248, and lot 1370 in this sale.

References: Houzeau & Lancaster 8733

£1,000-1,500
€1,450-2,200

1370 Mercator, Nicolaus. Institutionum astronomicarum libri duo, de motu astrorum communi & proprio, secundum hypotheses veterum & recentiorum praecipuas... cum tabulis Tychonianis solaribus, lunaribus, lunae-solaribus... *London: William Godbid for Samuel Simpson, 1676*

8vo (182 x 110mm.), [16], 288, 64pp., ILLUSTRATION: woodcut diagrams, BINDING: contemporary calf, *binding rubbed*

FIRST EDITION, although the appendix had been published previously in Mercator's *Hypothesis astronomica nova* (1664).

References: Houzeau & Lancaster 9235; Wing M1729

Provenance: Thomas Parker of the Inner Temple (the first Earl of Macclesfield), engraved armorial bookplate dated 1704, and signature on title-page

£300-400
€450-600

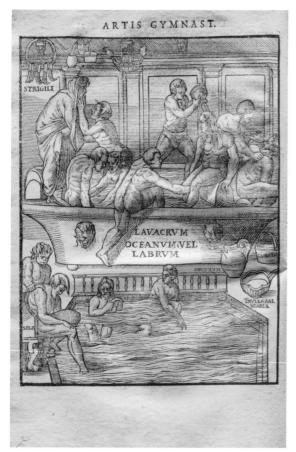

1371   1374

1371 Mercuriale, Girolamo (1530-1606). De arte gymnastica, libri sex... Secunda editione aucti, & multis figuris ornati. *Paris: Jacques du Puys, 1577*

4to (223 x 158mm.), ff. [4], 201, [13], ILLUSTRATION: woodcut initials and headpieces, woodcut illustrations (many full-page), BINDING: contemporary calf with blind-stamped panel on each cover, *small rust-hole on Q3 affecting a few letters, upper cover detached, binding rubbed*

First published in 1569. This is a reprint of the 1573 Venice edition, which was the first printed book to contain illustrations of gymnastics. "One of the earliest books to discuss the therapeutic value of gymnastics and sports generally for the cure of disease and disability, and an important study of gymnastics in the ancient world" (Garrison-Morton, p.310).

References: Krivatsy 3089

£600-800
€900-1,200

1372 Mercuriale, Girolamo. De arte gymnastica libri sex... Quarta editione correctiores, & auctiores facti. *Venice: Giunta, 1601*

4to (240 x 172mm.), [16], 308 (i.e. 326), [2 (blank)], [26]pp., ILLUSTRATION: woodcut printer's device on title-page, woodcut initials, woodcut illustrations (many full-page), BINDING: contemporary vellum, blue edges

References: Krivatsy 7784

£600-800
€900-1,200

1373 Mersenne, Marin (1588-1648). La vérité des sciences. Contre les septiques ou Pyrrhoniens. *Paris: Toussainct du Bray, 1625*

8vo (165 x 107mm.), [32], 1008pp., ILLUSTRATION: woodcut vignette on title, 4 pages of woodcut alchemical symbols, woodcut initials, BINDING: contemporary speckled calf, *occasional small wormholes, some light browning, binding rubbed at edges*

FIRST EDITION, RARE. The present work is one of several polemical studies written by Mersenne at the beginning of his career in support of traditional theological argument in the face of modern developments in science and Renaissance scepticism. The first of these works was *Quaestiones in Genesim* published in 1623, which attacked Renaissance interest in magic and kabala, and in particular Robert Fludd. The present work discusses at some length alchemy, and includes an attack on the Rosicrucians: "Mais il y en a d'autres qui veulent qu'un corps parfaitement temperé soit si parfait qu'il ne puisse contracter aucune maladie, qu'il puisse subsister éternellement, qu'il puisse marcher sur les eaus sans enfoncer, qu'il puisse guarir [*sic*] les maladies par son seul attouchement, qu'il puisse penetrer les murailles, voller par l'air, passer d'un lieu en un autre fort éloigné en un moment... se rendre invisible, &c. ce qu'on attribue aus magiciens & aus charlatans qu'on appelle, & qui se font nommer *freres de rose croix*..." (p. 566).

Provenance: F.F.L. (?), monogram dated 1683 on front flyleaf

£2,000-3,000
€2,900-4,350

1373

1374 Mersenne, Marin. Cogitata physico mathematica (Universae geometriae, mixtaeque mathematicae synopsis, et bini refractionum demonstratarum tractatus; Novarum observationum physico-mathematicarum... tomus III). *Paris: Antoine Bertier, 1644-1647*

3 volumes, 4to (235 x 175mm.), [44], 40, [8], 41-224, [8], 225-370, [16], 96, [12], 140, [28 (including a blank leaf)]; [32], 589, [1 (blank)]; [32], 62, [2], 63-235, [3]pp., first two title-pages ruled in red, ILLUSTRATION: woodcut vignette on title-page, woodcut initials, head-and tailpieces, woodcut illustrations and music, engraved illustration, BINDING: uniform contemporary vellum with blind fillets

For other works by Mersenne, see lots 1489 to 1491.

Provenance: William Jones, inscription on title-page of volume one

£10,000-15,000
€14,500-21,800

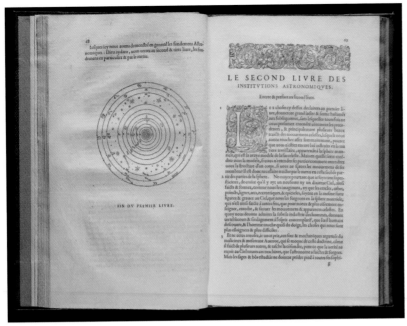

1375

1375 Mesmes, Jean Pierre de (1516-before 1584). Les Institutions astronomiques. *Paris: M. Vascosan, 1557*

folio (320 x 200mm.), [16], 214 (i.e. 314), [17]pp., errata on D4 recto, device on verso, ILLUSTRATION: woodcut diagrams, woodcut headpieces, 6- and 9-line initials, BINDING: nineteenth-century half calf by Hatton, *title-page repaired at outer edge*

Dedicated to Henri de Mesmes, sieur de Roissy (1531-1596), man of affairs and collector, and dedicatee (*qua* Memmius) of Lambin's edition of Lucretius. The de Mesmes family was extremely rich, and both Henri de Mesmes I and his son of the same name were great collectors. Naudé was librarian to Henri de Mesmes II.

References: Houzeau & Lancaster 2590

£2,500-3,500
€3,650-5,100

1376 Metius, Adriaan (1571-1635). Primum mobile, astronomice, sciographice, geometrice, et hydrographice nova methodo explicatum in 1. Sphaera, 2. Planisphaerio sive astrolabio, 3. Triangulis sphaericis, 4. Tabulis astronomicis et loxodromicis, 5. Lineamentis geometricis : opus absolutum 4 tomis distinctum... Editio nova, ab innumeris mendis vendicata, et instrumentis mathematicis aucta a Guilielmo Blaeu. *Amsterdam: Guilielmus Blaeu, 1633*

4to (201 x 147mm.), [4], 190, [8]; [4], 123, [93]; 160, 157-161, 154; [2], 165-260; 13, [1 (blank)] pp., ILLUSTRATION: woodcut device on title-pages, woodcut initials and diagrams, BINDING: contemporary calf, spine gilt in compartments, morocco lettering-piece, *M3 torn without loss, binding rubbed, spine chipped at head, upper joint splitting*

Metius studied at the universities of Franeker and Leiden before spending six months on Hven with Tycho Brahe. He became professor of mathematics and astronomy at Franeker in 1600 where Descartes attended his lectures. His brother Jacob was one of the inventors of the telescope.

References: Houzeau & Lancaster 2822; J.R. Christopherson, *On Tycho's Island* (2002), p.322 for biography

£1,000-1,500
€1,450-2,200

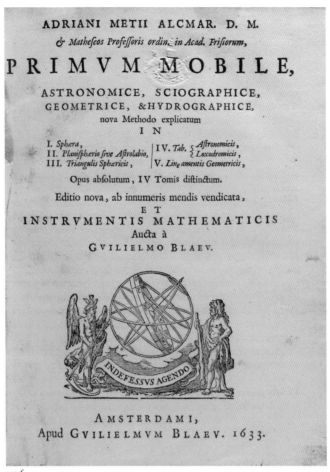

ADRIANI METII ALCMAR. D. M.

& Matheseos Professoris ordin. in Acad. Frisiorum,

PRIMVM MOBILE,

ASTRONOMICE, SCIOGRAPHICE,
GEOMETRICE, & HYDROGRAPHICE,
nova Methodo explicatum
I N

I. *Sphæra,*
II. *Planisphærio sive Astrolabio,*
III. *Triangulis Sphæricis,*
IV. *Tab.* { *Astronomicis,* / *Loxodromicis,*
V. *Lineamentis Geometricis,*

Opus absolutum, I V Tomis distinctum.

Editio nova, ab innumeris mendis vendicata,
E T
INSTRVMENTIS MATHEMATICIS
Aucta à
GVILIELMO BLAEV.

INDEFESSVS AGENDO

A M S T E R D A M I,
Apud GVILIELMVM BLAEV. 1633.

1376

1377 Metius, Adriaan. Manuale arithmetice & geometrie practice: in het welcke beneffens de Stock-rekeninghe ofte Rabdologia J. Nepperi... *Amsterdam: Henderick Laurentsz, 1634*

FIRST EDITION, 8vo (142 x 88mm.), [16], 246, [8]pp., 4 folding tables, ILLUSTRATION: woodcut initials, head- and tailpieces, woodcut illustrations, BINDING: contemporary mottled calf, spine gilt in compartments, red morocco lettering-piece, marbled edges, *small tear on I2 (affecting signature only), binding slightly rubbed*

For Napier, see lots 1510 and 1511.

References: Macdonald, *Napier*, pp.153-154

£400-500
€600-750

1378 Metius, Adriaan. Arithmeticae libri duo: et geometriae libri VI... Editio postrema priore multo auctior. *Leiden: Bonaventure and Abraham Elzevir (Franeker: Uldericus Balck), 1640*

4to (198 x 148mm.), [32], 118; [2], 426, [14]pp., title-page in red and black, ILLUSTRATION: woodcut device on title-page, woodcut initials, head- and tailpieces, woodcut diagrams, folding engraved plate, 2 folding woodcut plates, BINDING: contemporary vellum, *paper flaw in second A3, one woodcut shaved, some water-staining, boards warped*

Provenance: William Jones, inscription on title-page

£200-300
€300-450

1379 Meyer, Georg Friedrich (1645-1693). Doctrina triangulorum sive trigonometria, die Lehr von Messung der Trianglen. *Basel: Johann Rudolph Genath, 1678*, [16], 287, [1]pp., ILLUSTRATION: additional engraved title-page, woodcut initials, typographical headpieces, 38 woodcut and engraved plates (1 folding)

Ibid. Stereometria sive dimensio solidorum, das ist Aussmessung cörperlicher Dingen oder Visier-Kunst. *Basel: Johann Rudolph Genath, 1675*, [16], 127, [1 (blank)] pp., ILLUSTRATION: additional engraved title-page, woodcut initials, typographical head- and tailpieces, 29 engraved plates (2 folding)

FIRST EDITIONS, 2 works in one volume, oblong 16mo (72 x 88mm.), BINDING: contemporary vellum, *a few leaves shaved at foredge*

References: 2nd work: BL German STC XVIIc. M1011

£1,000-1,500
€1,450-2,200

1380 Meynier, Honorat de (c. 1570-1638). Paradoxes... contre les mathematiciens, qui abusent la ieunesse. Ensemble les definitions theorèmes et maximes, d'Euclides, d'Archimedes, de Proclus... Avec un abrégé des reigles de la géometrie... *Paris: Julian Jacquin, 1624*

24mo (111 x 54mm.), [8], 32, [9], 23, 91, [5 (blank)], [6], 34, [6], 24, [8], 88, [6], 58, 73, [1 (blank)], [8], 33, [3]pp., BINDING: contemporary vellum

FIRST EDITION, republished in 1652.

Provenance: A. Dutens, inscription on title-page

£400-600
€600-900

1381 Michelini, Famiano (?1592-1666). Trattato della direzione de' fiumi nel quale si dimostrano da' suoi veri principi i modi più sicuri, e meno dispendiosi di riparare a' danni, che sogliono farsi dall' acque. *Florence: stamperia della Stella, 1664*

4to (236 x 162mm.), [16], 89, 94-95, 92-93, 90-91, 96-151, [1]pp., title printed in red and black, ILLUSTRATION: woodcut initials and headpieces, 9 folding engraved plates, BINDING: contemporary calf, spine gilt in compartments, *quire M misbound, binding rubbed, joints splitting*

FIRST EDITION. Michelini was tutor to the brothers of Ferdinando II de' Medici, one of whom (Leopoldo) is the dedicatee of this work. In 1648 he was awarded the chair of mathematics at Pisa. This is the only work he wrote that was published in his lifetime.

References: Riccardi ii, 156

£400-600
€600-900

1382 Milliet de Chales, Claude François (1621-1678), *S.J.* Les principes generaux de la geographie. *Paris: Estienne Michallet, 1677*

12mo (165 x 88mm.), [12], 288, 281-286, [12]pp., ILLUSTRATION: woodcut vignette on title-page, woodcut initials, head- and tailpieces, woodcut illustrations, BINDING: contemporary calf with blind-stamped corners, spine gilt in compartments, morocco lettering-piece, *small marginal wormhole, binding rubbed, joints cracking at head*

References: Sommervogel II, 1040-1043

£150-200
€250-300

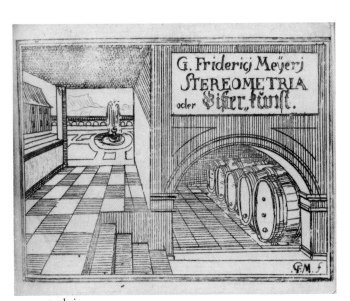

1379, actual size

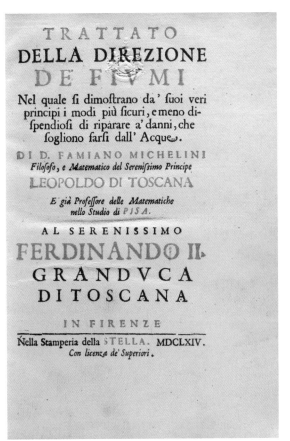

1381

1383 Milliet de Chales, Charles François, *S.J.* Traitté du mouvement local, et du ressort. Dans lequel, leur nature, & leurs causes, sont curieusement recherchées, & ou les lois qu'ils observent dans l'acceleration & les pendules, & encore dans la percussion & la reflexion des corps, sont solidement establies. *Lyon: Anisson and Posuel, 1682*

12mo (159 x 88mm.), [12], 465, [5]pp., ILLUSTRATION: woodcut initials, head- and tailpieces, woodcut diagrams, BINDING: contemporary speckled calf, spine gilt in compartments, speckled edges, *binding rubbed*

References: Sommervogel II, 1040-1043

£200-300
€300-450

1384 Milliet de Chales, Claude François, *S.J.* Cursus seu mundus mathematicus. Tomus primus (-quartus)… Editio altera ex manuscriptis authoris aucta & emendata, opera & studio R.P. Amati Varcin. *Lyon: Anisson, J. Posuel and Claude Rigaud, 1690*

4 volumes, folio (356 x 222mm.), [36], 691, [1 (blank)]; [28], 692; [24], 763, [1 (blank)]; [20], 755, [1 (blank)] pp., half-title in vol.1, titles printed in red and black, ILLUSTRATION: woodcut vignette on titles, woodcut diagrams in text, woodcut initials and headpieces, BINDING: contemporary panelled calf, spines gilt in compartments, *slight worming in lower margins at beginning of vol. 2, final leaf of vol. 4 rebacked with partial loss of a few lines of text, bindings slightly worn*

Second and enlarged edition of a work first published in three volumes in 1674.

References: Sommervogel II, 1040-1043

£600-800
€900-1,200

1385 Military and Geometrical tracts—Recorde, Robert (1510-1558). The pathway to knowledg [*sic*], containing the first principles of geometrie, as they most aptly be applied unto practise, both for use of instrumentes geometricall, and astronomicall and also for proiection of plattes in everye kinde... *(London: R. Wolfe, 1551)*, 2 parts, ff. [12 (last leaf a blank)], [34]; 46, text and preface printed in italic (see below), dedication (dated 28 January 1551/2) in Black Letter with Greek, running titles, ILLUSTRATION: woodcut figures in text, large device at end, [STC 20812]

Digges, Thomas (*c.* 1546-1595) *and* **Leonard Digges (*c.* 1515-1559).** An arithmeticall militare treatise named Stratioticos: compendiously teaching the science of numbers, as well in fractions as integers, and so much of the rules and aequations algebraicall and arte of numbers cossicall, as are requisite for the profession of a soldiour... Augmented... and lately finished, by Thomas Digges... *London: H. Bynneman, 1579*, [16], 191, [1]pp., largely printed in Black Letter, ILLUSTRATION: 2 folding woodcut plates at p.176, smaller figures in text, full-page woodcut royal arms on verso of title, woodcut initials, device, [STC 6848], *tiny hole in first leaf, tears in both plates repaired without loss*

2 works in one volume, 4to (190 x 120mm.), BINDING: eighteenth-century calf, gilt spine, red morocco lettering-piece, red edges

FIRST EDITIONS, and extremely fine copies. Recorde's work is an adaptation of Euclid and one of a number of pedagogic works from his pen, all written in English and often introducing new vocabulary into the language. Recorde, who came from Tenby and was for a time active in mining in Wexford, dedicated this work to Edward VI (see V. Larkey, "Robert Recorde's Mathematical Teaching and the Anti-Aristotelian Movement", *Huntington Library Bulletin* 7 (1935), 59-87).

Recorde's book is printed in a very particular "Arrighi" italic, originally introduced some twenty years earlier by Rastell (cf. Isaac, fig. 72), used in conjunction with a smaller font.

"Carpenters, Carvers, Joiners and Masons,
Painters and Limners with suche occupations,
Broderers, Goldesmithes, if they be cunning,
Must yelde to Geometrye thankes for their learning.
The Carte and the Plowe, who doth them well marke,
Are made by good Geometrye..." (Recorde's preface).

Thomas Digges shows what he considers a mathematician to be most explicitly in *Stratioticos*. He states that he had once been delighted with the elevated subtlety of mathematical demonstration but that, now more mature, he had spent his time "in reducing the Sciences Mathematical from Demonstrative Contemplations to Experimental Actions, for the Service of my Prince and Country" (*Stratioticos*, 1579, A2 recto). *Stratioticos* exemplifies this self-conscious choice of role and agenda. Its first book is on arithmetic and was based on work by Leonard Digges. The remainder of the text is Thomas Digges's own, and adapts elementary algebra for use by soldiers, as well as setting out the role of all in an army. The volume was dedicated to the earl of Leicester, and had been composed in response to hopes over the winter of 1577-78 that he would lead a force against the Spanish in the Netherlands (see the article in *ODNB* by Stephen Johnston). For a copy of the 1590 edition of Digges, see Macclesfield Science D-H, lot 634.

£6,000-10,000
€8,700-14,500

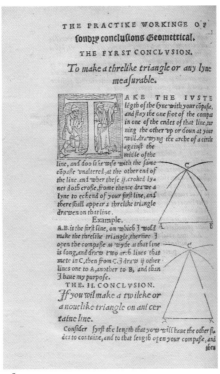

1385

1386 Milnes, James (1663-1739). Sectionum conicarum elementa nova methodo demonstrata. Editio secunda emendata, plurimisque in locis aucta & illustrata. *Oxford: e Theatro Sheldoniano, 1712*

8vo (190 x 119mm.), [8], 127, [1]pp., ILLUSTRATION: woodcut device of the Sheldonian Theatre on title-page, 21 folding engraved plates, BINDING: contemporary smooth calf, spine gilt in compartments, morocco lettering-piece, *one plate loose, extremities slightly rubbed*

This copy of the second edition has appended to it the extra sixth part that was added into the third edition of 1723 (pp. 117-127, [1], with one plate).

References: Carter, *OUP*, p.464

£400-600
€600-900

1387 Miscellanea curiosa mathematica: or, The literary correspondence of some eminent mathematicians in Great Britain and Ireland. Containing a choice collection of mathematical essays and dissertations on what is most valuable and really useful, not only in algebra, trigonometry, the doctrine of chances, astronomy, chronology, geometry, gunnery, infinite series, fluxions, fluents, exponentials, the quadrature of curves, &c. but likewise a curious collection of 160 new problems, with their solutions, in most branches of the mathematics... [edited by Francis Holliday]. *London: for Edward Cave, to be sold by J. Fuller and F. Holliday, 1749*

9 parts in one volume, 4to (231 x 172mm.), [2], ii-iii, [2], ix-xi, [1], 253, 154-200, 305-312pp., folding letterpress table, ILLUSTRATION: 9 folding engraved plates (one cut in half, without loss), BINDING: contemporary vellum-backed blue boards, *binding slightly soiled*

There was a second volume of this popular periodical published, containing a further five parts. Holliday, a grammar school teacher in Nottinghamshire, was also the translator of James Stirling's *Methodus differentialis.*

£300-400
€450-600

1388

HAGANOAE IN OFFICINA
IOHAN. SECERII, AN
NO M. D. XXXI.
Menſe Martio.

1389

AN
ESSAY
ON
The *Uſefulneſs* of
MATHEMATICAL LEARNING,
IN
A Letter from a *Gentleman* in
the CITY to his *Friend* in
O X F O R D.

Printed at the THEATER in *Oxford* for
Anth. Peiſley Bookſeller, 1701.

1389

ELEMENTA
GEOMETRIÆ
PRIORA DUO
Breviter Demonſtrata.

Apud Fulvium Urſinum in Numiſmate æreo.

A. D. MDCLXXIV.

1389

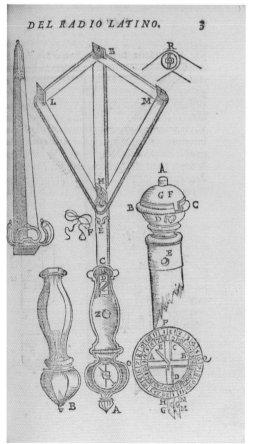

DEL RADIO LATINO.

180

1388 Miscellaneous Tracts—Alciati, Andrea (1492-1550). Libellus de ponderibus et mensuris. Item Budaei quaedam de eadem re, adhuc non visa... Alciati quoque & P. Melanchthonis, in laudem iuris civilis, orationes duae elegantissimae. *Hagenau: J. Secer, October 1530 (March 1531),* ff. [48], ILLUSTRATION: woodcut device on final leaf, [*IA* 102.874; VD16 A1669], *some printed marginalia cropped*

Gradi, Stefano [Stjepan Gradic] (1613-1683). Dissertationes physico-mathematicae quatuor. *Amsterdam: D. Elzevir [Leiden: Haak], 1680,* [30], 63pp., [Willems 1581]

Whiston, William (1667-1752). The Copernicus explain'd: or a brief account of the nature and use of an universal astronomical instrument, for the calcuation and exhibition of new and full moons... *London: for the author, [1715],* [2], 55, [5]pp., *imprint and some headlines cropped*

3 works in one volume, 12mo & 8vo (140 x 80mm.), BINDING: eighteenth-century mottled calf, spine gilt in compartments, red morocco lettering-piece, red edges

The second work is dedicated to Queen Christina of Sweden (1626-1689) and was written some years earlier, as Elzevir's preface makes clear. The author was from Ragusa (he wrote a poem on the earthquake of 1667), prefect of the Vatican Library, and a member of Christina's Academy. There is a street in Rome named after him (see also lot 1399).

£1,000-1,500
€1,450-2,200

1389 Miscellaneous Tracts—[Arbuthnot, John (c. 1667-1735)] An essay on the usefulness of mathematical learning, in a letter from a gentleman in the city to his friend in Oxford. *Oxford: at the theatre, 1701,* [2], 57pp., [Carter, *OUP,* p.438]

Fauré, J.P. de. Dissertation, découverte, et demonstrations de la quadrature mathematique du cercle, pour servir d'introduction à la connoissance exacte de cette vérité. *[Geneva?]: aux dépens de l'autheur, 1747,* 52pp.

Danti, Egnazio (1536-1586). Trattato del radio latino istrumento... per prendere qual si voglia misura, & positione di luogo, tanto in cielo come in terra... inventato dall illustrissimo... Latino Orsini... *Rome: Marc'Antonio Moretti & Giacomo Brianzi, 1586,* [16], 112pp., ILLUSTRATION: woodcut diagrams and figures, [Riccardi i, 393; Censimento 16 CNCE 37284]

Aldrich, Henry (1648-1710). Elementa geometriae priora duo breviter demonstrata. *[Oxford], 1674,* 2 parts, [12], 38; [2], 40pp., catchword on p.40 of part two CAP, ILLUSTRATION: woodcut diagrams, [Wing A898A], *small flaw in Cc2 with loss of a few letters*

4 works in one volume, 8vo (175 x 110mm.), BINDING: eighteenth-century smooth calf, spine gilt in compartments, morocco lettering-piece, red edges

Arbuthnot's pamphlet was reprinted in 1721 and 1745. The work by Danti is essentially of a trigonometrical nature. Fauré's pamphlet has at the end the following for "Ceux qui souhaiteront des exemplaires", advising them to write to the author at his address in Geneva, and to make sure that the letters are franked. In the Latin "Monitum ad lectorem" he describes himself as under the rule of Berne.

The text of the appendix to Aldrich's *Elementa* end as follows: "Jam ad utramque analysin satis est instructus qui priora haec duo elementa intellexerit; ut possit adeo si volet, haec problemata hoc loco aggredi. Meo autem institutio commodius videtur haec differre; futura scil. Analyseos geometricae exempla in appendice elementi tertii", followed by catchword. The only other copy known, which is at Christ Church, Oxford, has the same number of leaves. It would seem that neither is imperfect. The phrase "future scil. Analyseos" may simply point to something which was envisaged, but never actually printed. (For Aldrich, see note to Macclesfield Science D-H, lot 875, and the article in the *ODNB* by Stuart Handley.)

£2,000-3,000
€2,900-4,350

1390 Miscellaneous Tracts—B., J. The blazing star: or, a discourse of comets, their natures and effects: in a letter from J.B. to T.C. concerning the late comet seen on Sunday December the 11. 1664... *London: S. Speed, 1665,* [2], 48, [2]pp., last leaf with catalogue of books sold by Speed, [Wing B94], *errata torn at corner with slight loss*

Reyher, Samuel (1635-1714), *praeses.* De mundo... disputabit Laurentius Petri Aroselius... a.d. iv idus Majas anni 1666 Kiloni. *[Kiel, 1666],* ff. [16], ILLUSTRATION: woodcut planetary diagrams

Büthner, Friedrich (1622-1701). Admirandi & rari congressus ecliptici marti-solaris in signo martio scorpii quem elapsis totis 205 annis currens hic sol in eundem diem & locum seculo huic martio sive spectandum, sive speculandum, iterum reducet brevis astronomica & astrologica contemplatio. *Gdansk: D.F. Rhetius, [1659],* ff. [8], ILLUSTRATION: 2 manuscript illustrations in text, that on B1v full-page, that on B2 small

Philippi, Henricus (d. 1636), *S.J.* Quaestiones chronologicae de annis nati et passi salvatoris. *Cologne: J. Kinckius, 1630,* [4], 107, [1]pp., errata on last page, ILLUSTRATION: engraved arms of Ferdinand II (the dedicatee) on title-page

Marquardt, Andreas, *praeses.* Ηλιος φαινομενος seu Dissertatio optica-astronomica de diametro solis apparenti, quam... examini submittit praeses M. Andreas Marquardi respondente Jacobo Klein... a. 1662 d. 26 aug. hor. matutin. *Konigsberg: P. Mensenius & J. Segebadius, [1662],* ff. [8], PRESENTATION COPY but with part of inscription cut away

Newton, John (1621-1678). A help to calculation. Or two tables: the one of the decimal numbers and the other of their logarithmes... As also tables of declination... *London: J. Moxon, 1657,* [2], 10, [2], 110, [4]pp., advertisements for Moxon at end, [Wing N1060]

6 works in one volume, 4to (176 x 130mm.), BINDING: eighteenth-century calf, gilt spine, green morocco lettering-piece, red edges

The first work describes a comet seen in Hampshire and is entirely written with initals used in lieu of names: "Honest I.S. was going to N. Market, about one of the clock the last Thursday morning; and observing (as you know he is curious that way above his condition) the situation of the Stars in Taurus...".

Friedrich Büthner taught mathematics at the Gymnasium in Gdansk and was the author of a number of works, and in this pamphlet, dedicated to Jan Casimir, King of Poland, he discusses Copernicus ('Dux Copernicus Thorunensis'), Tycho, Kepler, and Longomontanus, with particular reference to observations by the last three. As the title makes clear, the astrological implications of certain observed phenomena are closely discussed. One might imagine, from the fact that the illustrations are done by hand, that very few copies of this pamphlet were printed.

Reyher's academic disputation is a survey of various systems of the world, both ancient Pythagorean and modern Copernican (Copernicus is said to have revived the Pythagorean system), Tychonic (these both with a woodcut diagram illustrative of the systems), and others. The verses at the end are by the polyhistor Daniel Morhof, and are about the various systems which man takes it upon himself to create:

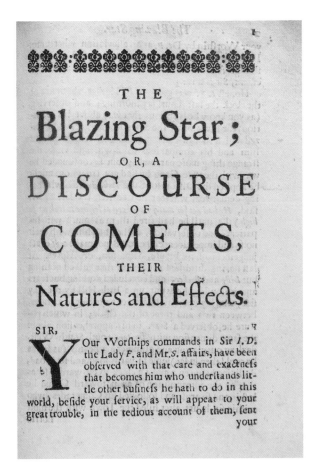

THE
Blazing Star;
OR, A
DISCOURSE
OF
COMETS,
THEIR
Natures and Effects.

SIR,

Your Worships commands in Sir *I. D.*
the Lady *F.* and Mr. *S.* affairs, have been
observed with that care and exactness
that becomes him who understands little other business he hath to do in this
world, beside your service, as will appear to your
great trouble, in the tedious account of them, sent
your

1390

QVÆSTIONES
CHRONOLOGICAE
DE ANNIS
NATI ET PASSI SALVATORIS
Conscripta à
R. P. HENRICO PHILIPPI Societatis Iesu
Theologo
AD SERENISS. POTENTISS. PRINCIPEM
FERDINANDVM III.
HVNGARIÆ BOHEMIÆ &c. REGEM,
Archiducem Austriæ &c.

PERMISSV · SVPERIORVM

COLONIÆ AGRIPPINENSIVM
ApudIOANNEM KINCKIVM, sub Monocerote,
ANNO MD.C.XXX.

1390

"Quos format Orbes ille [God], nos reformamus
Post Protoplasten huncce deuteroplastan.
Hic inter astra sceptra nostra jactamus,
Late tyranni, Olympici Imperatores..."

The respondens is Laurentius Petri Aroselius (1642-
1693), one of three brothers from Sala in Sweden, a
student at the University of Kiel. He seems to have
published nothing under his own name.

Philippi, who taught in Prague, wrote several works
on chronology, and for obvious reasons when
dealing with an historical personage, the date of
both Christ's birth and passion have exercised
greatly the minds of scholars from early times until
the present day (cf. lot 1413).

£5,000-6,000
€7,300-8,700

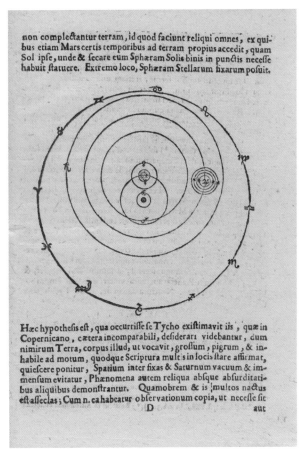

non complectantur terram, id quod faciunt reliqui omnes, ex quibus etiam Mars certis temporibus ad terram propius accedit, quam
Sol ipse, unde & secare eum Sphæram Solis binis in punctis necesse
habuit statuere. Extremo loco, Sphæram Stellarum fixarum posuit.

Hæc hypothesis est, qua occurrisse se Tycho existimavit iis, quæ in
Copernicano, cætera incomparabili, desiderari videbantur, dum
nimirum Terra, corpus illud, ut vocavit, grossum, pigrum, & in-
habile ad motum, quodque Scriptura multis in locis stare affirmat,
quiescere ponitur, Spatium inter fixas & Saturnum vacuum & im-
mensum evitatur, Phænomena autem reliqua absque absurditati-
bus aliquibus demonstrantur. Quamobrem & is multos nactus
est asseclas; Cum n. ea habeatur observationum copia, ut necesse sit
D   aut

1390

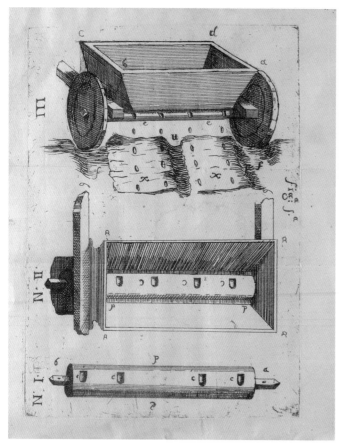

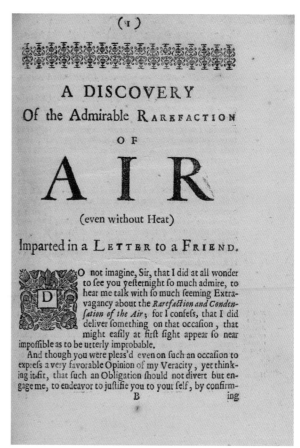

1391

1392

1391 Miscellaneous Tracts—Borro, Alessandro del (1672-1760). Il carro di Cerere overo i tre problemi di balistica... per la costruzione d'un nuovo instrumento... con cui si potranno seminare le campagne secondo qualsivoglia data proporzione... Opera consecrata all' impareggiabil merito dell'... cavalier Lamberto Blackvvell. *Lucca: Domenico Ciuffetti, 1699*, [8], 90, [8]pp., ILLUSTRATION: 3 folding engraved plates, [Riccardi i, 170]

Aristotle. Μηχανικα. Mechanica. *Paris: A. Wechel, 1566*, ff. [19], ILLUSTRATION: woodcut printer's device on title-page, woodcut illustrations, [*IA* 108.512; Mortimer, *Harvard French* 42], *without final blank leaf*

Gauger, Nicolas (c. 1680-1730). The mechanism of fire made in chimneys: or, the art of improving the effects and diminishing the expences thereof. Containing a treatise of new-invented chimneys. *London: for R. Bonwicke, T. Goodwin, J. Walthoe, M. Wotton, 1716*, xx, 103, [9]pp., ILLUSTRATION: 12 numbered engraved plates with 40 figures, *title-leaf cut down and remounted*

3 works in one volume, 4to (204 x 150mm.), BINDING: eighteenth-century mottled calf, spine gilt in compartments, red morocco lettering-piece, red edges

The dedication of the first work by Borro is in Latin and is to Sir Lambert Blackwell. Blackwell (*c.* 1665-1727) was a merchant at Livorno and was appointed by William III as envoy to Tuscany in 1689 and consul to Livorno in 1690 (see Ingamells p.96).

This edition of the *Mechanica* may well be the first separate edition of the Greek text. Gauger's work was published first in a translation made by Desaguliers, by Curll and Senex in 1715.

£1,000-1,500
€1,450-2,200

1392 Miscellaneous Tracts—Boyle, Robert (1627-1691). Tracts... of a discovery of the admirable rarefaction of the air... the duration of the spring of the air... the condensation of the air... the admirably differing extension of the same quantity of air rarefied and compressed. *London: T.N. for Henry Herringman, 1674,* [4], 28pp., [Wing B4059; Fulton 94], *some page numerals shaved*

Parker, Samuel (1640-1688), *Bishop of Oxford.* A free and impartial censure of the platonick philosophie being a letter written to his much honoured friend Mr N.B. *Oxford: W. Hall for Richard Davis, 1666,* [6], 115, [1 (blank)] pp., [Wing P463; Madan 2754], *lacking first leaf with imprimatur on verso*

Burnet, Thomas (1635?-1715). Reflections upon the theory of the earth, occasion'd by a late examination of it. In a letter to a friend. *London: for Walter Kettilby, 1699,* [2], 62pp., [Wing B5943A], *first and last leaves soiled*

Wallis, John (1616-1703). A discourse of gravity and gravitation, grounded on experimental observations: presented to the Royal Society, November 12. 1674. *London: John Martyn, 1675,* [2], 36pp., [Wing W574]

Alstrin, Erik (1683-1762), *praeses.* Disputatio academica de philosophia instrumentali eiusque pretio et emolumentis, quam... in... academia Upsaliensi, praeside... Mag. Erico Alstrin... publice examinandam sistit Petrus Djurberg... ad diem xx Octobris anni MDCCXXXI ante meridiem hora octava. *Uppsala: literis Wernerianis, [1731],* [8], 84pp., *slight browning*

Stempel, Friedrich Hannibal, *praeses.* De laterna magica dissertatio quam... sub praesidio M. Frid. Hannibalis Stempel Coburgensis publico eruditorum examini submittit Matth. Christianus Muller... XIX Ianuarii MDCCIIII. *Jena: typis Nisianis, excudebat H. Beyerus, [1704],* 36pp., ILLUSTRATION: folding engraved plate (loose)

Weidler, Johann Friedrich (1691-1755) *and* **Christian Samuel Rhostius.** De meteoro lucido singulari A. 1730 M. octobri conspecto dissertatio qua observationes madritensis et vitembergensis inter se comparantur... publice proposita D. xxiii iunii A.C. MDCCXXXI. *Wittemberg: J.C. Gerdes, [1731],* 32pp.

7 works in one volume, 4to (195 x 149mm.), BINDING: eighteenth-century mottled calf, spine gilt in compartments, red morocco lettering-piece, red edges

Parker's pamphlet is a discussion of two passages in Nathaniel Bisbie's *Tentamina physico-theologica* (1665). Parker, an erstwhile Puritan, was at this point a defender of the Church of England. He later developed Romish sympathies and was "foisted" on Magdalen College as President in 1687.

£800-1,000
€1,200-1,450

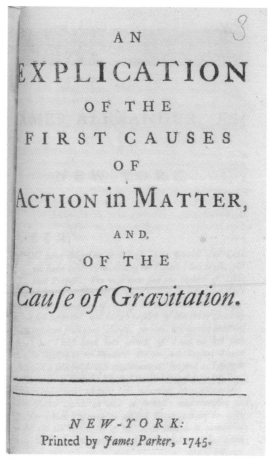

1393

1394

1393 Miscellaneous Tracts—[Ciruelo, Pedro Sanchez (1471-1560)] Tractatus arithmetice practice qui dicitur Algorismus cum additionibus utiliter adiunctis. *Paris: J. Gourmont, [c. 1516]*, ff. [14], woodcut device on title-page, [*IA* 140.452; Moreau II: 1303]

Beaulieu, Jean de. La lumiere des mathematiques contenant les definitions, les principaux theoremes, et problemes geometriques; la trigonometrie; la maniere de tracer... toutes sortes de plans... *Paris: chez l'autheur, 1670*, engraved throughout, 23 bifolia printed on one side of the sheet only (except for first), ILLUSTRATION: diagrams in text, folding plate of fortifications

Bosse, Abraham (1602-1676). Traité des pratiques geometrales et perspectives... *Paris: chez l'auteur (de l'imprimerie d'autheur d'An. Cellier), 1665*, [8], 140pp., engraved title, second engraved title and 67 plates printed on the recto and verso of leaves, nos. 6 & 7 *bis, lacking pls. 56 and 57 and with a2r (the engraved dedication) not imposed*

3 works in one volume, 8vo (175 x 110mm.), BINDING: eighteenth-century mottled calf, gilt spine, green morocco lettering-piece, red edges

The work by Ciruelo, who taught Philip II of Spain, was frequently printed in Paris from the mid 1490s (cf. GW 7052-7053). Of this edition there is one copy recorded in the British Library.

There was a copy of the work by Beaulieu in the Vitry collection (sale in these rooms, 10-11 April 2002, lot 49), which was dated *c.* 1660. This one is quite clearly dated 1670.

£1,500-2,000
€2,200-2,900

1394 Miscellaneous Tracts—Colden, Cadwallader (1688-1776). An explication of the first causes of action in matter, and of the cause of gravitation. *New York: James Parker, 1745*, vi, 43, [1]pp., [Evans 5564], *some catchwords cropped*

Bachstrom, Johann Friedrich (1686-1742). Nova aestus marini theoria ex principiis physico-mathematicis detecta... Examen acus magneticae spiralis... *Leiden: C. Wishoff, 1734*, [2], 85pp., ILLUSTRATION: 2 folding engraved plates, a few manuscript notes (cropped by the binder)

Boissière, Claude de. La propriete et usage des quadrans. *Paris: Guillaume Cavellat, 1557*, ff. 31, [1], ILLUSTRATION: woodcut illustrations in text, woodcut devices on title-page and recto of last leaf, [*IA 121.357*], *headline on D3 and second device cropped*

3 works in one volume, 8vo (146 x 87mm.), BINDING: eighteenth-century polished calf, spine gilt in compartments, red morocco lettering-piece, red edges

FIRST EDITIONS. Cadwallader Colden was born in Ireland of a Scottish family, and studied medicine in London. In 1710 he went to America, first to Philadelphia, and then to New York. He is chiefly famous for his *History of the five Indian nations of Canada*, but he was an interesting figure in the life of America in the mid-eighteenth century. In this little work, which is essentially a discussion of Newton's work (including in the Postscript to chapter I, his *Optics*), Colden sets out to clarify, as he sees it, with due diffidence, some of Newton's ideas. The work is dedicated to James Alexander. It was reprinted in London in 1746 by Brindley and in 1751 Dodsley published *The principles of action in matter the gravitation of bodies, and the motion of the planets explained from those principles*. This was translated almost immediately into French.

Bachstrom was born in Posnan, educated in Breslau and active in Torun and Warsaw as physician (he wrote various works on medicine), theologian and educationalist. A strict Lutheran, he was an early ecumenist, publishing in 1731 in Görlitz, *Liebreiche Vereinigung der drey Hauptreligionen*, and a strong opponent of what he saw as godless science (*Exercitatio sive specimen de cause gravitatis cui adiecta sunt nonnulla de originibus rerum tam quam fundamenta physices novae antatheisticae*, Copenhagen 1728). From 1729 until 1731 he was active in Constantinople, as educator and missionary, and played an important role in the Enlightenment in Turkey. On his return to Germany he led a wandering life for a number of years and published several books, including one on the art of swimming. He was an early advocate of women's education, particularly in practical subjects like medicine, and educated his two daughters in this wise. As tutor to one of the young Radziwill princes, who had a speech impediment, he went to Lithuania, but before this he published in Breslau in 1736-37 the two volumes of what can be considered a work of literature, his *Das bey zwey hundert Jahr lang unbekannte... Land de Inquiraner...*

Bachstrom met an unfortunate end. The old enmity between him and Jesuits and a row with the Radziwill family led to his imprisonment, and it was in prison that he died. His innocence was later vindicated and the priestly slander seen for what it was.

References: Brooke Hindle, "Cadwallader Colden's extension of the Newtonian Principles", *William and Mary Quarterly* xiii (1956) 459-476; A.R. Hoeman, *Cadwallader Colden* (Westport, Conn., 2002); for Bachstrom, see *Allgemeine Deutsche Biographie* 55, pp.664-667

£2,000-3,000
€2,900-4,350

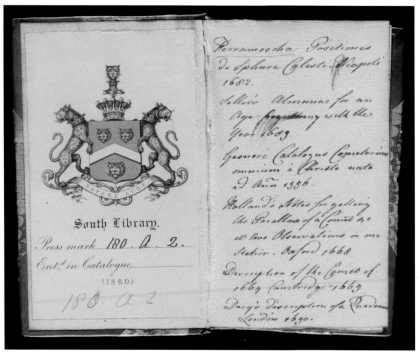

1395

1395 Miscellaneous Tracts—[Danforth, Samuel] An astronomical description of the late comet or blazing star, as it appeared in new England in the 9th, 10th, 11th, and in the beginning of the 12th Month, 1664. *Cambridge (Mass.): S. Green, 1665,* [2], 22pp., [Wing D173; Evans 99 (3 copies)]

Lavater, Ludwig (1527-1586). Cometarum omnium fere catalogus, qui ab Augusto... usque ad hunc 1556 annum apparuerunt, ex varijs historicis collectus. *Zurich: A. & J. Gesner, [1556],* ff. [40], device at end, [Zinner 2153; Vischer K50], *lacking final blank*

Holland, Richard (1596-1677). Notes shewing how to get the angle of parallax of a comet [etc.]. *Oxford: L. Lichfield for R. Davis, 1668,* [4], 20pp., [Wing H2433; Madan 2804]

Dary, Michael. Dary's Diarie. or, a description and use of a quadrant. *London: T.F. for G. Hurlock, 1650,* 39, [1]pp., ILLUSTRATION: double-page engraved plate, woodcut diagrams, [Wing D274a, OC only]

Ferramosca, Aegidius Leognanus. Positiones suas physicastronomicas de sphaera coelesti publice demonstrandas... in collegio neapolitano soc. Iesu. *Naples: Jacques Raillard, 1682,* [4], 88pp., ILLUSTRATION: 8 engraved plates, [not in Riccardi]

Almanach. An almanack for an age. *London: John Seller, [1684],* ff. [26], ILLUSTRATION: engraved throughout with single and double-page plates (one of the anatomical man) and tables, some rectos/versos blank, [Wing A2375 (2 copies)]

Almanach. [drop-title] The description and use of a perpetual almanack in two rundles. *[London, c. 1700],* 32pp., ILLUSTRATION: engraved frontispiece

7 works in one volume, 12mo (135 x 80mm.), BINDING: eighteenth-century English half calf

Provenance: The work by Lavater has the ownership inscription of Peter Le Neve, Norroy King of Arms (1661-1729)

£5,000-7,000
€7,300-10,200

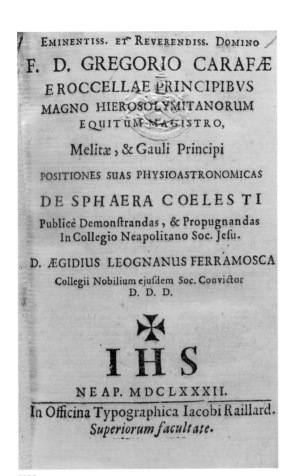

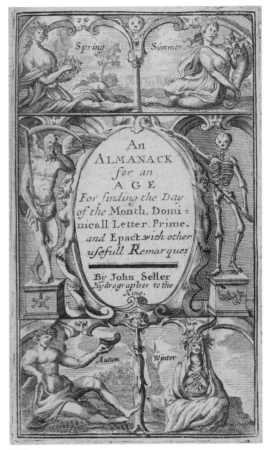

1395

1395

1396 Miscellaneous Tracts—Floutrières, Pierre de. Traitté d'horologeographie, auquel est enseigné a descrire et construire toutes sortes d'horologes au soleil, en quelque superficie plane que ce soit... *Paris: Michel Daniel, 1619*, 116pp. (A-C⁸, D², E-H⁸; D2 contains on the verso an "avis au lecteur", see below), ILLUSTRATION: woodcut diagrams

Slare, Frederick (1646/7-1727). An account of the nature and excellent properties of the Pyrmont waters... which are imported in flasks by Mr Burges... druggist. *London: J. Downing; sold by Tim. Goodwin, 1717*, xvi, 67, [1]pp., dedicated to Isaac Newton and John Bateman

The Welsh-monster: or, the rise and downfal of that late upstart, the R—t H—ble Innuendo Scribble [an attack on Robert Harley, Earl of Oxford, in verse, possibly by Edward Ward]. *London: [c. 1710]*, [4], 40pp., [Foxon W282]

3 works in one volume, 8vo (165 x 100mm.), BINDING: eighteenth-century half calf, spine gilt in compartments, morocco lettering-piece, red edges, *a few page numerals shaved*

On page 52 of the Floutrières is the bookseller's address to the reader explaining the origin of the following texts: "Comme l'impression de ce traitté des horologes estoit presques achevé, un gentil-homme estant en ma boutique, & voyant quelques feuilles d'iceluy... qu'un sien amy avoist eues de quelque mathematicien de ceste ville... entre lesquelles... deux traittez sur ce mesme suject... il estimoit aussi dignes d'estre communiquez au public... et m'ayant offert non seulement iceux traittez, mais usasis tous les autres si ie les voulois metre au iour, j'aurois accepté ces deux cy, a cause de leur briefueté, lesquels (amy lecteur) ie te presente...".

£800-1,000
€1,200-1,450

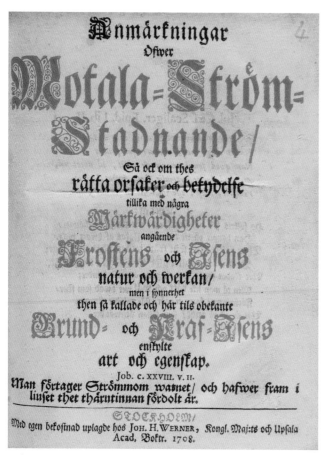

1397

1397

OMNIA REDEVNT AD SVA PRINCIPIA.

1397

Ansa inauditæ & mirabilis novæ Artis,

QVAM SPIRITVS DEI,

ARCANIS ALIQVOT PRO-
PHETICIS ET BIBLICIS NVMERIS,
ad vltima hæc tempora obsignare ac
operire voluit,

QVA, ORDO SEMPER A DE-
O OBSERVATVS, DVM NVMERIS,
AD PRÆCIPVAS VNIVERSALIORES Generalium Mutationum Prophetias, Pyramidalibus
vsus erat, certum cum destinaret tempus,
innuitur,

VIRIS OMNIVM FACVLTATVM
DOCTIS, STIMVLI ET ADMONITIONIS
LOCO EXISTENS, VT IVXTA EXPRESSVM
Mandatum Dei per arduos tales Numeros exquisitius investigent,
sedulò operam dantes, quò verius ex Divinæ Maiesta-
tis edicto intellectus, tandèm lucem
aspicere queat,

Demonstrationibus publicata certissimis hactenus nec lingua
nec idiomate vllo visis,

INVENTORE & AVCTORE,

JOHANNE FAVLHABERO

Arithmetico & Logista ordinario,

Nunc ob inæstimabilem subtus latitantem Sapientiam, ab ardente
Matheseos amatore, nec non eximij huius inuenti stupendo admira-
tore, è Germanico Norimbergæ apud Abrahamum VVagemann
impresso exemplari Latinè versa,

Missa Francofurtum Anno
JVDICIVM.

1397

1397 Miscellaneous Tracts—Faulhaber, Johann (1580-1635). Magia arcana coelestis, sive cabalisticus, novus... computus, de Gog et Magog, ex quo sapientes, prudentes... hac divina arte... imbuti, proprietates maximi christianorum hostis Gog & Magog observare secreto et curiose calculare poterunt, scito et miro teutonico, latino, graeco, & hebraico ex alphabeto occultis aenigmatis involutus & luce datus. *Ulm: for J. Remmelin (Nuremberg: A. Wagenman), 1613*, ff. [8]

Ibid. Tabula, magia arcana coelesti, Dn. Johannis Faulhaberi... construi edocta, et modo divulgata... *[Ulm, 1615]*, single folding letterpress sheet (289 x 600mm.) with chronogram giving date 1615

Ibid. [Begin:] Viro... nobilissimo... Dn. Philiberto Vernat... magicam praesentem tabulam, methodo faulhaberiana concinnatam, zelotes & mimetes eiusdem, bono affectu dicat dedicat. *[c. 1615]*, ff. [2 (folding)]

Ibid. Ansa inauditae & mirabilis novae artis, quam spiritus Dei, arcanis aliquot propheticis et biblicis numeris, ad ultima haec tempora obsignare ac operire voluit, qua, ordo semper a Deo observatus, dum numeris, ad praecipuas universaliores generalium mutationum prophetias, pyramidialibus usus erat ... innuitur... Nunc... e Germanico... latine versa. *Frankfurt (Nuremberg: A. Wagenman for J. Remmelin), 1613*, ff. [8]

Ziegler, Jakob (1561-1670), *of Zurich.* Fermentatio generationis et corruptionis causa. Ein kurtzer Bericht wie ein ding natürlich vergeben und ein anders daraus werden konne. *Basel: (J.G. Genath in Verlegung des authoris), 1647*, [8], 64, [4]pp., ILLUSTRATION: engraved title-page, emblematic engravings in text (with Latin mottoes), two maps, *slight browning*

Block, Magnus Gabriel (1669-1722). Anmärkingar ofwer Mosala-ström-stadnande sa ock om thes rätta orsaker och betyldelse tillika med några märkwärdigheter angående Frostens och Isens nature och werkan... *Stockholm: J.H. Werner, 1708*, [24], 114, [6]pp., title-page printed in red and black, ILLUSTRATION: folding engraved map

Engravings. Sixteen leaves, the first with nine subjects (probably having little to do with the remainder), and the remainder each with three sections, enclosing numerous small subjects of a religious, political, esoteric and possibly occult nature, the engravings cut out and mounted in the eighteenth century. *[Germany, c. 1640?]*

6 works in one volume, 4to (189 x 146mm.), BINDING: eighteenth-century half calf, spine gilt in compartments, red morocco lettering-piece, red edges

Faulhaber's *Magia* is dedicated to the emperor Matthias, whose interest (unlike Rudolf II's) in such things was negligible. *Ansa inauditae*, a short text with eight chapters of biblical quotations, has the quasi-imprint "Missa Francofurtum anno JUDICIUM", a chronogram for 1613, the first part of the "imprint" presumably referring to the text being put on sale at the Frankfurt Fair.

Provenance: Edward Paige, surgeon, inscription on title-page of Ziegler

£8,000-10,000
€11,600-14,500

1398 Miscellaneous Tracts—Doria, Paolo Mattia (1661-*c.* 1746). Discorso apologetico... nel quale di dimostra... che... il problema della duplicazione del cubo da esso sciolto... e libero da ogni vera, e sussistente opposizione... *Venice, 1735,* 102, [2]pp., last leaf with errata on recto, ILLUSTRATION: 1 engraved plate

Lagny, Thomas Fantet de (1660-1734). Methodes nouvelles et abbregées pour l'extraction et l'approximation des racines. Et pour resoudre par le cercle et la ligne droite, plusieurs problêmes solides & sursolides... Seconde edition. *Paris: J. Cusson, 1692 [printed M.DC. LXCII, with L crossed out],* 64pp., *marginal paper repairs to first 2 leaves*

Averani, Niccolo (d. 1721). Dissertatio de mensibus Aegyptiorum in gratiam Antoni Mariae Salvini adiectis notis P. Henrici Noris curante Ant. Francisco Gorio nunc primum edita. *Florence: C. Albizini, 1737,* xvi, 65pp., title printed in red and black, dedicated to Martin Ffolkes, ILLUSTRATION: engraved vignette on title, *without first leaf (?half-title/blank)*

Wendelin, Gottfried (1580-1667). Teratalogia cometica occasione anni vulgaris aerae 1652 (Canticum Abacuc cum paraphrasi). *[Antwerp: Verdussen, 1653?],* 43pp., dedication dated 25 January 1653, *marginal paper repairs to a few leaves*

Morin, Jean Baptiste (1583-1656). Trigonometriae conicae libri tres... adiungitur liber quartus, pro calculi tabulis logarithmorum... *Paris: sumptibus authoris, apud quem venales sunt & apud J. Libert, 1633,* [8], 108pp., ff. [25], 109-115, [1]pp., ILLUSTRATION: woodcut diagrams etc.

La Hire, Philippe de (1640-1718). De cycloide. *[Paris, ?1676],* 6pp., ILLUSTRATION: folding plate with 9 figures, [cf. lot 1179]

Rolle, Michel (1652-1719). Methodes pour resoudre les questions indeterminées de l'algebre. *Paris: J. Cusson, 1699,* [8], 68pp., [copies at Oxford and Aberdeen], *title-page shaved at foot*

7 works in one volume, 4to (203 x 145mm.), BINDING: eighteenth-century sprinkled calf, gilt spine, morocco lettering-piece, red edges

Wendelin was a Belgian astronomer and friend and correspondent of Huygens (cf. *Oeuvres* ii, 304), Mersenne and others. He was born near Liège and died at Rothenac. A student at Rome in 1603-04, he returned home in 1612 and held various ecclesiastical posts. He also founded some mathematical schools. The work here found has no title-page with imprint (what is given above is taken from a quasi half-title).

Michel Rolle, who gave his name to Rolle's theorem, published his treatise on algebra in 1690 and in 1691 his work on polynomials.

For Doria see note to Macclesfield Science D-H, lot 655; for Morin see entires under his name.

£8,000-12,000
€11,600-17,400

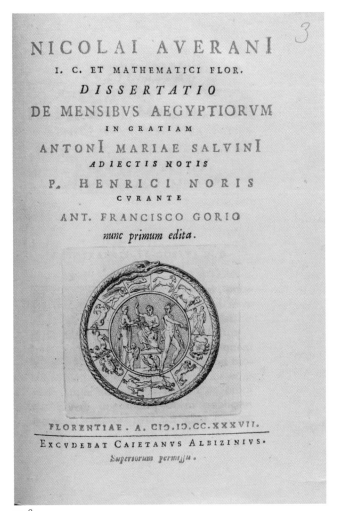

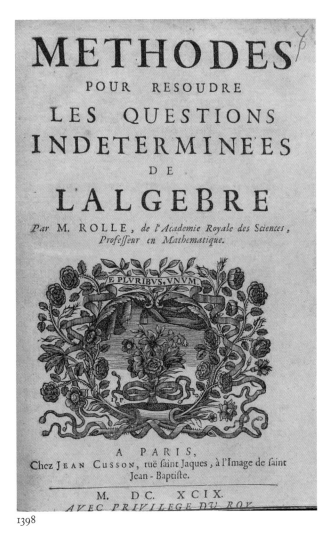

1398

1398

1399 Miscellaneous Tracts—Gradi, Stefano [Stjepan Gradic] (1613-1683).

Disputatio de opinione probabili cum P. Honorato Fabri Societatis Iesu theologo. *Rome: F. Tizzoni, 1678*, [16], 134, [2]pp., last leaf with errata

Académie Royale des Sciences. Reglement ordonné par le Roy... du 26 de janvier 1699. *Paris: Imprimerie royale, [1699]*, 12pp., ILLUSTRATION: engraved device, headpiece, initial and vignette

2 works in one volume, 4to (210 x 150mm.), BINDING: eighteenth-century mottled calf, spine gilt in compartments, red edges

In this lengthy pamphlet Gradi takes issue with Fabri on the subject of probability. Fabri had published in Lyon in 1670 the large folio of his *Apologeticus doctrinae moralis*, of which several dialogues were concerned "de opinione probabili" in various manifestations (cf. Sommervogel III, 516-517). Gradi, whose prolix and verbose work covers all manner of irrelevancies, must have been wheeled out as a safe defence. For another work by Gradi, see lot 1388.

The fifty rules and regulations for the Académie royale cover every aspect of its governance. The text was drafted by government lawyers, although the abbé Bignon's influence may be detected. The new legislation remained in force (with a few changes) right up to 1793, when the Académie was dissolved.

References: D.J. Sturdy, *Science and Social Status* (1995), pp.281-296

£1,000-1,500

€1,450-2,200

1400 Miscellaneous Tracts—Hájek, Tadeás (1525-1600). Aphorismorum metoposcopicorum libellus unus. Editio secunda. *Frankfurt: heirs of A. Wechel, 1584*, 79, [1 (blank)] pp., ILLUSTRATION: woodcut illustrations, [VD16 H235; Caillet 4926]

Divini, Eustachio (1610-1695). Lettera... all'ill. sig. conte Carl'Antonio Manzini. Si ragguaglia di un nuovo lavoro, e componimento di lenti, che servono a occhialoni, o semplici, o composti. *Rome: Giacomo Dragondelli, 1663*, [3]-62pp., [Riccardi i, 413], *lacking A1*

Hotman, François (1524-1590). Observationum, quae ad veterem nuptiarum ritum pertinent, liber singularis. *[Geneva]: Jean le Preux, 1585*, 101, [3]pp., last leaf blank

Taylor, John (1580-1653). A late weary, merry voyage, and journey: or, John Taylors moneths travells, by sea and land [in prose and verse]. *[London], 1650*, 24pp., [Wing T473A, Huntington copy only], *outer margin cropped close*

Peter, John. Artificial versifying, a new way to make Latin verses. Whereby any one of ordinary capacity, that only knows the A.B.C. and can count 9 (although he understands not one word of Latin, or what a verse means) may be plainly taught (and in as little time, as this is reading over) how to make thousands of hexameter and pentameter verses... The third edition... *London: T.J. for Samuel Tidmarsh, 1679*, [4], 18pp., ILLUSTRATION: 6 engraved tables (on 3 leaves) for hexameters and 5 (on 2 leaves) for pentameters, [Wing P1687, 2 copies only], *headlines cropped and occasionally cut away*

Royal Society of London. The charters and statutes of the Royal Society of London, for improving natural knowledge. *London, 1717*, 75, [1 (blank)] pp., *some underlining*

6 works in one volume, 8vo (155 x 90mm.), BINDING: eighteenth-century polished calf, spine gilt in compartments

The two letters from Rheticus at the end of the work by Hájek are dated 1563 and 1567. In the first Rheticus speaks of his work on Copernicus (what became the 1566 edition) which friends were begging him to take up "post praeteritam nuper Saturni & Iovis coniunctionem die 25 Augusti hora 7 cum dimidia post meridiem". These letters are printed in Burmeister iii, nos. 46 and 49.

John Peter describes himself on the title-page in Greek as a measurer of both heavens and earth, and he first published the work in 1677. At the end we find a very modern dictum:

"The fate of books depends not on the skill
Or worth of authors, but on th' readers will."

£5,000-7,000
€7,300-10,200

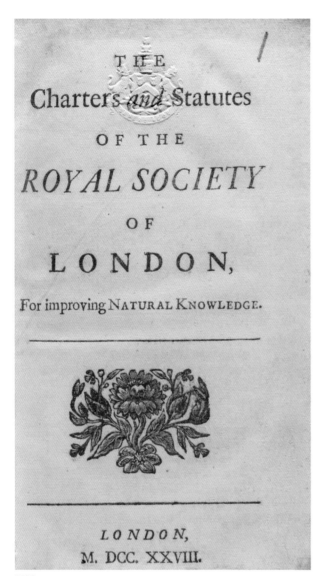

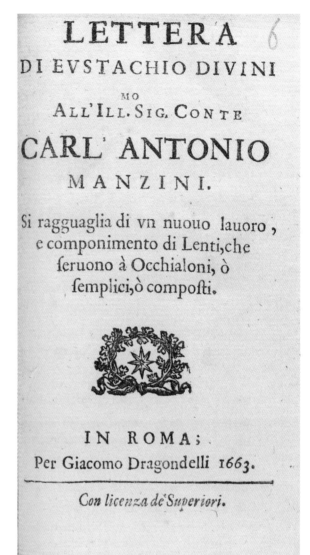

1400

1400

1401 Miscellaneous Tracts—Henisch, Georg (1549-1618). De numeratione multiplici, vetere et recenti. *Augsburg: D. Franck [ad insigne pinus], 1605*, FIRST EDITION, [5], 107pp., folding table at end

Sacro Bosco, Joannes de. [De sphaera] Libellus de anni ratione, seu ut vocatur vulgo, computus ecclesiasticus. Cum praefatione P. Melanthonis [*sic*, addressed to A. Firmin Gasser]. *(Wittemberg: Johann Crato), 1558*, ff. I3-K6 (end of text), folding table, ILLUSTRATION: woodcut, [Shaaber H385], *lacking the text of 'De sphaera' on ff. A-I2*

2 works in one volume, 8vo (145 x 85mm.), BINDING: eighteenth-century English sprinkled calf, gilt spine, red morocco lettering-piece, red edges

Many of Henisch's works date from the 1570s, and were published in Basel, like his edition of Hesiod, and his various medical works. His mathematical oeuvre had some currency: an English compilation by F. Cooke, *The principles of geometrie, astronomie, and geographie. Gathered out of G. Henischius, etc.* was published in 1591 (STC 13070). His catalogue of the printed books in the library at Augsburg was published in 1600, and his polyglot dictionary *Teutsche Sprache* in 1616.

£500-600
€750-900

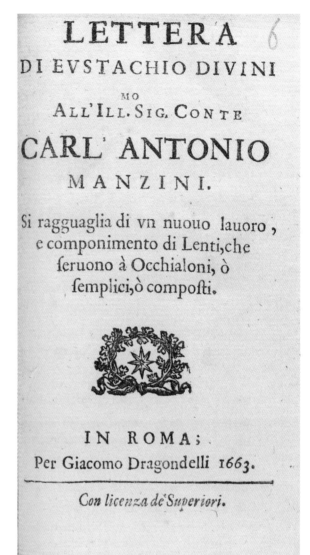

195

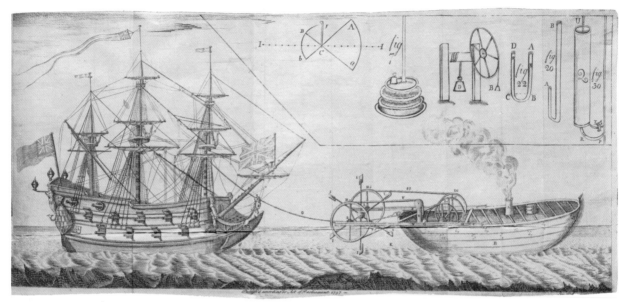

1402

1402 Miscellaneous Tracts—[Hale, *Sir* Matthew (1609-1676)] Observations touching the principals of natural motions; and especially touching rarefaction & condensation... by the author of Difficiles Nugae. *London: W. Godbid for W. Shrowsbury, 1677*, [14], 285, [3]pp., last 3 pages containing advertisements, [Wing H252; for *Difficiles Nugae* see Macclesfield Science D-H, lot 965], *without initial blank*

Hulls, Jonathan. A description and draught of a new-invented machine for carrying vessels or ships out of, or into any harbour, port, or river, against wind and tide, or in a calm... *London: for the author (sold by T. Boreman), 1737*, 48pp., small slip with Boreman's name pasted to foot of last page, ILLUSTRATION: folding engraved plate, [*English Maritime Books* 2170]

Computatio universalis seu logica rerum. Being an essay attempting in a geometrical method, to demonstrate an universal standard, whereby one may judge of the true value of every thing in the world, relatively to the person. *London: J. Moxon, 1697*, [3], 13pp., [Wing C5675 (3 copies listed)], *browned*

Gravesande, Willem Jakob Storm van 's (1688-1742). Essai d'une nouvelle theorie du choc des corps, fondée sur l'experience. *The Hague: T. Johnson, 1722*, [2], 54pp., ILLUSTRATION: engraved plate at end

4 works in one volume, 8vo and 12mo (154 x 90mm.), BINDING: eighteenth-century polished calf, spine gilt in compartments, green morocco lettering-piece, red edges

Hull's invention, which uses steam ("as in Mr Newcomen's engine", p.40), is shown in the accompanying plate mounted in a boat, and constitutes, in effect, a "tug-boat".

The dedication to the Royal Society of the *Computatio* has in manuscript the name S. Foly, clearly not the Irish bishop, who died in 1695. We cannot determine whether this should be treated as a contemporary attribution. "Axioms. 1 Ax. Time is as necessary to enjoy Happiness in, as an Estate is necessary to procure it. 2 Ax. The same proportion that the whole Happiness of a Man's life bears to his whole Time and Estate, the same proportion do the distinct parts of his Happiness bear to proportionable parts of his Time and Estate. 3 Ax. Happiness is worth as much as Time and as much Money, as are absolutely necessary to procure and enjoy it ...".

Gravesande's *Essai* appeared in this format also in the 1722 *Journal littéraire* published at The Hague, of which this is, apparently, an "offprint" (see note on verso of title).

£2,000-3,000
€2,900-4,350

THE

SHEPHERD of BANBURY'S

R U L E S

To judge of the

C H A N G E S

OF THE

W E A T H E R,

Grounded on Forty Years Experience.

To which is added,

A rational ACCOUNT of the Causes of such Alterations, the Nature of Wind, Rain, Snow, &c. on the Principles of the *Newtonian* Philosophy.

By JOHN CLARIDGE.

LONDON:

Printed for W. BICKERTON, in the *Temple Exchange, Fleet-street.* MDCCXLIV.

(Price 1 s.)

1403   1403

1403 Miscellaneous Tracts—[Hervey, John (1696-1743), *Baron Hervey*] Some remarks on the minute philosopher [Bishop Berkeley]. In a letter from a country clergyman to his friend in London. The second edition. *London: J. Roberts, 1732,* 66pp.

[Whiston, William (1667-1752)] A vindication of the new theory of the earth [by Thomas Burnet] from the exceptions of Mr Keill and others. *London: for B. Tooke, 1698,* [12], 52pp., [Wing W1698]

Claridge, John. The shepherd of Banbury's rules to judge of the changes of the weather. *London: W. Bickerton, 1744,* [2], viii, 64pp.

[Roubaix, Jacques de] [Dissertation physique sur le flux et reflux de la mer] A physical dissertation, concerning the cause of the variation of the barometer, the form of the globe of the earth, the diminution of heavy bodies, the flux and reflux of the sea; wherein some mistakes in Sir Isaack Newton's System are rectify'd... Written originally in French... Translated into English. *London: J. Peele, 1721,* [2], 74pp., [Wallis 145.05]

Robinson, Christopher. A view of Sir Isaac Newton's method for comparing the resistance of solids. *London, printed in the year 1734,* [2], ii, 50pp., ILLUSTRATION: 2 folding engraved plates by John Mynde with numerous figures, [Wallis 141]

5 works in one volume, 8vo (195 x 115mm.), BINDING: eighteenth-century half calf, spine gilt in compartments, morocco lettering-piece, red edges

£800-1,200

€1,200-1,750

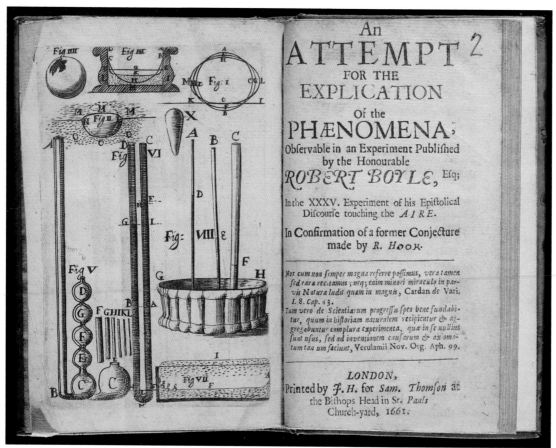

An
ATTEMPT 2
FOR THE
EXPLICATION
Of the
PHÆNOMENA,
Obſervable in an Experiment Publiſhed
by the Honourable
ROBERT BOYLE, Eſq;

In the XXXV. Experiment of his Epiſtolical
Diſcourſe touching the *A I R E*.

In Confirmation of a former Conjecture
made by *R. HOOK*.

*Nos cum non ſemper magna reſerre poſſimus, vera tamen
ſed rara recitamus ; neq; enim minori miraculo in par-
vis Natura ludit quam in magnis,* Cardan de Vari.
L. 8. *Cap.* 43.
*Tum vero de Scientiarum progreſſu ſpes bene fundabi-
tur, quum in hiſtoriam naturalem recipientur & ag-
gregabuntur complura experimenta, quæ in ſe nullius
ſunt uſus, ſed ad inventionem cauſarum & axioma-
tum tantum faciunt,* Verulamii Nov. Org. Aph. 99.

LONDON,
Printed by *J. H.* for *Sam.* Thomſon at
the Biſhops Head in St. *Pauls*
Church-yard, 1661.

1404

1404 Miscellaneous Tracts—H[ooke], R[obert] (1635-1702). An attempt for the
explication of the phaenomena, observable in an experiment published by the
Honourable Robert Boyle, Esq. in the xxv. experiment of his epistolical discourse
touching the aire. *London: J.H. for Sam. Thomson, 1661*, [6], 50pp., ILLUSTRATION:
engraved plate, [Wing H2612; Keynes, *Hooke* 2], *bottom edge cut close but not
affecting text*

Sturm, Leonhard Christoph (1669-1719). Gründlicher Unterricht, von der
Allen, so wohl denen welche in Bau-Sachen dem Aerario vorstehen, alls auch
Baumeistern, Oeconomis und curieusen Reisenden zuwissen sehr nöthigen
Wissenschafft, von Häng- oder Sprengwercken, auff Veranlassung einer grossen
Bossheit, welche ein Zimmermann gegen ihm in dergleichen Werck begangen,
und von unverständigen Bau-Herrn ist secundiret worden, öffentlich...
auffgestellet, sammt einer Vorrede in Form eines architectonischen Bedenckens,
was einem Architecto zuthun sey im Fall er bauen soll, wo eines grosen Herrn
höchst-vernünfftige Commodität und die allgemeinen Reguln der Bau-Kunst
einander schnurstracks zu wider sind, nebst dazugehorigen... Figuren. *[Schwerin &
Leipzig: J.H. Russworm, 1713]*, [34], 74, [8]pp., ILLUSTRATION: 17 engraved plates,
imprint cropped

2 works in one volume, 8vo (150 x 85mm.), BINDING: eighteenth-century mottled
calf, spine gilt in compartments, red morocco lettering-piece, red edges.

HOOKE'S FIRST SCIENTIFIC PUBLICATION, RARE. The pamphlet is concerned with
capillary action and takes its starting point, as the title makes clear, in Boyle's
experiment as published in *New Experiments* (Oxford, 1660), here reprinted
(pp.1-5). A Latin translation was published in Holland in 1662.

£7,000-10,000
€10,200-14,500

1405 Miscellaneous Tracts—Kepler, Johann (1571-1630). Strena seu de nive sexangula. *Frankfurt: Godefrid Tampach, 1611,* [2], 1, 4-24pp. (i.e. 12 leaves), ILLUSTRATION: 3 small woodcut diagrams, [Caspar 39], *lower margins not quite trimmed straight, small tear in margin of last leaf*

Swammerdam, Johannes (1637-1680). Ephemeri vita: or the natural history of the ephemeron, a fly that lives but five hours. *London: for H. Faithorne and J. Kersey, 1681,* [8], 44, [8]pp., PRESENTED TO THE ROYAL SOCIETY BY THE TRANSLATOR, EDWARD TYSON, June 8 1681, *lacking all plates*

Canal de Picardie—Devis général des ouvrages à faire au canal de Picardie pour la jonction navigable de la riviere de Somme à l'Oise, depuis Saint Quentin jusqu'à Pont, qui est la partie supérieure de ce projet; depuis Pont jusqu'à Fargnier, qui est le centre; & depuis Fargnier en deux branches, pour la partie inférieure, dont l'une sera conduite à Chauny, & l'autre à la Fere. *(Paris: H. Guerin), 1730,* 62pp., ILLUSTRATION: large folding engraved map

Lorenzini, Stefano. The curious and accurate observations... on the dissections of the cramp-fish... now done into English... with figures after the life. By J. Davis. *London: Jeffery Wale, 1705,* [8], 75, [1]pp., last page with advertisement, ILLUSTRATION: 5 engraved plates each with several figures

[Woodward, John (1665-1728)] Brief instructions for making observations in all parts of the world: as also for collecting, preserving and sending over natural things... Drawn up at the request of a person of honour: and presented to the Royal Society. *London: Richard Wilkin, 1696,* [2], 20pp., *without imprimatur leaf*

Biörner, Eric Julius (1696-1750). Prodromus tractatum de geographia Scandinaviae veteri, et historiis gothicis: exhibens succinctum judicium de Scythiae, Suethiae, et Gothiae etymo, ut et runarum in cippis helsingicis ac medelpadicis inventarum aetate, usu atque explicatione. *Stockholm: J.L. Hornn, [1726],* [4], 48, [6]pp., p.29 a fly-title, ILLUSTRATION: woodcut illustrations of stones with runes by I. Pering, [copy in Royal Library, Stockholm]

6 works in one volume, 4to (220 x 160mm.), BINDING: eighteenth-century mottled calf, spine gilt in compartments, red morocco lettering-piece, red edges

Kepler's *Strena* or *New Year's Gift* is dedicated to Johann Matthaeus Wackher von Wackhensels. It begins with a typically humanist, playful *jeu de mots* and a discussion of "nothing" with allusion to the lecherous sparrow, sacred to Venus, a topos found in ancient Greek and Latin poetry (famously in Catullus) and how the author, on his way to his patron's house with no present, is overtaken by a snow storm where the snow flakes come, as it were, out of nothing. This gave him the idea for something which a poor mathematician "nihil habens, nihil accipiens", could give as a present.

Its serious content ("sed ad rem veniamus ioco misso") is a discussion of snow crystals and their hexagonal construction. "Why is it," Kepler asks, "that when we see snowstars (stellulae nivales) they are always hexagonal, and never pentagonal or heptagonal... The cause lies not in the material but in the agent...". Kepler adduces various examples from the natural world of geometric construction or packing — bee-hives, pomegranates, pea-pods etc.

He writes: "For in general equal spheres (globi) when collected in any vessel, come to a mutual arrangement in two modes according to the two modes of arranging them in a plane. If equal spheres are loose in the same horizontal plane and you drive them together so tightly that they touch each other, they come together either in a three-cornered or in a four-cornered pattern. In the former case six surround one; in the latter four. Throughout there is the same pattern of contact between all the pellets except the outermost. With a five-sided pattern uniformity cannot be maintained. A six-sided pattern breaks up into three-sided. Thus there are only the two patterns as described.

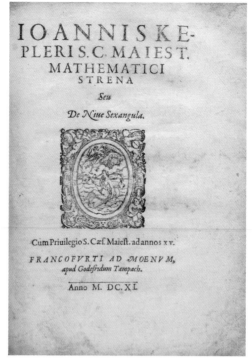

1405 1405

"Now if you proceed to pack the solid bodies as tightly as possible, and set the files that are first arranged on the level on top of others, layer on layer, the pellets will be either squared, or in triangles. If squared, either each single sphere of the upper range will rest on a single sphere of the lower, or, on the other hand, each single sphere of the upper range will settle between every four of the lower. In the former mode any sphere is touched by four neighbours in the same plane, and by one above and one below, and so on throughout, each touched by six others. The arrangement will be cubic, and the spheres, when subjected to pressure, will become cubes. But this will not be the tightest pack. In the second mode not only is every sphere touched by its four neighbours in the same plane, but also by four in the plane above and by four below, and so throughout one will be touched by twelve, and under pressure spherical spheres will become rhomboid. This arrangement will be more comparable to the octahedron and pyramid. This arrangement will be the tightest possible, so that in no other arrangement could more pellets be stuffed into the same container" (*The Six-cornered snowflake*, Oxford 1966, translated by Colin Hardie, with "pellet" changed to "sphere").

This is what is called the "Kepler conjecture". This natural method of stacking the spheres (like a greengrocer stacking oranges) creates one of two similar patterns called cubic close packing and hexagonal close packing. Each of these two arrangements has an average density of pi over square root of 18 (nearly equals 0.74048). The Kepler conjecture says that this is the best that can be done - no other arrangement of spheres has a higher average density than this.

It seems in its origin to go back to a problem posed by the Englishman Thomas Harriot who corresponded with Kepler, and who tried, without success, to interest Kepler in atoms etc. (there is a brief reference in this text on p.1 to Epicurus and his atoms), but who had sought in 1591 an explanation of how one constructed piles of bullets or cannon balls.

The pamphlet rarely appears at auction. There was a copy in the Honeyman sale, and there has been one since.

£15,000-20,000
€21,800-29,000

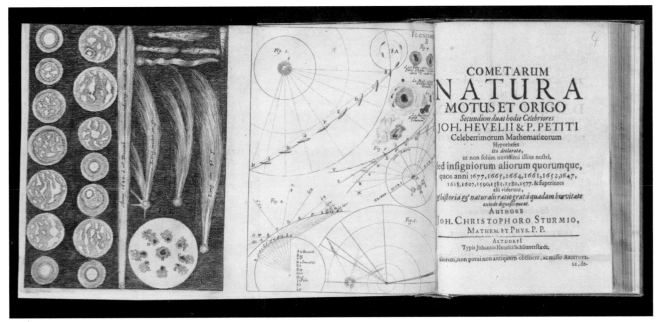

1406

1406 Miscellaneous Tracts—Longomontanus, Christian Sørensen (1562-1647) *and* **John Pell (1611-1685).** Controversiae de vera circuli mensura anno 1644 exortae, inter Christianum Severini... et Ioannem Pellium. Pars prima [with additional letters from Mydorge (to Charles Cavendish), Roberval, J. Hobbes, Le Pailleur and Jacobus Golius]. *Amsterdam: J. Blaeu, 1647*, 96pp., title printed in red and black, ILLUSTRATION: woodcut diagrams in text, *small tear in A4 and B1*

Lansberge, Philipp van (1561-1632). Chronologiae sacrae libri III. In quibus annorum mundi series, ab orbe condito ad eversa per Romanos Hierosolyma... ostenditur. *Middelburg: widow and heirs of S. Moulert, 1625*, 181, [1]pp.

Mutoli, Pier Maria, *pseud.* [Borelli, Giovanni Alfonso (1608-1679)] Del movimento della cometa apparsa il mese di dicembre 1664. Spiegato in una lettera... al P. Stefano de Angeli. *(Pisa: G. Ferretti, 1665)*, 22pp., PRINTED ON THICK PAPER, [Riccardi ii, 164 (not seen)]

Sturm, Johann Christoph (1635-1703). Cometarum natura motus et origo secundum duas... Joh. Hevelii & P. Petiti hypotheses... *Altdorf: J.H. Schönnerstädt, (1681)*, [4], 52pp., ILLUSTRATION: 2 engraved plates printed on a folding leaf, [BL STC XVIIc. S3063], *blank foot of title-leaf removed*

Regnartius, Valerianus. Astrolabiorum seu utriusque planisphaerii universalis et particularis usus. Per modum compendii traditus. *Rome: B. Zannetti, 1610* [with III partially inked in after X], 57, [3]pp., "ad radium 1000..." [added in manuscript] with on p. [60] (with first line cropped) "the table of sines (to Rad.1) before wanting is supplied by Mr. Carleton, Apr. 6th 1671: George Fairfax", *G5 (pp.57-58) cut down to edge of text*

5 works in one volume, 4to (190 x 135mm.), BINDING: eighteenth-century English polished calf, gilt spine, red morocco label, red edges

The first item was actually published by Pell who had solicited various friends for demonstrations against Longomontanus. The final item by Regnartius is recorded with date 1610 (as in BL) but here the three vertical strokes can be seen lightly added, in what was meant to be a reissue. George Fairfax (Taylor, *Tudor & Stuart*, p. 273) who flourished in the last thirty years of the century was a mathematical practioner and teacher. Carleton we have not traced.

Provenance: The Lansberge belonged to John Morris (see Tom Birrell, *The Library of John Morris*, 1976) with his motto 'erchetai nyx'; P. de Cardonnel (see Noel Malcolm, *Hobbes Miscellanies*, 2003, chapter 9) and Sir Edward Sherburne (see Tom Birrell, 'I' in A. Hunt & others, *The Book Trade and its Customers*, 1997).

There are several of Pierre de Cardonnel's books in the library, and others belonging to him were given to him by John Morris. Birrell (p. xix) records a copy of Jodocus a Megen *Peregrinatio Hierosolymitana* (1580) originally owned by Sir John Doddridge (1555-1628), from whom it passed to his nephew, thence to Morris, who seems to have given it to Cardonnel in about 1651; to this may be added an unnoticed Hebrew book at Eton College (Isaac Abarbanel, *Sefer Mif' aloth Elohim*, Venice 1592), with inscription "Sum Joannis Morris nunc ex bibl. P. de Cardonnel, 1651". Of two books belonging to Morris in the possession of the American Antiquarian Society, one belonged to Cardonnel in 1651, and both later belonged to Increase Mather (Birrell p. 67 nos. X30 and X31).

£2,000-3,000
€2,900-4,350

1407 Miscellaneous Tracts—Mohr, Georg (1640-1697). Euclides Danicus, bestaende in twee deelen. Het eerste deel: handelt van de meetkonstige werckstucken, begrepen in de ses eerste boecken Euclidis: het tweede deel: geest aenleyding om verscheyde werckstucken te maecken... *Amsterdam: Jacob van Velsen for the author, 1672*, [4], 36pp., ILLUSTRATION: 3 folding plates with numerous figures, signed by the author in authentication, [not in BL, copy in Christ Church, Oxford]

Ibid. Compendium Euclidis curiosi: dat is, meetkonstigh passer-werck, hoe me meet een gegeven opening van een passer en een liniael, de werck-stucken van Euclides, ontbinden kan... *Amsterdam: J. Jansson van Waesberge, 1673*, 24pp., ILLUSTRATION: folding plate at p.5, [not in BL, copy in Christ Church, Oxford]

S., J.D. Gegen-übung auf ein mathematisch Tractaetlein, Compendium Euclidis Curiosi genant, worin nebst kurtzem Anweis um verscheidene Euclidische Aufgaben mit einer gegebenen Oeffnung des Zirkels noch auf andere Ahrt zu machen... *Amsterdam: J. Jansson van Waesberge, 1673*, 24pp., ILLUSTRATION: 2 folding plates

Pilkington, Gilbert. The turnament of Tottenham. Or, the wooing, winning, and wedding, of Ribbe, the reeu's daughter there... (A briefe description of the towne of Tottenham High-Crosse... written by Wilhelm Bedwell). *London: J. Norton, 1631*, ff. [22], without final blank leaf, [STC 19925]

Bedwell, William (1561-1632). Mesolabium architectonicum... invented long since by Mr Thomas Bedwell... and now published... *London: J. N[orton] for William Garet, 1631*, ff. [13], without final blank leaf, ILLUSTRATION: 2 engraved plates, [STC 21825]

Schöner, Lazarus (*c.* 1543-1607). De numeris geometricis. Of the nature and proprieties of geometricall numbers... Englished... by Thomas Bedwell. *London: R. Field, 1614*, [6], 82pp., with folding table at end, without initial blank leaf, [STC 21825]

Sturm, Johannes (1507-1589). De accurata circuli dimensione et quadratura cum sylvula epigrammatum... *Louvain: F. Simons, 1633*, [24], 72pp.

Hood, Thomas (*fl.* 1582-1600). The making and use of the geometricall instrument, called a sector... *London: J. Windet and sold by S. Shorter, [1598]*, ff. [5], 50, [1], Black Letter, last leaf with errata, ILLUSTRATION: woodcut diagrams, [STC 13695]

8 works in one volume, 4to (185 x 130mm.), BINDING: eighteenth-century mottled calf, spine gilt in compartments, red morocco lettering-piece, red edges, *occasional cropping, upper joint weak*

Georg Mohr was a Dane by birth, but spent much of his life in Holland (where he had gone in 1662) before visiting England and France and then returning to Denmark. In a letter to Leibnitz (30 September 1675), Oldenburg writes of Mohr, whom he wrongly terms a Fleming, but of whom he says that he is "algebrae et mechanices probe peritus", that he has recently left England for Paris and has left with John Collins ("Collinius noster") "a certain work written in the Flemish tongue, a copy of which I was glad to communicate to you,

1407

because, according to Collins, the said Mohr asserted, this work... complete's Cardan's rules... and supplies roots of equations of the kind which are represented by surds..."(Oldenburg, *Correspondence* XI, letter 2754).

Mohr is famous as the proponent of the practice of carrying out virtually all geometrical processes with a compass alone, an activity which many will vividly remember from their schooldays. Lorenzo Mascheroni (1750-1800) who is credited with proving that all Euclidean constructions can be carried out with compasses alone, in a book published in Pavia in 1797 and dedicated to Napoleon (*Geometria del compasso*), did not prove this until 125 years after Mohr.

Mohr proves in the book that a line segment can be divided in golden section with compass alone. The book is in two parts: the first consists of the constructions of the first six books of Euclid, the second, of various constructions. The problem of finding the intersection of two lines, which is of some theoretical importance, is solved incidentally in the second part in connection with the construction of a circle through two given points and tangents to a given line.

Mohr's work has his signature of authentication, something which the imprint draws attention to: "voor de Autheur, wellcke geen exemplaren voor de sijne erkent, als die hy selver met zijn handt onderteeckent heest".

The anonymous German work also found here has been attributed to Mohr (for a discussion see K. Andersen and H. Meyer, "Georg Mohr's three books and the *Gegenübung auf Compendium Euclidis Curiosi*", *Centaurus* 28 (1985), 139-144).

£5,000-7,000
€7,300-10,200

1408 Miscellaneous Tracts—Morin, Jean (1583-1656). La Science des longitudes... reduite en exacte et facile pratique par luy-mesme, sur le globe celeste; tant pour la terre que pour la mer... Avec la censure de la nouvelle théorie... du père Leonard Duliris. *Paris: aux depens de l'autheur... chez lequel le livre se vend: ensemble chez Iacques Villery, 1647,* [8], 62pp., ILLUSTRATION: woodcut figures

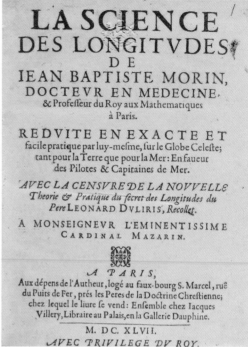

Ibid. Response... a l'apologie scandaleuse du P. Leonard Durilis [*sic*] Recollect, touchant la science des longitudes; pour les navigations. *Paris: aux despens de l'autheur... chez Iacques Villery... et chez Jean le Brun, 1648,* 88pp., ILLUSTRATION: woodcut figures

Zarlino, Giuseppe (1517-1590). De vera anni forma, sive de recta eius emendatione. *Venice: in officina Varisciana, 1580,* [8], 134pp., last leaf of preliminaries with errata, sheets C-D printed as a table in red and black, ILLUSTRATION: woodcut plate at p.75 (intended to be cut out to form a wheel with volvelle), woodcut diagrams etc., [Censimento 16 CNCE 40778], *without final blank, preliminaries a little damp-stained, tables a little cropped*

Weidler, Johann Friedrich (1691-1755). Institutiones geometriae subterraneae. *Wittenberg: widow Gerdes, 1726,* 80pp., ILLUSTRATION: 4 engraved plates, *one plate shaved*

Segner, Johann Andreas von [János András] (1704-1777). Ad... Georgium Erhardum Hambergerum... Dissertatio epistolica qua regulam Harrioti de modo ex aequationum signis numerum radicum tam verarum quam spuriarum eas componentium, cognoscendi, demonstrare, simulque rationem structurae instrumenti novi, sectionibus conicis secundi generis plerisque, ac omnibus primi, describendis apti, exponere conatur Ioannes Andreas Segner. *Jena: C.F. Buch, [1728],* 23, [1]pp.

5 works in one volume, 4to (200 x 150mm.), BINDING: eighteenth-century sprinkled calf, gilt spine, green morocco label, red edges

Zarlino is famous as a composer and musical theorist (see C.V. Palisca, *Humanism in Italian Renaissance musical thought* (1985), and the long article in Grove), but this work on the calendar is uncommon and not noticed by musicologists.

Weidler, who succeeded Wolf in the chair of mathematics at Wittenberg, was a fellow of the Royal Society and wrote many books on mathematics, hydraulics (1728), astronomy, and technology. This work is connected with the geometry of mining, a field in which, as the author says in his preface, the Germans excelled.

It was Segner, of Hungarian family by birth, but generally known under his German name, who introduced the concept of surface tension. In this his first work (dated at the end 7 September 1728) he discusses Harriot's rule as outlined in Harriot's *Artis analyticae praxis*.

£6,000-10,000
€8,700-14,500

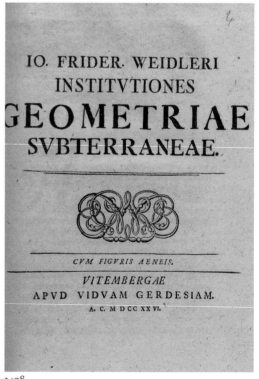

1409 Miscellaneous Tracts—Napier, John (1550-1617), *Baron Merchiston.* Rabdologiae, seu numerationis per virgulas libri duo: cum appendice expeditis-simo[*sic*] [etc.]. *Edinburgh: A. Hart, 1617,* [12], 154pp., plus 4 folding engraved tables, at p. 101, 105, 106 (lettered A-C) and 130, [STC 18357; Dibner 107; Norman 1574]

Dionysius Periegetes. Denys Alexandrin, de la situation du monde. Nouvellement traduit du grec en françois [in verse], & illustré de commentaires… par Benigne Saumaize. *Paris: A. Perier, 1597,* ff. [6], 114 [*sic*=124]

A brief description of the four-foot gauging rule, [etc.]. *[London, c. 1650?],* 47pp., *lacking preliminaries, a few leaves shaved in margin*

3 works in one volume, 12mo (135 x 70mm.), BINDING: eighteenth-century English calf, spine gilt, red morocco lettering-piece, red edges

Napier's *Rabdologia* (from the Greek for staff or 'virgula') deals with mechanical calculation using small rods of boxwood, silver or ivory (the so-called Napier's bones) for the purposes of counting, and metal plates for multiplication and division. "Each of the ten rods had numbers inscribed as geometric squares, which, in multiplication, were arranged by digit and the products recorded and added. Later the rods were mounted on a rotatable cylinder, and an arrangement of these in a box, constituted a calculator" (Dibner).

The translation into French verse of *De situ orbis* is a rare item. The translator, Benigne de Saumaise (1560-1640?), was conseiller at the parlement of Dijon and a very minor poet. This seems to be his only book.

References: La description de la terre habitée de Denys d'Alexandrie ou la Leçon de géographie, edited by Christian Jacob (Paris: A. Michel, 1990) is a modern edition of the text. The original edition is in the BNF, but there is no copy in the British Library.

Provenance: Pierre de Cardonnel, inscription on title-page of the Dionysius Periegetes dated 1646 (see note to lot 1406)

£15,000-20,000
€21,800-29,000

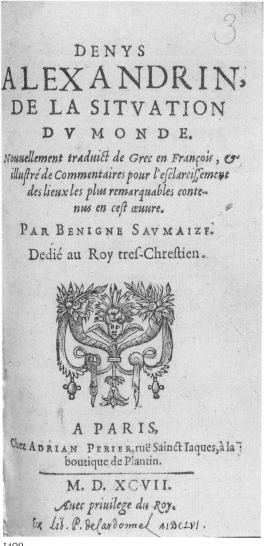

1409

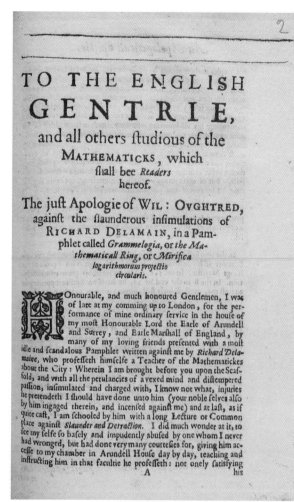

Aquila

1410   1410

1410 Miscellaneous Tracts—Oughtred, William (1575-1660). The circles of
proportion and the horizontal instrument. The former shewing the maner how to
work proportions... and is newly increased with an additament for navigation... the
later teaching how to work most quaestions, which may be performed by the
globe: and to delineat dialls upon any kind of plaine. Hereunto is annexed the
excellent use of two rulers for calculation... Translated into English... by William
Forster (To the English gentrie... the just apologie... against the slaunderous
insimulations of Richard Delamain, in a pamphlet called Grammelogia...).
London: A. Mathewes, to be sold by N. Bourne, 1633 (part 3: [A. Mathewes, 1634?]),
3 parts, [8], 152, [8]; [2], 74, [4]pp.; ff. [16], ILLUSTRATION: 3 engraved plates in
part 1, woodcut diagrams, [STC 18899b/c & 18901a], *first plate cropped at edge,
lacking A1 (blank) and X4 (errata?) in part one and last two leaves in part two with
errata*

Hyginus, Gaius Julius. Poeticon astronomicon. *Venice: Erhard Ratdolt, 22 January
1485,* ff. [56], 32 lines, Roman letter, ILLUSTRATION: astronomical woodcuts,
[H 9063; BMC v 289; Klebs 527.3; Sander 3473; Redgrave 48; Goff H561]

2 works in one volume, 4to (180 x 120mm.), BINDING: eighteenth-century mottled
calf, spine gilt in compartments, red morocco lettering-piece, red edges

For Oughtred, see lots 1559 to 1561. The Hyginus is copiously annotated on
some leaves (notably the first recto, which is blank) in Latin in a contemporary
hand.

£2,500-3,000
€3,650-4,350

1411 Miscellaneous Tracts—Parker, Gustavus. An account of a portable barometer, with reasons and rules for the use of it. *London: W. Haws, 1700*, [10], 38, 31-70, 81-104, [4]pp. (A-P⁴), date printed MDCXCX, last leaf with advertisement for Hawes [*sic*], [Wing P391; Taylor, *Tudor & Stuart* 526], *M1 torn at corner with loss, browned throughout*

[Moranus, G.] Animadversiones in elementorum philosophiae sectionem I. De corpore editam a Thoma Hobbes. *Brussels, 1655*, 50, [2]pp., ILLUSTRATION: folding engraved plate, *running titles shaved or cropped, folding plate trimmed at edge,* RARE

Beveren, Cornelis van. Dissertatio de quadratura circuli, ut de demonsrtatio [*sic*] methodi Do. de Fermat de maximis & minimis investigandis. *Utrecht: Franciscus Halma, 1679*, [10], 20, [3]pp., last leaf with errata (spelled "Arrata") on recto, ILLUSTRATION: woodcut illustrations and diagrams

Scheuchzer, Johann Jakob (1672-1733). Enchiridion mathematicum. *Zurich: Bodmer for the author, 1714*, [6], 40pp., ILLUSTRATION: folding engraved table at beginning

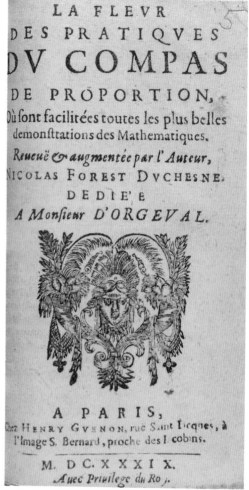

1411

Forest Duchesne, Nicolas (1595-1650). La fleur des pratiques du compas de proportion... augmentée par l'auteur. *Paris: Henry Guenon, 1639*, [14], 112pp., dedication followed by preface "au lecteur" and privilege leaf, ILLUSTRATION: folding engraved plate at p.1, folding printed table at p.104, engraved and woodcut illustrations and diagrams in text (2 full-page), *ink staining on pp.1-2 obscuring words*

5 works in one volume, 8vo (156 x 88mm.), BINDING: eighteenth-century polished calf, spine gilt in compartments, red morocco lettering-piece, red edges

The first work contains a criticism of Hobbes as geometer by the Jesuit mathematician André Tacquet (pp.13-29).

We have located no copy of the Beveren in the Dutch NSTC. Whether he can be the same as the translator of Racine's *Mithridate* into Dutch, we have not determined.

£1,500-2,000
€2,200-2,900

1412 Miscellaneous Tracts—Pighius, Albertus (*c.* 1490-1542). Adversus novam Marci Beneventani astronomiam… in qua, tota ferme Alphonsina positio, hactenus a paucissimis recte intellecta, a Purbachio etiam in multis perperam explicata, mathematica demonstrata est [and other works]. *(Paris): Simon de Colines, (3 May 1522)*, ff. [6], 70, ILLUSTRATION: woodcut diagrams in text, [Renouard, *Colines*, pp.40-41]

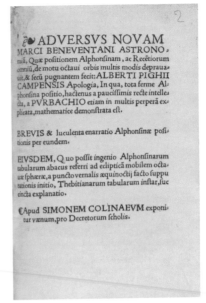

1412

Archimedes. Opera… per Nicolaum Tartaleam Brixianum… emendata… commentariolis sane luculentis… aperta [etc.]. *(Venice: V. Ruffinelli for N. Tartaglia, April 1543)*, ff. 35, [1], ILLUSTRATION: woodcut diagrams in text, arms of Wentworth on title, contemporary ownership inscriptions of William Buxt[on?] and William Hall, extensive later notes in ink on ff. 20 & 28 verso

Flamand, Claude (1570-1611). Geometria, oder kurtzer klarer und doch gnugsamer Bericht zum Erd and Landmessen, sampt allen so darzu gehörig… Allen Liebhabern dieser edlen Kunst insonderheit Ingeniern und Bawmeistern… in französische Sprach an Tag gegeben… in unsere Muttersprach übersetzet und mit Figuren erkläret [by Wieland]. *Frankfurt: N. Hoffman for Lucas Jennis, 1616*, [12], 183pp., ILLUSTRATION: woodcut diagrams etc., [VD17 39121329T]

Fortunatus, *monk of Padua.* Decas elementorum mysticae geometriae quibus praecipua divinitatis arcana explicantur. *Padua: (L. Pasquati for) P.P. Tozzi, 1617*, 71, [1]pp., ILLUSTRATION: engraved title, woodcut diagrams, eighteenth-century inscription of George Douglas on title

1412

Bramer, Benjamin (1588-1649). Bericht und Gebrauch eines proportional Limals: neben kurtzen Underict eines Parallel Instruments. *Marburg: Paul Egenolff, 1617*, 58pp., ILLUSTRATION: 2 woodcut plates (forming one image) at p. 10, woodcut portrait on verso of title, diagrams in text, [VD17 23:236796Q]

Manfredi, Eustachio (1674-1739). Mercurii ac solis congressus in astronomica specula bononiensis scientiarum instituti observatus die ix. Novembris 1723. *(Bologna: C. Pisarri, 1723)*, 37, [3]pp., last leaf with imprimatur and colophon, ILLUSTRATION: 2 engraved plates at end, [Riccardi ii, 83]

6 works in one volume, 4to (188 x 130mm.), BINDING: eighteenth-century English mottled calf, spine gilt, red edges

1412

The Archimedes is a reprint of the 1503 *Tetragonismus* which included *Measurement of the circle* and *Quadrature of the parabola*, plus *On the equilibrium of planes* and Book I of *On floating bodies*, which Tartaglia published unrevised from the 1503 edition and the manuscript (codex B) which belonged to Andreas Coner.

£4,000-5,000
€5,800-7,300

1413 Miscellaneous Tracts—Postel, Guillaume (1510-1581). De universitate liber, in quo astronomiae doctrineve coelestis compendium terrae aptatum... exponitur. *Paris: J. Guellart, 1552*, ff. 56, [4], Italic type, ILLUSTRATION: woodcut map and diagrams

Bottrigari, Ercole (1551-1612). Trattato della descrittione della sferea celeste in piano di C. Tolomeo... tradotto in parlare italiano... *Bologna: A. Benacci, 1572*, [116], 93, [3]pp., last leaf with register and device, [Riccardi i, 186-187, "raro e poco conosciuto"; Censimento 16 CNCE 32435]

Zeccadori, Francesco (1660-1703). Problemata arithmetica primo mathematicorum studiorum trimestri solute discursibus institutes iuxta logisticam P. Aegidii Grancisci de Gottignies. *Rome: N.A. Tinassi, 1677*, [8], 19pp., [Riccardi ii, 662]

Courcier, Pierre (1608-1692), *S.J.* Supplementum sphaerometriae sive triangularum & aliarum in sphaera figurarum quoad areas mensuratio. *Pont-à-Mousson: C. Cardinet, 1675*, 76pp., ILLUSTRATION: woodcut figures, [Sommervogel II, 1577]

Philippi, Henricus (1575-1636), *S.J.* Introductio chronologica... *Cologne: J. Kinch, 1621*, [20], 72pp., [Sommervogel VI, 381], *heavily browned*

Zimmermann, Johann Jakob (1644-1693). Iovis per umbrosa Dianae nemora venantis deliciae Würtembugicae, id est: insignis & infrequenter visa Jovis in luna occultatio, die ult. Martii elapsi mensis, sub coelo & instrumentis noricis observat... *Nuremberg: J.A. Endter, May 1686*, ff. [12], ILLUSTRATION: engraved plate, [for another work by Zimmermann see Macclesfield Science A-C, lot 261]

Commentarius de kalendario, quae eius proma origo... et quomodo sit restituendum... Scriptus in Neapolitana Nemetum [Newustadt] schola, recognitus auctusque, & in latimum ex germanico sermone translatus. *Heidelberg: J. Mylius, 1585*, 55, [3]pp., errata and woodcut device on verso of last leaf

7 works in one volume, 4to (198 x 135mm.), BINDING: eighteenth-century mottled calf, spine gilt in compartments, green morocco lettering-piece, red edges

FIRST EDITION of Postel's *De universitate* and a rare book (the 1563 edition of Martin Le Jeune, who was also involved in this edition, is more commonly found). Postel was one of the great figures of the sixteenth century, orientalist, kabbalist, mathematician and much else besides, the author of many books, endowed with "une intelligence miraculeuse et prodigieuse dont il fait prevue dans des fascinantes acrobaties intellectuelles..." (Rosanna Goris in *Dictionnaire des lettres françaises xvie siècle*).

Zimmermann, a Copernican and follower of Jacob Böhme, was a man of heterodox religious ideas. His interest in astronomy was closely allied to his chiliastic views (the later seventeenth century was rich in such) and had a highly valued career in a number of towns, including Hamburg, where he worked as a press-corrector, and at the very end of his life was on the point of emigration to Pennsylvania, where there was a strong pietist community. He died in Rotterdam where he and his family had gone to embark for the New World. The splendid poetic title of this account of an eclipse viewed using Nuremberg-made instruments conjures up "Jupiter hunting through the shady groves of Diana" (i.e. the Sun and the Moon).

The last work in the volume is anonymous but was composed at the Latin School in Neustadt, written originally in German, and in more than one edition ("aliquoties recusum"), which was translated into Latin. The printer tells us that having obtained a copy of this translation, he has caused it to be printed for international circulation. There is a copy in Munich, but the work is not common.

£15,000-20,000
€21,800-29,000
See illustrations on next page

SVPPLEMENTVM
SPHÆROMETRIÆ
SIVE
TRIANGVLARIVM
& aliarum in Sphæra figurarum
quoad areas menſuratio.

Per R. P. PETRVM COVRCIER Soc. IESV,
Sacræ Theologiæ Doctorem.

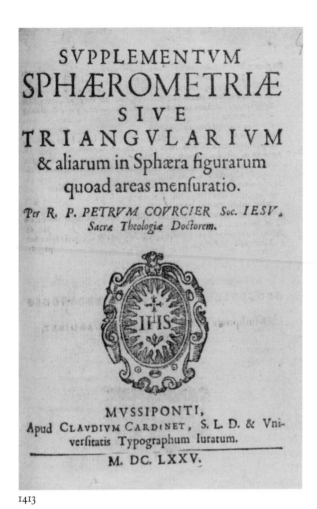

MVSSIPONTI,
Apud CLAVDIVM CARDINET, S. L. D. & Vni-
verſitatis Typographum Iuratum.

M. DC. LXXV.

1413

Occultatio Iovis in Luna,
Die ult. Martij ſt. Anno 1686. Noribergæ obſervata.

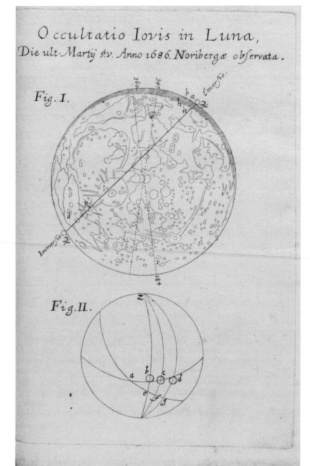

Fig. I.

Fig. II.

1413

FRANCISCI ZECCADORI
PROBLEMATA
ARITHMETICA

Primo Mathematicorum ſtudiorum trimeſtri ſoluta
diſcurſibus inſtitutis iuxta Logiſticam P. Ægidij
Franciſci de Gottignies Societatis IESV.

AD

Eminentiſſimum, & Reuerendiſſimum

PRINCIPEM

ALDERANVM
CYBO

S. R. E. CARDINALEM AMPLISSIMVM.

ROMAE, Typis Nicolai Angeli Tinaſſij. 1677.
SVPERIORVM PERMISSV.

1413

1414

1414 Miscellaneous Tracts—Proclus Diadochus (5th century AD). La sfera...
tradotta da Maestro Egnatio Danti... con le annotazioni, & con l'uso della sfera
del medesimo. *Florence: Giunta, 1573*, 2 parts, [8], 55; 33, [2]pp., ILLUSTRATION:
woodcut diagrams, [Riccardi i, 391], *1 slightly cropped at foot*

Montanari, Geminiano (1633-1687). La fiamma volante gran meteora veduta
sopra l'Italia la sera de 31 Marzo 1676. Speculazioni... *Bologna: Manolessi, 1676*,
95, [1]pp., [Riccardi ii, 172]

Salignac, Bernard, *of Bordeaux*. Arithmeticae libri duo, et algebrae totidem, cum
demonstrationibus. *Frankfurt: A. Wechel, 1580*, [8], 152 [i.e. 150, pp.57 & 98
omitted], [2]pp., 2 folding tables, [Adams S129]

3 works in one volume, 4to (185 x 125mm.), BINDING: eighteenth-century mottled
calf, spine gilt in compartments, morocco lettering-piece, red edges

£600-700
€900-1,050

1415 Miscellaneous Tracts—Rome. Accademia Fisico-Matematica. Cometicae observationes habitae ab academia physicomathematica romana anno 1680 & 1681. *Rome: Tinassi, 1681*, 35pp., ILLUSTRATION: engraved frontispiece and large folding plate, [rare; copy in BL], *title leaf cut down at lower edge, a few slight marginal worm-holes*

Baron, Charles. Theses mathematicae propugnabuntur a Carolo Baron... die vi Julii anni 1686 a tertia ad vesperam in regio Ludovico Magni Collegio Societatis Jesu. *(Paris: G. Martin, 1686)*, [8], 52pp., ILLUSTRATION: handsome scientifically symbolic engraved head-pieces and initials, [not in BNF, BL, Harvard, etc.], *lower margins cropped close*

Young, John. [drop-title] The improvement of the marsh [Romney-Marsh], and of the country near about it: being an account of some proposals for furnishing the marsh with fresh-water, with reasons for the same, reflections thereon, and objections answered. To which is subjoyned a farther proposal for the mending the sea-walls about Dimchurch. *[London, 1700?]*, 24pp.

Ceva, Giovanni (1647-1734). De re numaria quoad fieri potuit geometrice tractata. *Mantua: A. Pazzoni, 1711*, [4], 60pp., [Riccardi i, 342]

Sault, Richard (d. 1702). A new treatise of algebra, according to the late improvements. Apply'd to numeral questions and geometry. With a converging series for all manner of adfected equations. *[London: R. Baldwin, c. 1700]*, [4], 66, [2]pp., last leaf with advertisement on recto, [Taylor, *Tudor & Stuart* 289], *some leaves cropped at margins with damage to head-lines, page numbers, and a few letters, especially pp.37–38*

Snell, Charles (*c.* 1667-1733). The tradesman's director; or, a short and easy method of keeping his books of accompts. *London: R. Baldwin, 1697*, ff. [12], [Wing S4391A, BL only]

6 works in one volume, 4to (206 x 150mm.), BINDING: eighteenth-century half calf, gilt spine, red morocco lettering-piece, red edges

Richard Sault ran a mathematical school in London from 1693, and was involved with the publisher John Dunton. He translated Malebranche, and this work was first published as part of Leybourn's *Pleasure with profit* (1694) (see *ODNB*). Charles Snell was a writing-master in London.

£6,000-10,000
€8,700-14,500

1415

1415

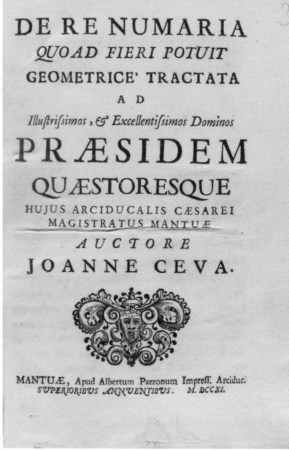

1415

1416 Miscellaneous Tracts—Vaulezard, Jean Louis de. Traitté... du quadrant analematique, par lequel avec l'ayde de la lumiere du soleil, on trouve en un instant sans aiguile aimantée la ligne meridienne. La description des horloges solaires, & la pluspart des phoenomenes appartenant au soleil. Plus le moyen de construire un horloge solaire pour le moyen de trois ombres du soileil en un mesme jour... *Paris: J. Le Brun, 1644*, [4], 50; 9 (last page misnumbered 51) pp., ILLUSTRATION: engraved plates pasted to the edges of pp. 18, 26, 48 and 50, *title-leaf folded at top edge and slightly soiled, a few leaves shaved*

Cospi, Antonio Maria. L'interpretation des chiffres ou reigle pour bien entendre & expliquer facilement toutes sortes de chiffres simples... Augmentée & accommodée... à l'usage des langues francoise & espagnolle, par F.I. N[iceron] P.M. *Paris: A. Courbé, 1641*, [6], 90pp.

[Eisler, Tobias (1683-1753)] Das auss neue wohl zubereitete Tinten-Fass: oder Anweisung wie man gute schwarze, buntfärbige auch andere curiöse Tinten auf mancherlei Weise zubereiten, auch wie man mit Gold, Silber und andern Metallen aus des Feder auf Pappier, Pergament und andere Dinge schreiben solle... *Helmstadt: zu finden in Buchladen, 1732*, 52pp.

Academia Scientiarum Imperialis Petropolitana. Catalogue des livres imprimés aux dépens de l'Academie... qui se vendent en sa librairie. *St Petersburg: Academy of Sciences, 1748*, ff. [7], listing books, engravings, maps and books "sous presse"

[Vittori, Mariano (d. 1572), *bishop of Rieti*] Chaldeae, seu aethiopicae linguae institutiones. Opus utile, ac eruditum [revised by A. Veneri]. *Rome: Sacra Congregatio de Propaganda Fide, 1630*, [6], 86pp.

5 works in one volume, 12mo (160 x 90mm.), BINDING: eighteenth-century half calf, spine gilt in compartments, red morocco lettering-piece, red edges

Vaulezard was a member of the circle of Marin Mersenne and a mathematician who published in 1650 *Les cinq livres des zététitiques* of Viète.

The work by Cospi, secretary to the Grand Duke of Tuscany and a jurist by training, was published in Italian in 1639. It is an uncommon book, although there are copies at the Mazarin library and the BNF. This French version is from the hands of the well-known Minim priest and writer on perspective, Jean François Nicéron. This French translation is also rare.

The anonymous pamphlet on ink is by the Pietist schoolmaster Tobias Eisler, who edited a number of religious works.

The Ethiopic grammar is a revision of the work originally published in 1552 by Vittori, which, as is remarked in the preface, had long been out of print. The original edition is rare (copy at Christ Church, Oxford) and this 1630 edition has long been a collector's item (Thomas Grenville, for example, had two copies).

£10,000-15,000
€14,500-21,800

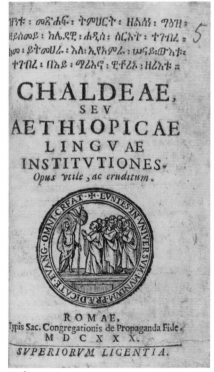

1416

1417

1417 Miscellaneous Tracts—Zonca, Vittorio (b. *c.* 1580). Novo teatro di machine et edificii per varie et sicure operationi... opera necessaria ad architectti, et a quelli chi di tale studio si dilettano. *Padua: Francesco Bertelli, 1656*, [6 (including title-page)], 8, 17-115, [1 (blank)] pp., ILLUSTRATION: engraved title-page, woodcut initials, head- and tailpieces, 3 engraved plates (one double-sided) and full-page engraved illustrations by Pietro Bertelli, replacement plate pasted to p.56, *lacking quire B, a few leaves shaved at foot*

Poleni, Giovanni (1683-1761). De castellis per quae derivantur fluviorum aquae habentibus latera convergentia liber. *Padua: Giuseppe Comino, 1718*, FIRST EDITION, [6], 65, [3]pp., ILLUSTRATION: woodcut device on title-page, woodcut initials and headpieces, 1 engraved plate, *without final blank*

2 works in one volume, folio (274 x 182mm.), BINDING: eighteenth-century mottled calf, spine gilt in compartments, red morocco lettering-piece, red edges

Zonca's compendium of machines (including a printing press, various grinding devices and a perpetual screw), powered by water, animals or men, was originally published in Padua in 1607. According to Riccardi, this edition has the best impressions of the plates.

Poleni wrote on a vast range of subjects, from architecture to astronomy. He held the chair of astronomy and then of physics at the University of Padua. This work is on hydraulics and hydrodynamics. He formerly edited a great edition of Vitruvius.

References: Riccardi ii, 669 & 292

£1,000-1,500
€1,450-2,200

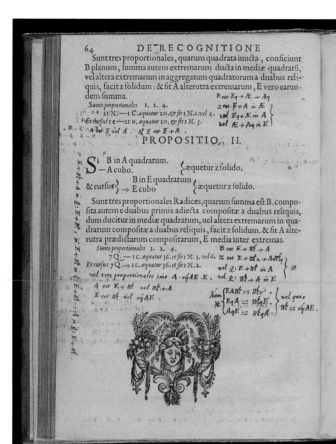

Sunt tres proportionales, quarum quadrata iuncta, conficiunt B planum, summa autem extremarum ducta in mediæ quadratū, vel altera extremarum in aggregatum quadratorum a duabus reliquis, facit z solidum: & fit A alterutra extremarum, E vero earundem summa.

$$B \text{ est } Eq + Æ + Aq$$
$$z \text{ est } E + A \text{ in } Æ$$
$$\text{vel } Eq + Æ \text{ in } A$$
$$\text{vel } Æ + Aq \text{ in } E$$

Sunto proportionales 1. 2. 4.

21 N. — 1 C. æquatur 20. & fit 1 N. 1. vel 4.
Et rursus 1 C. — 21 N. æquatur 20. & fit 1 N. 5.

R. ... A est E vel A. ... E est E + A.

PROPOSITIO II.

Si   B in A quadratum. — A cubo.   æquetur z solido.

& rursus   B in E quadratum + E cubo   æquetur z solido.

Sunt tres proportionales Radices, quarum summa est B, composita autem e duabus primis adiecta compositæ a duabus reliquis, dum ducitur in mediæ quadratum, vel altera extremarum in quadratum compositæ a duabus reliquis, facit z solidum. & fit A alterutra prædictarum compositarum, E media inter extremas.

Sunto proportionales 1. 2. 4.

7 Q. — 1 C. æquatur 36. et fit 1 N. 3. vel 6.
Et rursus 7 Q. — 1 C. æquatur 36. et fit 1 N. 2.

vel tres proportionales sint A . √AE . E .

$$B \text{ est } E + Æ + A$$
$$z \text{ est } E + Æ + A \text{ in } E$$
$$\text{vel } Q: E + Æ \text{ in } A$$
$$\text{vel } Q: Æ + A \text{ in } E$$

A est E + Æ vel Æ + A.
E est Æ vel √AE.

Nam $\begin{cases} EAÆ = ÆE \\ EqA = ÆqE \\ AqE = ÆqA \end{cases}$ vel quia   Æ = √qAE.

FRANCISCI
VIETAE FONTENAEENSIS
DE ÆQVATIONVM EMENDATIONE
TRACTATVS SECVNDVS.

De Solennibus quinque modis præparandarum Æquationum, aduersus earum in numeris
ΔΥΣΜΗΧΑΝΙΑΝ.

Ac Primum.

De Expurgatione per Vncias, quæ Remedium est aduersus Πολυπαθειαν.

CAPVT I.

AGNITA æquationum constitutione, Analysta ad præparandum eas quæ suam alioquin mechanicè respuant, aut demum ægrè subeunt, tuto se confert, & sua præparatione efficit ευμηχεσιας. & præparandi quidem generalis doctrina est, vt noua zetesis instituatur, vel Plasmatis, aut Syncriseos vestigia repetantur, ac denique nullus non tentetur transmutandi modus: sed non desunt Analystæ singula-

I

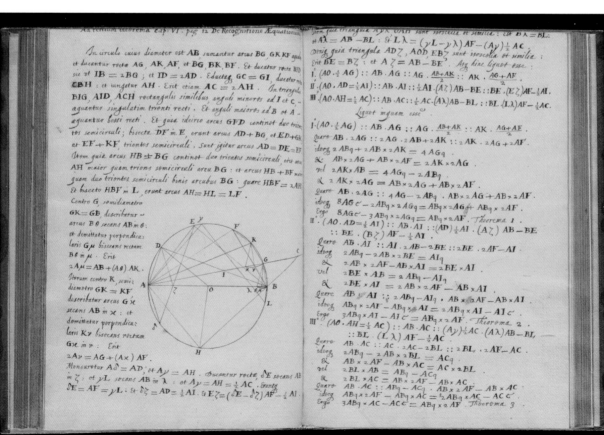

1418 Miscellaneous Tracts—Viète, François (1540-1603). De aequationum recognitione et emendatione tractatus duo [edited with a preface by Alexander Anderson]. *Paris: Jean Laquehay, 1615*, [12], 135pp., title printed in red and black, manuscript annotations, *some annotations shaved*

Stancari, Vittorio Francesco (1678-1709). Schedae mathematicae... Eiusdem observationes astronomicae (Vita authoris... [by E. Manfredi]). *Bologna: G.P. Barbiroli, 1713*, [20], 102pp., ILLUSTRATION: 4 numbered engraved folding plates, [Riccardi ii, 475-476]

2 works in one volume, 4to (205 x 145mm.), BINDING: eighteenth-century mottled calf, spine gilt in compartments, red morocco lettering-piece, red edges

THIS IMPORTANT COPY OF VIÈTE IS COPIOUSLY ANNOTATED THROUGHOUT BY WILLIAM OUGHTRED, THE GREAT ENGLISH MATHEMATICIAN. The annotations are to be found in the text and margins (with an extra slip pasted in on p.63) and more particularly at the end with four pages (on four leaves, all slightly shaved at head) of manuscript material, the first of which is a discussion "ad tertium theorema cap. VI p. 12 De recognitione aequationum" (2 pages with a diagram) and "De expurgatione per uncias" (2 pages).

Oughtred was born and educated at Eton before going to King's College, Cambridge in 1592, where he seems to have begun his (independent) study of mathematics. Taking orders in 1603, he was preferred to the living of Albury in Surrey in 1610 which he held until his death in 1660. He was introduced to the great collector and maecenas Thomas Howard, Earl of Arundel (1586-1646), the patron of Hollar and Harvey, and he knew Henry King, poet and bishop of Chichester, one of whose sons studied with him.

His interest in mathematics is attested by a letter from the "ever memorable" John Hales of Eton, written in 7 October 1616: "amongst all the solutions which you sent me, none there was which gave me not full and sufficient satisfaction... onely one excepted... concerning the projecture of an oblique circle...", and his correspondence with Robinson, Derand, Sir Charles Cavendish, John Wallis and others from the 1630s is all of a mathematical nature, to be found in Rigaud, *Correspondence* (the originals are now in Cambridge).

Oughtred's works were largely published in the 1630s, although some were written earlier, and his *Arithmeticae in numeris et speciebus institutio: quae totius mathematicae quasi clavis est*, published in 1631 (STC 18898), circulated widely and was much praised. In the notes to this volume he refers to this work on page 79.

For Anderson (1581/2-after 1621) and his connection with Viète, see Macclesfield Science A-C, lot 165. In this work Anderson demonstrated Viète's transformation and reduction of algebraic equations, and proved the dependence of the solution of cubic equations on the trisection of angle.

The rare work by Stancari, published posthumously with a preface and life of the author by Eustachio Manfredi, is the first book in Italy to include infinitesimal calculus (the Bolognese school were great admirers of Leibnitz, who is here described as the inventor of calculus). According to the *Vita* (a useful summary of Italian mathematical knowledge at the time), it was in 1701 that Stancari began to study calculus with Gabriele Manfredi (1671-1751), also from Bologna, who had introduced it first to Italy, later working also with Giuseppe Verzaglia from Cesena.

£20,000-25,000
€29,000-36,200

1419 Miscellaneous Tracts—Waller, William. [Begin:] Honour'd Sirs, It is not the Vanity of appearing in print, that I give you this Second Trouble, but to give you the present State of the Mines [in Cardiganshire]. *[London, 1704]*, 22pp. (printed on versos only from p.3), ILLUSTRATION: large folding map of Cardiganshire and 10 smaller folding plates, *a few leaves shaved at foot*

Cole, Benjamin (1695-1755). The description and use of a new quadrant, for finding the latitude at sea: invented and made, by Benjamin Cole... To which are added... instructions for the use of that... instrument, invented by John Hadley... *London, 1748*, 32pp., ILLUSTRATION: folding engraved plate, [*English Maritime Books* 377; Taylor, *Hanoverian*, pp.114 & 123]

Evans, Robert. An essay on the new invented circular motions, now in great use in jack-work and clock-work. Demonstrated, by a new invented piece of jack-work, made by Robert Evans; who has His Majesties Letters Patent for the sole making of the same. *London: for the author, 1717*, 24pp., [ESTC T55773]

Desaguliers, John Theophilus (1683-1744). Physico-mechanical lectures... *London: for the author, to be sold by the author... & R. Bridger & W. Vream, 1717*, [4], 80pp.

Wells, Edward (1667-1727). [The young gentleman's course of mathematicks] The young gentleman's mechanicks... *London: J. Knapton, 1713*, 78pp. (mechanicks only), ILLUSTRATION: 9 folding engraved plates

Machine nouvelle pour la conduite des eaux, pour les bâtimens, pour la navigation, & pour la pluspart des autres arts. *Paris: S. Mabre-Cramoisy, [1660?]*, 14, [2]pp., last page with description of plate, ILLUSTRATION: single engraved plate, [copies in BL and BNF]

[Parent, Antoine] [Recherches de mathématique et de physique] Supplément a plusieurs problêmes (sur le mouvement d'un vaisseau; sur a résistances des figures; sur le vol des oiseaux; sur la perspective générale publiés en differentes occasions...). *(Paris: J. Quillau, 1715)*, 52, [2]pp., ILLUSTRATION: single engraved plate with 10 figures (loosely inserted), *plate shaved*

7 works in one volume, 8vo & 12mo (180 x 105mm.), BINDING: eighteenth-century half calf, spine gilt in compartments, red morocco lettering-piece, red edges

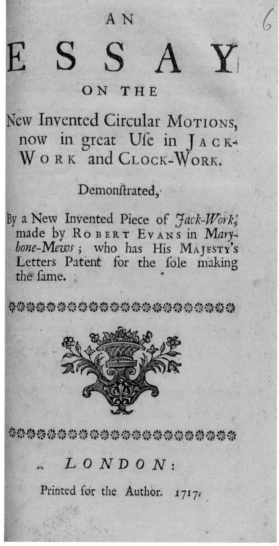

1419

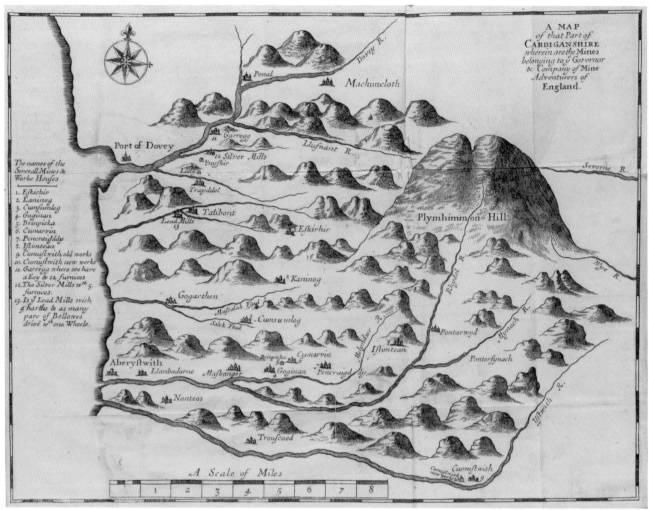

The names of the
Severall Mines &
Worke Houses
1. Eskirhir
2. Kaninog
3. Cumsumlog
4. Goginan
5. Brinpieka
6. Cumarvin
7. Pencraigddu
8. Istumtean
9. Cumystwith old works
10. Cumystwith new works
11. Garrego where we have
a Key & 22. furnaces
12. The Silver Mills with 5.
furnaces.
13. Is y Lead Mills with
4 harths & as many
pare of Bellowes
drive wth one Wheele.

A MAP
of that Part of
CARDIGANSHIRE
wherein are the Mines
belonging to y Governor
& Company of Mine
Adventurers of
England.

Penal
Machuneloth
Dovey R.
Port of Dovey
Garrego
Llusnant R.
Silver Mills
Ynysfair
Lada
Trayddol
Severne R.
Tatibont
Lead Mills
Eskirhir
Plymhimmon Hill
Kaninog
Rhydol R.
Gogarthen
Massalak Elud
Wye R.
Salek Flud
Cumsumlog
Melindwr R.
Brinpicka
Cumarvin
Istumtean
Pontarwyd
Mynach R.
Aberystwith
Goginan
Pencraigddy
Ponterfynach
Llanbadarne
Massbanger
Nanteos
Ystwith R.
Trouscoed
Cumystwith
new works
Cumystwith

A Scale of Miles

| 1 | 2 | 3 | 4 | 5 | 6 | 7 | 8 |

1419

William Waller's account of the mines in Cardiganshire is the first work of its kind. In 1698 he had issued *An essay on the value of the mines, late of Sir Carbery Price, writ for the satisfaction of all the partners* (Wing W552), his intention being purely commercial: to set forth the advantages of these mines in order to sell the shares profitably. In this pamphlet he referred to a paper he had written in 1693 showing that "with sufficient stock he would be able in a few years, with six hundred men, to bring in a dear profit from one of the said veins of seventy thousand five hundred pounds per annum".

In this work, whose text is remarkably brief and is essentially limited to a description of the plates, Waller provides a map of that part of Cardiganshire containing the mines belonging to the governor and company of mine adventurers of England, and with it a plan of Bwlch yr Escair, Bwlch Caninog, Cwmsymlog, Goginan, Brinpica, Cwnarvin, Pencraggddu, Ystum tuen, Cwmystwyth and the new lead mines at Cwmystwyth.

There is a modern facsimile of this rare pamphlet, which appears in two issues, one as described here with no title-page, edited by David Bick.

£5,000-7,000
€7,300-10,200

1420 Mizauld, Antoine (1510-1578). Ephemerides aeris perpetuae: seu popularis & rustica tempestatum astrologia, ubique terrarum & vera, & certa. *Paris: Jacob Kerver, 1554*

16mo (115 x 73mm.), ff. 171, 174-175, [1 (blank)], ILLUSTRATION: woodcut initials and headpieces, BINDING: near-contemporary vellum, *lacking leaves 172-173 (containing a list of Mizauld's works)*

Originally published in 1546, this is the second edition. Kerver also published a French edition in the same year. Mizauld studied medicine in Paris but is best known as an astrologer and a confidant of Marguerite de Valois.

References: Houzeau & Lancaster 4833

£600-800
€900-1,200

1421 Moivre, Abraham de (1667-1754). Animadversiones in D. Georgii Cheynaei tractatum de fluxionum methodo inversa. *London: Edward Midwinter for Daniel Midwinter and Thomas Leigh, 1704*

8vo (192 x 113mm.), [14], 129pp., ILLUSTRATION: woodcut diagrams, BINDING: eighteenth-century speckled calf, panelled and blind-tooled, spine gilt in compartments, *extremities rubbed*

De Moivre first published on the calculus in *Philosophical Transactions* 19 (1695) pp.52-56, "Specimina quaedam illustra doctrinae fluxionum...", a short piece clearly drawing on Newton's *Principia* dealing with the application of the method of fluxions to geometrical problems. Cheyne's work *Fluxionum methodus inversa* (1703), according to David Gregory, prompted Newton to publish in 1704 his *De quadratura* as part of *Opticks*. (For a copy of *De quadratura* by itself bound with other items on the calculus, see Macclesfield Science D-H, lot 858.)

£1,000-1,500
€1,450-2,200

1422 Moivre, Abraham de. The doctrine of chances: or, a method of calculating the probabilities of events in play. The second edition... more correct than the first. *London: H. Woodfall for the author, 1738*

4to (280 x 220mm.), [4], xiv, [2 (blank)], 258pp., large paper copy, ILLUSTRATION: mezzotint portrait engraved by Faber after Highmore's painting, engraved headpieces and initials, BINDING: contemporary crimson morocco, gilt border on covers, spine gilt in compartments, green morocco lettering-piece, gilt edges, *without most of final leaf (see footnote)*

De Moivre's work, already adumbrated in the *Philosophical Transactions* in 1711 with his *De mensura sortis*, was first published in 1718. This is the second and much improved edition (there was a third in 1756). His book on annuities was dedicated to the Earl of Macclesfield, whose personal interest in annuities seems to have been quite substantial, and part of the *Annuities upon lives* is subsumed into this second edition of his major work.

Mathematically, this is de Moivre's most important work. In it he "developed a series of algebraic and analytic tools for the theory of probability, like a 'new algebra' for the solution of the problem of coincidences which foreshadowed Boolean algebra, the method of generating functions, or the theory of recurrent series for the solution of differential equations. In the *Doctrine* de Moivre offered an introduction which contains the main concepts such as probability, conditional probability, expectation, dependent and independent events, the multiplication rule, and the binomial distribution" (Ivo Schneider in *ODNB*).

Loosely inserted at the end are two leaves of contemporary manuscript with a long list of errata, and a small printed slip of errata, which is probably cut down from the final leaf.

£800-1,000
€1,200-1,450

1422

1424

1423 Moivre, Abraham de. The doctrine of chances: or, a method of calculating the probabilities of events in play. The third edition. *London: A. Millar, 1756*

4to (284 x 224mm.), [4], xi, [1], 348pp., ILLUSTRATION: engraved medallion portrait of the author on title-page, woodcut and engraved initials, head- and tailpieces, BINDING: contemporary calf, spine gilt in compartments, *binding rubbed, joints weak*

References: Kress 5546; cf. Norman 1529 (1st edition)

£500-700
€750-1,050

1424 Moivre, Abraham de. Miscellanea analytica de seriebus et quadraturis, [etc.] (Supplementum - Approximatio ad summam terminorum binomii… in seriem expansi. Autore A.D.M.R.S.S.). *London: J. Tonson & J. Watts, 1730*

2 parts in one volume, 4to (290 x 225mm.), [8], 250, 22, [2]; 7pp., ILLUSTRATION: mezzotint portrait of the author by Faber after Highmore, BINDING: contemporary English black morocco, fine gilt floral border on covers, gilt spine, *some slight browning*

References: Norman 1531

£4,000-5,000
€5,800-7,300

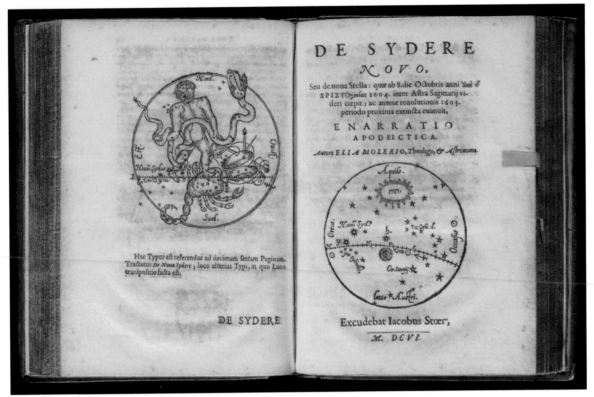

1425

1425 Molerius, Elias. Astronomicus... hoc est, accurate descriptio, ocularis demonstratio, & elegantissimis typis illustratio, quae ex delineatione ecleipsium [solis] & [lunae] annorum 1605 & 1607... declaratur... Cui adiunguntur... Enarratio de sydere novo annorum 1604 & 1605. *[Geneva]: J. Stoer, 1607*, 2 parts, [16], 199, [1]; 24pp., ILLUSTRATION: woodcut plates inserted at pp. 26, 68, 93 and 195, woodcut diagrams, *a few plates cropped*

Ibid. Εκλειψσεων magnorum luminarium solis, et lunae cum sacris scripturae sacrae locis. Συνκρισις... *[Geneva]: J. Stoer, 1607*, XLIII pp.

Maestlin, Michael (1550-1631), *praeses*. Disputatio de multivariis motuum planetarum in coelo apparentibus irregularitibus, seu regularibus inaequalitatibus, earumque causis astronomicis. Quam... defendere conabitur die 21 & 22 Februarii... M. Samuel Hafenreffer. *Tübingen: ex officina Gruppenbachiana, 1606*, [4], 92pp.

3 works in one volume, 4to (195 x 140mm.), BINDING: seventeenth-century English calf, later morocco lettering-piece, red edges, *extremities slightly rubbed, head of spine chipped*

Elias Molerius was a pupil at the Lausanne academy of Gervasius Curianus (according to his prefatory epistle) and many of his observations seem to have been made at Lausanne. The preface is signed "Paterniaci", i.e. Payerne in the canton of Vaud.

Samuel Hafenreffer (1587-1660), a physician and writer of a number of medical works, belonged to the family of the Tübingen theologian Matthias Hafenreffer (1561-1619), whose pupils included Johann Valentin Andreae and Johann Kepler, who speaks warmly of Hafenreffer's mathematical and scientific knowledge, and whom Kepler terms "praeceptor colendissimus". Hafenreffer was very much a "spiritual father" to Kepler.

£1,500-2,000
€2,200-2,900

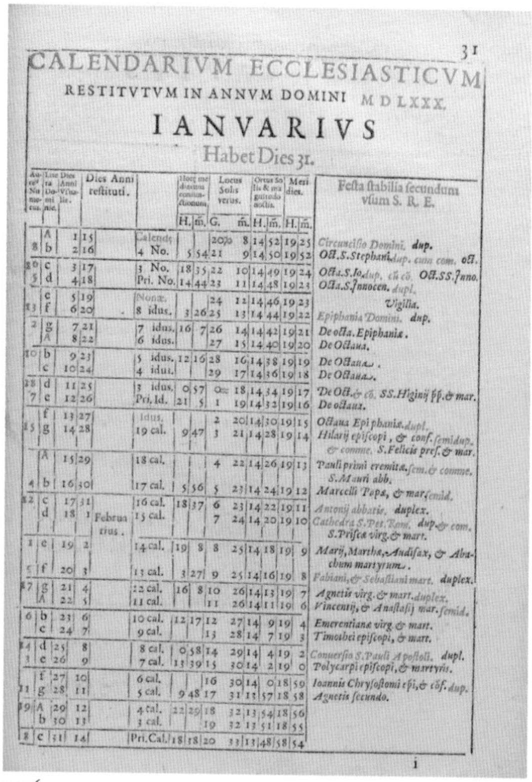

CALENDARIVM ECCLESIASTICVM 31
RESTITVTVM IN ANNVM DOMINI M D LXXX.
IANVARIVS
Habet Dies 31.

1426

DIOPTRICA NOVA.
A
TREATISE
OF
DIOPTRICKS,
In Two PARTS.
Wherein the
Various Effects and Appearances
OF
Spherick Glasses,
BOTH
Convex and Concave, Single and Combined,
IN
TELESCOPES and MICROSCOPES,
Together with
Their Usefulness in many Concerns of Humane Life,
ARE EXPLAINED.
By William Molyneux of Dublin Esq;
Fellow of the ROYAL SOCIETY.
Ex Visibilibus Invisibilia.
London: Printed for Benj. Tooke, MDCXCII.

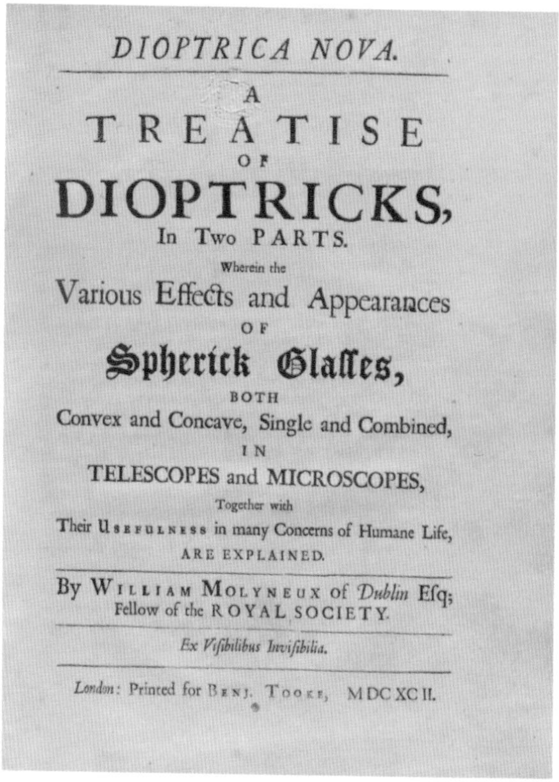

1427

1426 Moleti, Giuseppe (1531-1588). Tabulae gregorianae motuum octavae spherae ac luminarium ad usum calendarij ecclesiastici, & ad urbis Romae meridianum supputatae... Adiecti sunt libri duo De corrigendo calendario, & de usu computi ecclesiastici. *Venice: Pietro Deuchino, 1580*

4to (253 x 186mm.), ff. [8], 50; 88; 37, [1], tables at end printed in red and black, ILLUSTRATION: woodcut initials and headpieces, woodcut diagrams, BINDING: contemporary calf, spine gilt in compartments, morocco lettering-piece, blue speckled edges, *binding slightly rubbed*

FIRST EDITION. Moleti was professor of mathematics at the University of Padua. This work was commissioned by Gregory XIII to assist his reform of the calendar.

References: Censimento 16 CNCE 30732; Houzeau & Lancaster 12738

£600-800
€900-1,200

1427 Molyneux, William (1656-1698). Dioptrica nova. A treatise of dioptricks, in two parts. Wherein the various effects and appearances of spherick glasses, both convex and concave, single and combined, in telescopes and microscopes... are explained. *London: for Benjamin Tooke, 1692*

4to (245 x 189mm.), [16 (including licence leaf)], 301, [3 (including advertisement leaf)] pp., ILLUSTRATION: 43 folding engraved plates of diagrams, BINDING: eighteenth-century calf, *some plates browned, occasional light staining*

FIRST EDITION. THE FIRST TREATISE ON OPTICS PUBLISHED IN ENGLISH. This work includes at the end Halley's famous theorem for finding the foci of lenses.

References: Wing M2405; Taylor, *Tudor & Stuart* 489; British Optical Association i, 145

£3,000-4,000
€4,350-5,800

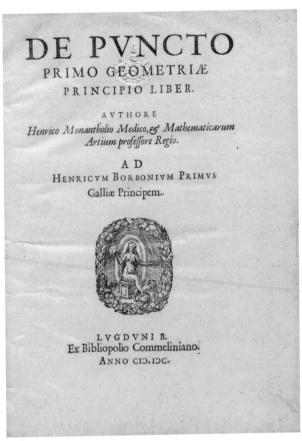

1428

1428 Monantheuil, Henri de (?1536-1606). De puncto primo geometriae principio liber. *Leiden: Commelin, 1600*

4to (230 x 167mm.), [8], 35, [1 (blank)] pp., ILLUSTRATION: woodcut device on title-page, woodcut initials and headpieces, woodcut initials, BINDING: later vellum-backed blue boards

FIRST EDITION. Monantheuil was a student of Ramus in Paris and became professor of mathematics at the Collège royale in 1574. He was a supporter of Henry IV, to whom this treatise is dedicated.

£300-400
€450-600

1429 Monforte, Antonio (1644-1717). De stellarum motibus. Opus posthumum (Antonii Monfortii vita a Iacobo Salerno... recollecta). *Florence: A.M. Albizini, 1720*

4to (215 x 160mm.), [28], 228, [2 (blank)] pp., ILLUSTRATION: engraved portrait of the author, woodcut diagrams, BINDING: contemporary Italian vellum

Originally from Basilicata, Monforte went in the suite of the Venetian ambassador to Constantinople, where apparently (according to Poggendorff) he became the "maestro di cappella" of the Sultan. He is, however, not mentioned in Grove.

At the end of this copy are bound a substantial number of leaves from a book of astronomical tables (17th century).

References: Riccardi ii, 167

£500-700
€750-1,050

1430 [Monginot, François de] A new mystery in physick discovered, by curing of fevers & agues by quinquina or Jesuites powder. Translated from the French, by Dr. Belon, with additions. *London: for Will. Crook, 1681*

12mo (137 x 77mm.), [60], 99, [1 (blank)] pp., BINDING: contemporary sheep, *lacking F3-6 (last 4 leaves, containing advertisements), slightly water-damaged, binding rubbed*

References: Wing M2416; Wellcome IV, p.154

£100-150
€150-250

1431 Monier, Pierre (1641-1703). Histoire des arts qui ont raport au dessein, divisée en trois livres où il est traité de son origine, de son progres, de sa chute, & de son rétablissement... *Paris: Pierre Giffart, 1698*

12mo (163 x 92mm.), [52], 349, [17]pp., ILLUSTRATION: engraved frontispiece, engraved and woodcut initials, head- and tailpieces, BINDING: contemporary calf, spine gilt in compartments, *binding rubbed*

FIRST EDITION. Monier was *peintre du roi* and a professor at the Académie royale de peinture et sculture. For the English translation published the following year, see lot 1432.

£100-150
€150-250

1432 Monier, Pierre. The history of painting, sculpture, architecture, graving; and of those who have excell'd in them: in three books. Containing their rise, progress, decay, and revival; with an account of all the most considerable productions of the best artists in all ages: and how to distinguish the true and regular performances, from those that are otherwise. *London: for T. Bennet, D. Midwinter, T. Leigh and R. Knaplock, 1699*

8vo (187 x 115mm.), [30], 192, [16]pp., ILLUSTRATION: engraved frontispiece, BINDING: contemporary calf, spine gilt in compartments, *binding rubbed, spine worn, joints cracking*

References: Wing M2419

£200-300
€300-450

1433 Monier de Clairecombe, Jean. A new and universal practice of mercantile arithmetick... in two parts. *London: Tho. Ilive for John Nicholson, John Sprint and Ralph Smith, 1707*

8vo (195 x 122mm.), [12], 206, 152, 157, [1], 161-191, [5]pp., BINDING: contemporary speckled calf, spine gilt in compartments, *some foxing, binding rubbed (particularly spine), joints cracking*

£100-150
€150-250

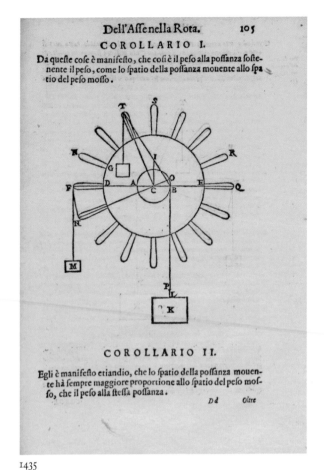

1434   1435

1434 Monte, Guidobaldo del (1545-1607). Planisphaeriorum universalium theorica.
Pesaro: Girolamo Concordia, 1579

FIRST EDITION, folio (263 x 180mm.), [8], 128, [2]pp., last leaf with errata and
imprint on recto, ILLUSTRATION: woodcut diagrams in text, some full-page,
BINDING: sixteenth-century English calf, blind-stamped fillets on covers, flat spine

References: Riccardi ii, 179; Censimento 16 CNCE 16712

Provenance: William Jones, signature. Earlier note of price 6s.2d.

£3,000-4,000
€4,350-5,800

1435 Monte, Guidobaldo del. Le mechaniche... tradotte in volgare dal Sig. Filippo
Pigafetta: nelle quali si contiene la vera dottrina di tutti gli istrumenti principali da
mover pesi grandissimi con picciola forza. *Venice: Francesco de Franceschi, 1581*

4to (218 x 159mm.), ff. [8], 127, [1], ILLUSTRATION: woodcut vignette on title,
woodcut illustrations and diagrams in text, woodcut head-pieces and initials,
BINDING: eighteenth-century panelled calf gilt, *tear in text of a4 without loss, some
light browning in first few leaves, small wormhole in margin of last few leaves, binding
rubbed*

"Guidobaldo was Galileo's patron and friend for twenty years and was possibly the
greatest single influence on the mechanics of Galileo" (*DSB*).

References: Riccardi ii, 178; Censimento 16 CNCE 16714

£600-800
€900-1,200

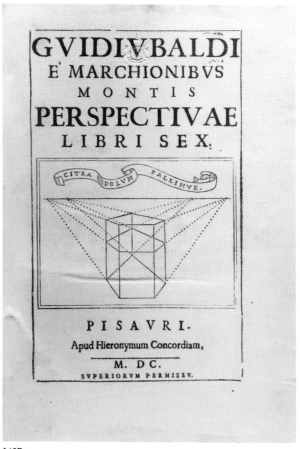

1436

1437

1436 Monte, Guidobaldo del. In duos Archimedis aequeponderantium libros paraphrasis scholiis illustrata. *Pesaro: Girolamo Concordia, 1588 (1587),* [4], 202, [2]pp., each page within ruled borders, ILLUSTRATION: woodcut vignette on title, woodcut diagrams in text, woodcut initials

Scaletti, Carlo Cesare. Scuola mecanico-speculativo-pratica in cui si esamina la proporzione, che hà la potenza alla resistenza del corpo grave... opera utile all'uso civile, e militare necessaria ad ogni matematico, ingegniero, architetto, machinista et bombardiere. *Bologna: Costantino Pisarri, 1711,* [14], 188pp., ILLUSTRATION: engraved frontispiece, 12 engraved plates, *tear in text of M4 without loss, a few plates trimmed at fore-edge*

FIRST EDITIONS, 2 works in one volume, folio (292 x 195mm.), BINDING: eighteenth-century mottled calf

References: Riccardi ii, 179 & 427

£2,000-3,000
€2,900-4,350

1437 Monte, Guidobaldo del. Perspectivae libri sex. *Pesaro: Girolamo Concordia, 1600*

folio (312 x 219mm.), [4], 310, [2]pp., ILLUSTRATION: woodcut illustration on title, woodcut diagrams in text, woodcut initials, BINDING: eighteenth-century calf gilt, spine gilt in compartments, *occasional light staining in margins*

FIRST EDITION of this landmark in the history of the science of perspective, which provided a definitive analysis of the mathematics of perspectival projection. For a detailed analysis of the book see Martin Kemp, *The science of art* (1990), p.89 ff.

References: Riccardi ii, 179; Vagnetti EIIb41

£1,500-2,000
€2,200-2,900

1438

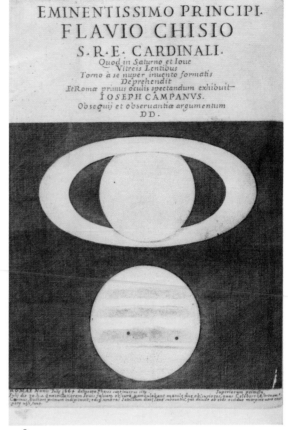

1438

1438 Monte, Guidobaldo del. Problematum astronomicorum libri septem. *Venice: Bernardo Giunta, Giovanni Battista Ciotti, 1609*, ff. [6], 128, ILLUSTRATION: woodcut diagrams, [Riccardi ii, 180]

Campani, Giuseppe (1635-1715). Lettera al D. Cassini intorno all'ombre delle stelle medicee nel volto di Giove, ed altri nuovi fenomeni celesti scoperti co' suoi occhiali. *Rome: Fabio di Falco, 1665*, 11pp., printed on thick paper, ILLUSTRATION: 2 engraved plates of the satellites of Jupiter and one folding plate of telescope, [Riccardi i, 219], RARE

Fernel, Jean (1497-1558). Cosmotheoria, libros duos complexa. *Paris: Simon de Colines, 1528*, ff. [6], 46, ILLUSTRATION: large woodcuts, small woodcut diagrams, [Renouard, *Colines*, p. 116], *outer edges of a few leaves cropped, very slightly affecting edges of some large circular woodcuts*

Cavina, Pietro Maria, *of Faenza.* [drop-title] Viro illustrissimo Annibali Carolo Ferniano... domino suo summo colendo... Acta thesium bononiensium. *(Faenza: ex typographia Zarafallii (Zarafagli), 1677)*, 12pp., ILLUSTRATION: woodcut diagrams, [Riccardi i, 333]

Beck, Matthias Friedrich, *editor.* Al-Taqwim sanat 209. Ephemerides Persarum... e libello arabice, persice atque turcice msto. praeda militis germani ex Hungaria, nunc... V commentariorum libris illustratae. *Augsburg: Jakob Koppmayer for L. Kroniger & heirs of T. Goebel, 1695-1696*, 2 parts, ff. [5], [24 (with 12 double-page engraved tables etc.)], [2], 12, [2]; 80pp., ILLUSTRATION: engraved plate in commentary at p. 2, *3 leaves of printed table in section numbered 1-12 cropped at bottom*

5 works in one volume, folio (300 x 190mm.), BINDING: eighteenth-century mottled calf, spine gilt, red morocco lettering-piece, red edges, *a few leaves shaved in outer margin*

The letter by Campani discusses observations made by him with a telescope of his own devising, of the so-called Medicean planets. The text is in Italian, but there are quotations in Latin, a reference to the Jesuit Honorat Fabri's *Dialogi* published in Lyon (on p. 3, highlighted in contemporary manuscript) and a letter to Claude Basset also in Latin. The bulk of the text is concerned with Saturn, and considerable mention is made of Huygens. The two handsome plates are: 1. a plate of the planet Jupiter with its ring, observed at Rome in July 1664, dedicated to Cardinal Flavio Chigi, and 2. a splendid large folding plate of Campani's telescope, dedicated to Colbert.

The text to the unusual item by Cavina is in both Latin and Italian and consists of letters to various savants, one to Magliabechi, one to Enea Lupari, and one to Antonio Vincenzo Maioli of Faenza, in which is discussed a 'flamma volans' observed at Faenza (and elsewhere). This is given an elaborate treatment in 15 double sections with text and commentary (printed in roman and italic types in columns).

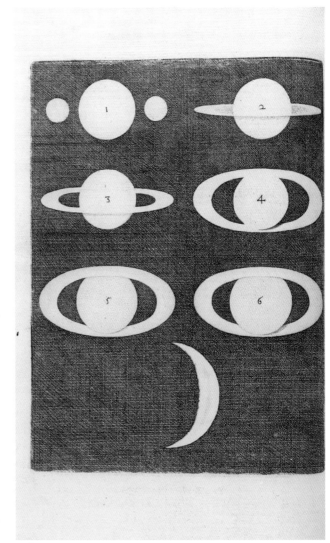

1438

Fernel's *Cosmotheoria* is here in its first edition dedicated to João I of Portugal, and handsomely produced by Colines. The text discusses the composition of the world, water, air etc. This copy has considerable underlining at various points.

Provenance: The last item has the signature of Thomas Smith, orientalist, traveller and fellow of Magdalen College, Oxford (1638-1710), who possessed a large library.

£20,000-25,000
€29,000-36,200

1439 Monte, Guidobaldo del. De cochlea libri quatuor. *Venice: Evangelisto Deuchino, 1615*

FIRST EDITION, folio (311 x 212mm.), [4], 160pp., ILLUSTRATION: engraved vignette on title, woodcut illustrations and diagrams in text, BINDING: contemporary vellum

References: Riccardi ii, 180

£700-900
€1,050-1,350

1440 Monte, Guidobaldo del. Mecanicorum liber. *Venice: Evangelisto Deuchino, 1615*

folio (295 x 202mm.), ff. [4], 104, ILLUSTRATION: woodcut device on title, woodcut illustrations and diagrams in text, BINDING: contemporary vellum, *upper outer corners lightly damp-stained throughout*

Second edition of Monte's first work, first printed in 1577 and instrumental in promoting understanding of Archimedes.

Georgius Frommius, an early owner of this copy, was the author of *Dissertatio astronomica de mediis quibusdam ad restituendam astronomiam necessariis* (1642), written as part of the debate that followed the publication of Jean-Baptiste Morin's *Astronomia restituta.*

References: Riccardi ii, 178

Provenance: Georgius Frommius, professor of mathematics at Copenhagen; Samuel Karl Kechel of Hollenstein, ownership inscription on title and note of gift from the former inside lower cover

£500-700
€750-1,050

1441 Montebruni, Francesco. Ephemerides novissimae motuum coelestium... ad longitudinem inclytae urbis Bononiae... Cum catalogo insigniorum fixarum ad annum 1650 (ad annum 1660) earumque ortu, & occasu pro altitudine poli grad. 44. Ex Philippi Lansbergi mathematici celeberrimi recentissimis, & exactissimis observationibus summo studio supputata... Pars prima (-secunda). *Bologna: Giovanni Battista Ferroni, 1650*

4to (245 x 178mm.), [8], xxxix, [1 (blank)], 307, [5], 309-633, [3]pp., ILLUSTRATION: woodcut device on title-page and final verso, woodcut initials and tailpieces, woodcut illustrations, folding engraved plate, BINDING: contemporary calf, spine gilt in compartments, *plate torn and repaired and slightly stained, a few leaves soiled, binding rubbed, upper joint cracking, spine chipped at head*

FIRST EDITION, RARE. The years 1640 to 1645 had been previously published in Bologna in 1640.

References: Houzeau & Lancaster 15161; Riccardi ii, 180

£1,000-1,500
€1,450-2,200

1442 Moon. The transit of the moon and of a known fixed star being given to find her right ascension [with various astronomical tables]. *[England, c. 1750]*

4to (230 x 175mm.), ff. [42], containing 11+ 55pp. of text and a number of blank leaves, manuscript in ink on paper (watermarked arms of England with letters LVG), BINDING: contemporary half calf, *slightly rubbed*

The text begins with a reference to an observation recorded September 12 1742 in the morning, and the basis for calculation is taken as September 11 1742, 19h, 44 minutes, 22 seconds. A further date is given on p. [8]: "July 22 1743 the place of the star... was" with a reference to the British Catalogue of Stars, and here there is a reference to Shirburn.

The tables concern the movements of sun and moon. That on pp.17-18 gives "The mean longitude of the moon her apogee & node for the meridian of Shirburne Castle in Oxfordshire" and runs from 1689 to 1800.

This manuscript is probably connected with the group observations made at the Shirburn observatory in the mid to late eighteenth-century, now in the Bodleian Library, Oxford.

£500-700
€750-1,050

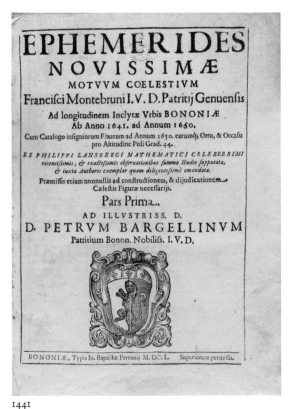

1441

1442

1443 [Montmort, Pierre Rémond de (1678-1719)] Essay d'analyse sur les jeux de hazard. Seconde edition revûe & augmentée de plusieurs lettres. *Paris: Jacque Quillau, 1713*

4to (252 x 179mm.), xlii, 414, [2]pp., ILLUSTRATION: engraved device on title-page, engraved and woodcut headpieces, woodcut initials and tailpieces, 4 folding engraved plates, engraved illustrations, 2 folding letterpress tables, BINDING: contemporary calf, spine gilt in compartments, red morocco lettering-piece, red speckled edges, *binding rubbed*

PRESENTATION COPY, INSCRIBED BY MONTMORT TO WILLIAM JONES on the flyleaf: "A Monsieur Jones, Par son tres humble et trest obeissant serviteur, Remond de Monmort".

Montmort studied under Malebranche and came to England in 1700 to meet Newton. He was elected to both the Royal Academy and the Académie royale. This treatise, originally published in 1708, was the first on gaming since that of Huygens in 1657 (see Macclesfield Science D-H, lot 1084, for the first English translation of Huygens' work).

Provenance: William Jones, presented by the author

£1,000-1,500
€1,450-2,200

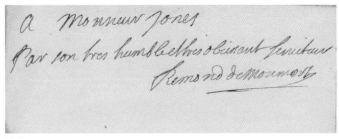

1443

1444 Moore, *Sir* Jonas (1617-1679). Moor's arithmetick in two books. The first treating of the vulgar arithmetick... The second of arithmetick in species or algebra... To which are added two treatises: 1. A new contemplation geometrical upon the... ellipsis. 2. The two first books of Mydorgius his conical sections, analized by... W. Oughtred, Englished and completed with cuts (A canon of the squares and cubes of all numbers under 1000...). *London: J.G. for Nath. Brook, 1660*

5 parts in one volume, 8vo (165 x 100mm.), [16] (first leaf blank), 224; [4], 95; [4], 33; [4], 39; [1], 48, [1]pp., ILLUSTRATION: folding engraved plate at beginning of Contemplationes and folding engraved plate with 8 figures at end, 5 folding engraved plates relating to section on Conics with 34 and 12 figures, BINDING: contemporary sheep, spine gilt later, *lacking portrait, binding slightly rubbed*

As the work of Frances Wilmoth has made clear, Jonas Moore was a distinguished figure. A Lancastrian by birth (he was born near Pendle) with little formal education, he came into contact with various figures, including Oughtred, and came to play an important part in the draining of the fens, of which he produced a famous map. After the Restoration he entered government service and directed the Ordnance, playing an important role in the Dutch wars of the 1670s. The author of many books, he was intimately connected with the foundation of the Royal Observatory at Greenwich, the governance of the mathematical school at Christ's Hospital and many other activities.

This work, first published in 1650, contains an eloquent plea for the practical aspects of mathematics: 'among the rest of the arts, to which arithmetick puts forth her helping hand, navigation acknowledgeth a great assistance: no man can pretend to any moderate skill in it without arithmetick'. The section on algebra is dedicated to Colonel Giles Strangeways since 'by your means I was chosen surveyor in the work of draining the great level of the fenns...'.

Moore owned a large library, sold in 1684 after his death. A copy of the catalogue is in the Macclesfield Library and will be offered for sale at a later date.

For Mydorge and his *Conica* see lots 1505 to 1508.

References: Wing M2564; see F.H. Wilmoth, *Sir Jonas Moore: practical mathematics and Restoration science* (1993)

£300-500
€450-750

1444

1445 Moore, *Sir* **Jonas.** [Moor's arithmetick in two books] Arithmetick in species or symbols... *London: J.G. for Nath. Brook, 1660*

8vo (165 x 105mm.), [4], 95, [1]; 33, [3]; [4], 39pp. only, ILLUSTRATION: engraved portrait of the author, folding engraved plate with 8 figures at end, 5 folding engraved plates relating to section on Conics with 34 and 12 figures, plate for Contemplationes cut out and the figures pasted to relevant pages, BINDING: contemporary calf, *incomplete, upper cover detached*

References: Wing M2564

£300-400
€450-600

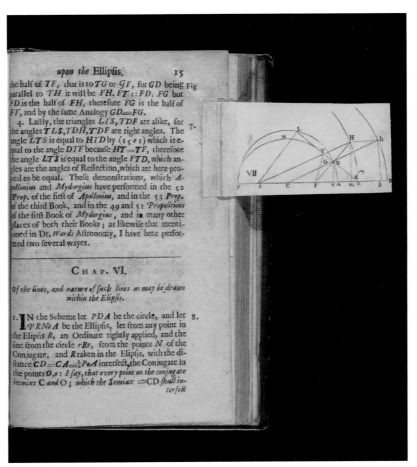

1445

1446 Moore, *Sir* **Jonas.** A mathematical compendium; or, useful practices in arithmetic, geometry, and navigation... the second edition, with many large additions. *London: Robert Harford, 1681*

2 parts in one volume, 12mo (126 x 74mm.), [24], 120, [180]pp., advertisement leaf at end, ILLUSTRATION: engraved and letterpress tables (one pasted onto A1), engraved plate at end, BINDING: contemporary mottled calf, spine gilt

References: Wing M2573

£200-300
€300-450

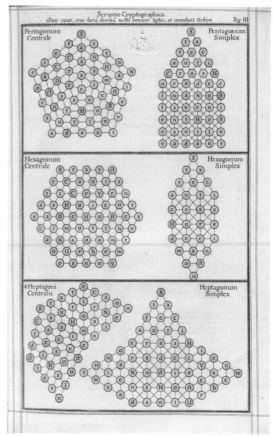

1447

1450

1447 Morgan, Sylvanus (1620-1693). Horologiographia optica. Dialling universall and particular: speculative and practicall. In a threefold praecognita... Illustrated by diverse opticall conceits, taken out of Augilonius, Kerrcherius, Clavius, and others. Lastly topothesi, or, a feigned description of the court of art. Full of benefit for the making of dials, use of the globes... Together with many useful instruments and dials in brasse, made by Walter Hayes, at the Crosse Dagger in More Fields. *London: R. & W. Leybourn for Andrew Kemb and Robert Boydell, 1652*

4to (180 x 135mm.), [16 (including additional engraved title and 'On the frontispiece')], 144pp., ILLUSTRATION: additional engraved title and woodcut diagrams in text, woodcut initials and head-pieces, BINDING: eighteenth-century vellum-backed marbled boards, *a little browned in places, engraved title cropped within plate mark at lower edge*

The liminary verses include some by William Leybourn the publisher and some by Edward Barwick 'On my friend Mr. Silvanus Morgan, his Book of Dialling':

The use of Dials all men understand
To make them few: & I am one of those.
I am not one of the Mathematick Band:
Nor know I more of Vers, then Vers, from Prose.
But though nor Diallist I am, nor Poet:
I honour those in either doe excell;
...[2 lines omitted]
Consider then the pains the Author too,
And thank him, as thou benefit'st by's Book.

References: Wing M2741

£600-800
€900-1,200

1448 More, Henry (1614-1687). Remarks upon two late ingenious discourses [by Sir Matthew Hale]: the one, an essay touching the gravitation and non-gravitation of fluid bodies: the other, observations touching the Torricellian experiment; so far forth as they may concern any passages in his Enchiridion metaphysicum. *London: Walter Kettilby, 1676*

8vo (150 x 90mm.), [48 (first leaf blank, here lacking)], 192pp., ILLUSTRATION: woodcut diagram on p.160, BINDING: eighteenth-century polished calf, spine gilt in compartments, green morocco lettering-piece, red edges

A handsome copy. For an account of this work, see A. Rupert Hall, *Henry More, and the scientific revolution* (Cambridge, 1996).

References: Wing M2675

£600-800
€900-1,200

1449 Morin, Jean Baptiste (1583-1656). Astronomia iam a fundamentis integre et exacte restituta. Complectens ix partes... longitudinum coelestium nec-non terrestrium. *Paris: the author & J. Libert, 1640 (parts 6 [-9]: Paris: P. Menard, 1657)*, 2 parts, [8], 162, [8], 163-282, [4], 283-360, [2]pp., achevé d'imprimer on p. 282 dated 12 June 1638 and at end 3 January 1639, the Menard imprint for part 6 and 7 is printed on a slip pasted over the original imprint, which is dated 1639

Ibid. Coronis astronomiae... qua respondetur ad Introductionem in Theatrum astronomicum... C. Longomontani, [etc.]. *Paris: the author & J. Libert, 1641,* [8], 40, [2]pp.

Ibid. Defensio astronomiae... contra... Georgii Frommii Dani dissertationem astronomicum (Appendix ad longitudinum scientiam - J.B. Morinus... ab Ismaelis Bullialdi convitiis... vindicatus. - Anonymi epistola castigatoria adversus G. Frommium... circa fundamentalem astronomiae restitutionem). *Paris: the author, 1644,* [6], 48; 8; 8; 19pp.

3 works in one volume, 4to (215 x 160mm.), ILLUSTRATION: woodcut diagrams, BINDING: contemporary vellum, edges coloured

Menard would seem to have reissued the entire 9 parts of the *Astronomia* in 1657 (as in the British Library copy). The *Appendix ad longitudinem scientiam* is sometimes bound after part 9 of the *Astronomia* but would seem to have been printed as part of the group of items dated 1644.

£600-700
€900-1,050

1450 Morland, *Sir* Samuel (1625-1695). A new method of cryptography, humbly presented to the most serene majesty of Charles the II. *[London], 1666*

folio (350 x 225mm.), 12pp., ruled in red, ILLUSTRATION: 10 engraved plates printed in red (2 with manuscript notes etc.), engraved diagrams in the text, some coloured by hand, BINDING: early eighteenth-century calf, spine gilt, *one corner rubbed and worn*

References: Wing M2781A (2 copies only, Folger and Yale Center for British Art)

Provenance: label with 3367 (lot number) pasted to upper cover; signature Ent (possibly Sir George Ent, physician, 1604-1689) and price in pencil 1 guinea on fly-leaf

£5,000-6,000
€7,300-8,700

1451 Morland, *Sir* **Samuel.** The description and use of two arithmetick instruments. Together with a short treatise, explaining and demonstrating the ordinary operations of arithmetick. As likewise, a perpetual almanack, and several useful tables. *London: Moses Pitt, 1673*

8vo (151 x 89mm.), ff. [63] (various foliations and paginations), 16pp. [A-G⁸ (-G8); B⁸; *⁸], ILLUSTRATION: engraved frontispiece portrait, 6 engraved illustrations, 7 engraved plates (3 folding), BINDING: contemporary calf, spine gilt in compartments, morocco lettering-piece, mottled edges, *binding rubbed*

FIRST EDITION of this treatise describing Morland's calculating machine, originally invented in 1666.

The final 16 pages contain "A table shewing the beginning of every King's reign, from the Conquest...", "Advice touching the posts, and roads..." and "Forreign weights and measures", signed at the end by Jonas Moore. This copy has the engraved illustrations in quire A printed directly onto the paper rather than pasted on, as found in other copies.

References: Wing M2777; Taylor, *Tudor & Stuart* 358

Provenance: Nathaniel Herne, early inscription on title-page

£2,000-2,500
€2,900-3,650

1452 Morland, *Sir* **Samuel.** The doctrine of interest, both simple & compound: explained in a more exact and satisfactory method then [*sic*] has hitherto been published. Discovering the errors of the ordinary tables of rebate for annuities at simple interest, and containing tables for the interest and rebate of money for days, months, and years, both at simple and compound interest, also tables for the forbearance, discomps, and purchase of annuites. As likewise, equation of payments made practicable and useful for all merchants and others. Together with divers other useful reflections. *London: A. Godbid and J. Playford, to be sold by Robert Boulter, 1679*

FIRST EDITION, 8vo (150 x 98mm.), [52], 203, [1]pp., BINDING: contemporary mottled calf, spine gilt in compartments, morocco lettering-piece, mottled edges, *binding rubbed, joints cracking at head*

References: Wing M2778; Goldsmiths 2300

£300-400
€450-600

1453 Morland, *Sir* **Samuel.** Elévation des eaux par toute sorte de machines réduite à la mesure, au poids, à la balance, par le moyen d'un nouveau piston, & corps de pompe, & d'un nouveau mouvement cyclo-elliptique. *Paris: Etienne Michallet, 1685*

4to (242 x 183mm.), [16], 49, [2], 50-60, [2], 61-110, [2], 12, 43, [1]pp., one double-page printed table, title-page, text on pp.34-35, 44-45 and one sub-title printed in red, ILLUSTRATION: 34 engraved plates, engraved portrait, BINDING: contemporary speckled calf, *title-page from a shorter copy and rebacked, binding rubbed, upper joint partly split, spine label detached*

FIRST EDITION. Morland, appointed 'Master of Mechanicks' by Charles II in 1681, is best known for his work on hydrostatics. The present work was written as a result of his efforts to raise water at Versailles. The manuscript version of 1683 in the British Library contains an account of steam power to raise water. Other copies do not appear to contain the portrait.

£1,500-2,000
€2,200-2,900

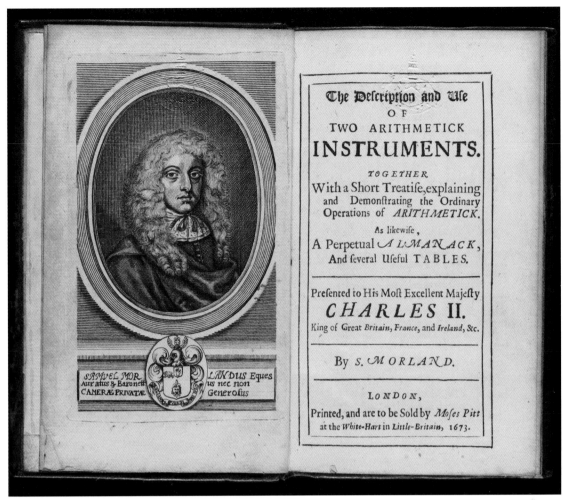

1451

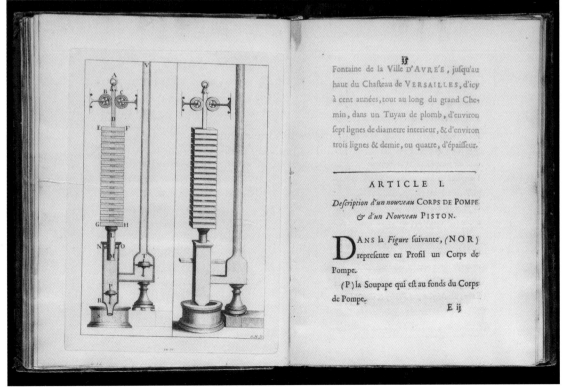

1453

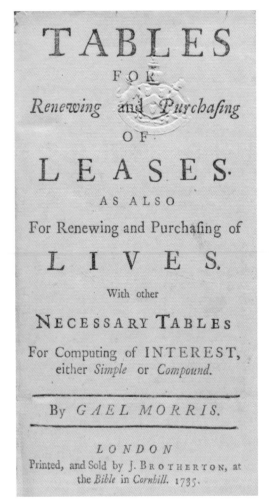

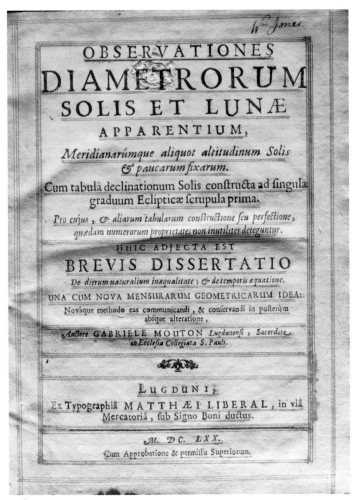

1455   1458

1454 Morris, Gael (*fl.* 1752-1765). Tables for renewing and purchasing of leases, as also for renewing and purchasing of lives. With other necessary tables for computing of interest, either simple or compound. *London: J. Brotherton, 1735*

12mo (135 x 73mm.), iv, 48, [2], 92pp., BINDING: contemporary speckled calf gilt, *binding slightly rubbed*

FIRST EDITION. According to Taylor (*Hanoverian*, p.241), Morris was an astronomer at Greenwich and he composed the preface to Halley's astronomical tables of 1752.

References: Goldsmiths 7269; Kress 4232

£200-300
€300-450

1455 Morris, Gael. Tables for renewing and purchasing of leases, as also for renewing and purchasing of lives. With other necessary tables for computing of interest, either simple or compound. *London: J. Brotherton, 1735*

FIRST EDITION, 12mo (138 x 74mm.), iv, 48, [2], 92pp., BINDING: contemporary speckled calf gilt, morocco lettering-piece, *extremities very slightly rubbed*

References: Goldsmiths 7269; Kress 4232

£200-300
€300-450

1456 Motte, Andrew (d. 1734). A treatise of the mechanical powers, wherein the laws of motion, and the properties of those powers are explained and demonstrated in an easie and familiar method. *London: for Benjamin Motte, 1727*

8vo (204 x 114mm.), [8], 222, [2]pp., ILLUSTRATION: woodcut initials and headpieces, woodcut diagrams, 3 engraved plates, BINDING: contemporary mottled calf gilt, spine gilt in compartments, morocco lettering-piece, *binding rubbed*

Motte is chiefly known as the first English translator of Newton's *Principia* (see lot 1526).

£300-400
€450-600

1457 Mourgues, Michel (1650-1713), *S.J.* Nouveaux elemens de geometrie. *Toulouse: Jean Pech, 1680*

12mo (142 x 80mm.), [12], 142pp., ILLUSTRATION: woodcut vignette on title-page, woodcut initials and headpieces, woodcut diagrams, BINDING: contemporary vellum, *binding slightly soiled*

FIRST EDITION. Mourgues taught rhetoric and mathematics in Toulouse.

References: Sommervogel V, 1344

£200-300
€300-450

1458 Mouton, Gabriel (1618-1694). Observationes diametrorum solis et lunae apparentium meridianarumque aliquot altitudinum solis et paucarum fixarum... Huic adjecta est brevis dissertatio de dierum naturalium inaequalitate... *Lyon: Matthieu Liberal, 1670*

4to (225 x 166mm.), [12 (including portrait)], 448pp., title-page ruled in red, ILLUSTRATION: engraved portrait of the dedicatee, Camille de Neufville, Archbishop of Lyon, woodcut initials, head- and tailpieces, woodcut diagrams, BINDING: contemporary calf, *T2 torn and repaired, binding worn, upper cover detached*

FIRST EDITION of Mouton's only book, in which he proposed a universal unit of measurement based on the length of the earth's meridian.

References: Norman 1560

Provenance: William Jones, inscription on title-page

£800-1,000
€1,200-1,450

1459 Mouton, Gabriel. Observationes diametrorum solis et lunae apparentium meridianarumque aliquot altitudinum solis et paucarum fixarum. *Lyon: Matthieu Liberal, 1670*

FIRST EDITION, 4to (224 x 166mm.), [12 (including portrait)], 448pp., ILLUSTRATION: engraved portrait of the dedicatee, Camille de Neufville, Archbishop of Lyon, woodcut initials, head- and tailpieces, woodcut diagrams, BINDING: contemporary calf, *A3 torn in margin, binding rubbed, upper joint splitting*

References: Norman 1560

£800-1,000
€1,200-1,450

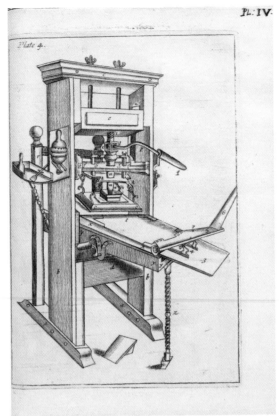

1462   1463

1460 Moxon, Joseph (1627-1700). Practical perspective; or perspective made easie. *London: for Joseph Moxon, 1670*

FIRST EDITION, folio (299 x 201mm.), [6], 66 pp., ILLUSTRATION: 60 engraved plates on 42 sheets (2 folding, one with overlay), 2 engraved illustrations in text (one on hinged slip), BINDING: contemporary calf, *some light soiling, occasional short tears in lower margins, binding worn, upper cover detached*

References: Wing M3018; Vagnetti EIIIb63; Berlin Catalogue 4721

Provenance: Thomas Ledyard, inscription on title; William Jones, inscription on flyleaf

£2,500-3,000
€3,650-4,350

1461 Moxon, Joseph. A tutor to astronomy and geography. Or an easie and speedy way to know the use of both the globes, coelestial and terrestrial... The third edition corrected and enlarged. *London: Thomas Roycroft for Joseph Moxon, 1674*

4to (198 x 153mm.), [6], 271, [9]pp., ILLUSTRATION: additional engraved title-page, engraved illustrations in text, woodcut diagrams in text, BINDING: contemporary mottled calf, *tear in upper corner of engraved title repaired without loss, some light soiling in margins, binding rubbed at edges*

First published in 1654, Moxon's work on globes was based on Tycho Brahe's system. This third edition is dedicated to Samuel Pepys. At the end of the text is a one-page advertisement for books, maps and instruments sold by Joseph Moxon.

References: Wing M3024; cf. Taylor, *Tudor and Stuart* 291 (note)

£300-400
€450-600

1462 Moxon, Joseph. Regulae trium ordinum literarum typographicarum; or the rules of the three orders of print letters... Shewing how they are compounded of geometrick figures, and mostly made by rule and compass... *London: J. Moxon, 1676*

4to (200 x 150mm.), [4], 52pp., ILLUSTRATION: 39 engraved plates of letters, BINDING: eighteenth-century mottled calf, gilt spine

Dedicated to Sir Christopher Wren, these types are modelled on Dutch originals. Moxon writes: "I finding therefore that the Holland letters in general are in most esteem, and particularly those that have been cut by... Christofel van Dijck, and some very few others, have elected them for a patern in Romans and Italicks... When the Stadthouse at Amsterdam was finishing, such was the curiosity of the Lords that were the Overseers of the Building, that they offered C. van Dijck aforesaid 80 Pounds Sterling (as himself told me) for drawing in Paper the Names of the several Offices that were to be painted over the Doors...".

References: Wing M3020; Bigmore and Wyman ii, 62

£1,500-2,500
€2,200-3,650

1463 Moxon, Joseph. Mechanick exercises: or, the doctrine of handy-works (applied to the art of printing). *London: J. Moxon, 1694 [but 1700]-1683*

a mixed edition, 7 parts in 2 volumes, 4to (195 x 143mm.), [8], 58, [4], 59-114, [4], 115-169, [5], 171-234, [4], 1-46; 394, [2 (blank)] pp., ILLUSTRATION: 59 engraved plates (some folding), 2 engraved portraits, 7 small engraved slips loosely inserted in section on house-carpentry (volume 1), BINDING: eighteenth-century mottled calf, spines gilt in compartments, *paper flaw at head of V4 (volume 1) without loss, one plate (volume 1) cut down and mounted with tears repaired, some other plates slightly trimmed, the 2 portraits on conjugate leaves (volume 2) cut down, mounted and bound after p.4, bindings slightly rubbed;* sold not subject to return

FIRST EDITION OF THE EARLIEST MANUAL ABOUT PRINTING. Moxon's *Mechanical exercises* were intended to describe the chief trades of the day, issued in monthly numbers, each number consisting of 16 pages and one or more engraved plates. Volume 1, which contains sections on smithing, joinery, house-carpentry, turning and bricklaying, was originally published in 14 parts between 1677 and 1680. The second volume, concerned solely with printing, was published in 1683, delayed, as Moxon explains in his *Advertisement*, "by the breaking out of the [Popish] Plot, which took off the minds of my few Customers from buying them, as formerly".

The present copy of volume 1 is a mixture of second and third editions. It contains a general title dated 1694, followed by five sections with subtitles, dated between 1693 and 1701, the first four paginated continuously, the last with separate pagination, and 26 engraved plates. The second volume, a first edition, contains 24 numbered sections with continuous pagination, 33 plates (bound at the end) and 2 engraved portraits.

References: Wing M3014, 3015 & 3017; Bigmore & Wyman ii, p. 54; Norman 1561

£5,000-7,000
€7,300-10,200

1464

1464 Moxon, Joseph *and* **Thomas Tuttell (*fl.* 1695-1702).** Mathematicks made easie, or a mathematical dictionary... The third edition corrected and much enlarged, with the definition, explanation, nature and meaning of the principal mathematical instruments. *London: for J. Moxon & T. Tuttell, 1700-1701*

2 parts in one volume, 8vo (165 x 96mm.), [24], 191, [9 (advertisements)]; [4], 22pp., ILLUSTRATION: engraved advertisement, 4 engraved plates (2 folding), BINDING: eighteenth-century speckled calf, *a few headlines and catch-words shaved, frontispiece and one folding plate slightly trimmed, short tear in one plate*

This third edition includes Thomas Tuttell's *Description and explanation of mathematical instruments*, as well as two engraved plates of mathematical instruments and a fourteen-page catalogue of globes, mathematical instruments and books sold by Moxon.

References: Wing M3008; Taylor, *Tudor and Stuart* 540

£200-300
€300-450

1465 [Mullen, Allen (d. 1690)] An anatomical account of the elephant accidentally burnt in Dublin on Fryday, June 17 in the year 1681: sent in a letter to Sir Will. Petty, fellow of the Royal Society: together with a relation of new anatomical observations in the eyes of animals, communicated in another letter to the Honourable R. Boyle, Esq., fellow of the same society. *London: for Sam. Smith, 1682*

FIRST EDITION, 4to (220 x 172mm.), 72pp., ILLUSTRATION: woodcut headpieces, 2 folding engraved plates, BINDING: later vellum-backed blue boards, *without final 4 pages of advertisements, slight foxing, binding a little soiled*

References: Wing M3057; Cole 961

£500-700
€750-1,050

1466 Mulerius, Nicolaus (1564-1630). Tabulae frisicae lunae-solaris quadruplices; e fontibus Cl. Ptolemaei, Regis Alfonsi, Nic. Copernici, & Tychonis Brahe, recens constructae. *Alkmaar: Jacobus Meesterus, veneunt Amstelrodami apud Wilhelmum Janssonium, 1611*

4to (236 x 170mm.), 136 (including engraved title), [4], 137-464, [28], 77, [3]pp., calendar printed in red and black, ILLUSTRATION: engraved title-page incorporating portraits of Hipparchus, Alfonsus, Tycho Brahe, Copernicus and Ptolemy, woodcut coat-of-arms on A4 verso, a few woodcut diagrams in text, BINDING: contemporary vellum, signed by Mulerius by A4 verso, *binding soiled*

FIRST EDITION. Having trained and practised for many years as a physician, while maintaining an interest in mathematics and astronomy, Mulerius was appointed professor of medicine and mathematics at the newly-founded University of Gröningen in 1614. In 1608 he had obtained letters patent for a set of eclipse tables based on the work of Ptolemy, Copernicus and Tycho Brahe; by the time the work was published in 1611 a fourth source, the Alfonsine tables, had been included. By relating the motions of the sun and moon, Mulerius's work made the calculation of eclipses much easier. A second part to the work concerning the other planets, written in 1612, was never published and exists in manuscript only. In 1617 Mulerius published a new, corrected edition of Copernicus's *De revolutionibus*, the first to contain explanatory notes (see Macclesfield Science A-C, lot 559).

References: Houzeau & Lancaster 12750

£1,000-1,500
€1,450-2,200
For illustration see frontispiece

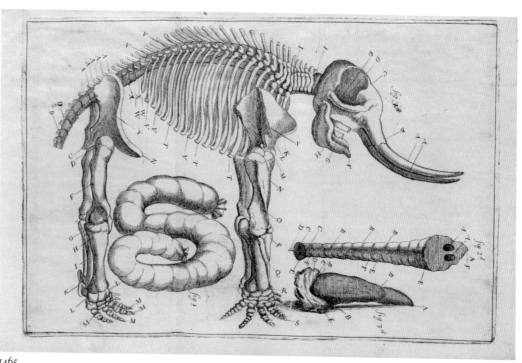

1465

1467 Muller, John (1699-1784). A mathematical treatise: containing a system of conic-sections; with the doctrine of fluxions and fluents, applied to various subjects. *London: T. Gardner for the author, and sold by W. Innys, R. Manby and J. Nourse, 1736*

4to (249 x 188mm.), [4], iv, [4], 227, [3 (errata)] pp., ILLUSTRATION: 14 folding engraved plates, BINDING: contemporary mottled calf, spine gilt in compartments, 3 slips of manuscripts and diagrams loosely inserted at pp. 72, 85 & 106, the first 2 in the hand of William Jones

FIRST EDITION of Muller's first work. Muller, a native of Germany, was appointed first, in 1741, headmaster and later professor of fortification and artillery at the Royal Military Academy, Woolwich. He later wrote works on both fortification and artillery.

£300-400
€450-600

1468 Müller, Johann Heinrich (1674-1731). Collegium experimentale, in quo ars experimentandi... de aere, aqua, igne ac terrestribus, explanatur ac illustratur. *Nuremberg: J.E. Adelbulner for W.E. Endter, 1721*

4to (204 x 167mm.), [8], 302, [16]pp., title printed in red and black, ILLUSTRATION: 14 folding engraved plates, BINDING: contemporary speckled calf, *tear in text of Aa4 (without loss)*

FIRST EDITION. Müller was professor of mathematics at Altdorf.

£200-250
€300-400

1469 Müller, Philipp (1585-1659). Miracula chymica et misteria medica. Libris quinque enucleta, quorum summam pagina versa exhibet. *Rouen: Jean Berthelin, 1651*

12mo (133 x 75mm.), [24], 193, [1 (blank)] pp., ILLUSTRATION: woodcut device on title-page, woodcut initials and illustrations, typographical head- and tailpieces, BINDING: contemporary sheep, *small stain on B2, one marginal wormhole, binding rubbed, upper cover detached*

Originally published in 1611.

References: Wellcome IV, p.195; Ferguson p.417

£150-200
€250-300

1470 Multum in parvo or tables of generall use exactly calculated with the superficial and solid measure of most bodys. *London: P. Lea, at the Atlas & Hercules, [c. 1700]*

12mo (132 x 67mm.), engraved throughout, ILLUSTRATION: engraved title, double-page folding twin-hemispherical map of the world, 2 double-page plates (points of the compass and zones of the world), 15 double-page tables, and one single-page plate at end, BINDING: contemporary panelled calf, spine gilt, *binding slightly rubbed*

Philip Lea was a map and globe maker active at the address above from 1687-1700, and just after.

£700-1,000
€1,050-1,450

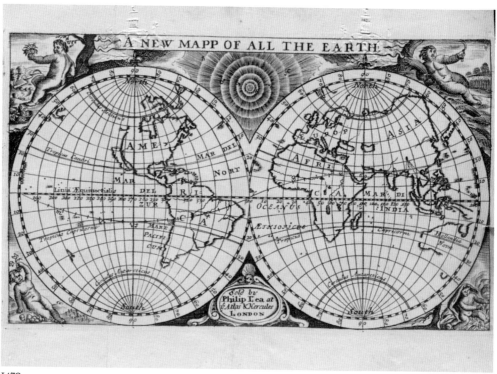

1470

1471 Muñoz, Jeronimo (*c.* 1520-*c.* 1591). Traicté du nouveau comete, et du lieu ou ils se font, et comme il se verra par les parallaxes combien ils sont loing de la terre, & du pronostic d'iceluy... Plus, un cantique sur ladicte estoille ou apparence lumineuse. *Paris: Martin le Jeune, 1574*

8vo (150 x 92mm.), ff. 40, [12], ILLUSTRATION: woodcut device on title-page, woodcut diagrams, BINDING: eighteenth-century speckled calf, spine gilt in compartments, contemporary annotations in Latin, *annotations shaved, slightly rubbed*

This work first appeared in Valencia in 1573 with the title *Libro del nuevo cometa* (Palau 185065). Translated by Guy le Fevre de la Boderie (1541-1598), "le prince des poètes kabbalistes chrétiens", friend of Plantin and one of the editors of the great Antwerp Polyglot Bible, it was in this edition that it was disseminated in Europe, where it was commented upon by Cornelius Gemma, the imperial doctor Hájek, and Tycho Brahe in his *Astronomiae Instauratae Progymnasmata*, who compared his own observations with those of Muñoz. He also published in 1578 a pamphlet of eight pages on the comet of 1577. Of manuscript works, there is a probably autograph work on astrology which is a commentary on a work by Abu-Al-Saqr Abd al'Aziz ibn Uthman ibn Ali al-Qabisi (Alcabitius), translated in the twelfth century into Latin by Juan of Seville, and printed at various times in the fifteenth and sixteenth centuries. Muñoz was a native of Valencia where he also studied at the University and held two chairs. He later moved to Salamanca, where he died.

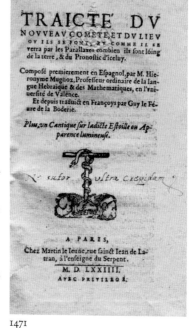

References: Palau 185066 (giving date as 1584)

Provenance: contemporary motto on title, "Ne sutor ultra crepidam" ("Let the cobbler stick to his last", Horace)

£2,000-3,000
€2,900-4,350

1471

1472 Murdoch, Patrick (d. 1774), *F.R.S.* Mercator's sailing, applied to the true figure of the earth. With an introduction, concerning the discovery and determination of that figure. *London: A. Millar, 1741*

FIRST EDITION, 4to (222 x 173mm.), xxxii, 38pp., ILLUSTRATION: woodcut head- and tailpieces, 3 folding engraved plates, BINDING: contemporary speckled calf, spine gilt in compartments, *without final advertisement leaf, binding slightly rubbed*

£200-300
€300-450

1473 [Murdoch, Patrick] Neutoni genesis curvarum per umbras. Seu perspectivae universalis elementa; exemplis coni sectionum et linearum tertii ordinis illustrata. *London: A. Millar, 1746*

8vo (201 x 122mm.), x, [2], 126pp., ILLUSTRATION: 12 folding engraved plates, BINDING: contemporary speckled calf gilt, spine gilt in compartments, morocco lettering-piece, *I2 torn in margin without loss, binding slightly rubbed*

References: Wallis 300

£300-400
€450-600

1474 Music—Aristoxenus (b. *c.* 375-360 BC). Aristoxeni... Harmonicorum Elementorum libri III. Cl. Ptolemæi Harmonicorum, seu de Musica lib. III. Aristotelis de obiecto Auditus fragmentum ex Porphyrii commentariis. *Venice: Vincenzo Valgrisi, 1562*, 165, [1]pp., separate titles for the treatises by Ptolemy, Aristotle and Porphyry, ILLUSTRATION: devices on title and at end, diagrams, [RISM Écrits p.95; Gregory & Bartlett i, 111; Censimento 16 CNCE 3007], *lacking final blank*

Printz, Wolfgang Caspar (1641-1717). Historische Beschreibung der Edelen Sing- und Kling- Kunst. *Dresden: Johann Christoph Mieth, 1690*, FIRST EDITION, [6], 223, [17 ("Register")] pp., ILLUSTRATION: engraved additional title and 5 engraved plates, titles in red & black, woodcut and type-set music examples, [RISM Écrits p.671; Gregory & Bartlett i, 218]

2 works in one volume, 4to (192 x 135mm.), BINDING: eighteenth-century half calf, red morocco lettering-piece, *extensive browning in the second work (lighter on the plates), additional title cropped at head*

FIRST EDITION of the most important work of Greek music theory, Aristoxenus's *Harmonics*, in the Latin translation by Antonius Gogava, together with the *Harmonics* of Ptolemy (second century AD), *De audibilibus* (here ascribed to Aristotle) and the commentary on Ptolemy by Porphyry (third century AD). Aristoxenus's *Harmonics* is the earliest such work to have been preserved in substantial fragments, and by far the most important. Our knowledge of Greek music scales derives almost entirely from Aristoxenus, a disciple of Aristotle born in Tarentum.

£3,000-4,000
€4,350-5,800

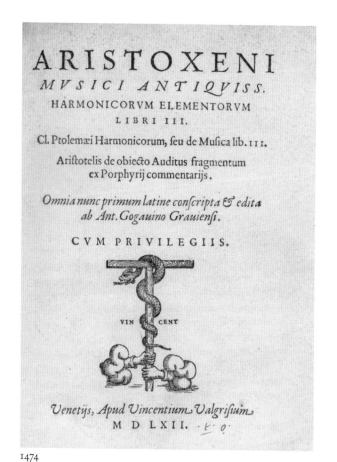

Baſſa

1474   1475

1475 Music—Caroso, Fabritio (*c.* 1530-after 1605). Il ballarino... diviso in due trattati; nel primo de' quali si dimostra la diversità de i nomi, che si danno à gli atti, et movimenti, che intervengono ne i Balli... nel secondo s'insegnano diverse sorti di balli, & balletti sì all'uso d'Italia, come à quello di Francia, & Spagna. Ornato di molte figure, et con l'intavolatura di liuto, & il soprano della musica nella sonata di ciascun ballo. *Venice: Francesco Ziletti, 1581*

2 parts in one volume, 4to (224 x 158mm.), ff. [7], 16; 184, [4], printed music and lute tablature, ILLUSTRATION: woodcut device on both title-pages, woodcut initials, head- and tailpieces, 22 full-page copperplate engraved illustrations by Giacomo Franco, BINDING: eighteenth-century sprinkled calf gilt, spine gilt in compartments, red speckled edges, *lacking B4 with engraved portrait of Caroso, occasional slight staining, small loss in outer margin of last few leaves*

FIRST EDITION, second issue.

Caroso's was the first important illustrated book about dancing. The first part describes the figures and positions used in contemporary social dances (illustrated by the plates) and the second is given over to the various types of dance popular in France and Spain at the time (with extensive examples of the appropriate music for them). Caroso was an Italian dancing master who produced two manuals of dance, providing a vast amount of detail about the dances of the period.

This is the standard first edition of this work: the first (dedication) issue, also of 1581, bore the arms of the dedicatee, Bianca Cappello, on the first title-page (see Magriel, p.42).

References: Censimento 16 CNCE 9679; Mortimer, *Harvard Italian* 106; RISM Ecrits p.207; RISM C 1233; Magriel p.43 (the first issue is illustrated); Gregory & Bartlett i, 53; Lipperheide 3055

£3,000-4,000
€4,350-5,800

1476 Music—A Treatise of Daunses, wherin it is shewed, that they are as it were accessories and depe[n]dants (or thinges annexed) to whoredome: where also by the way is touched and proved, that Playes are ioyned and knit togeather in a rancke or rowe with them. *[London: H. Middleton?], 1581*

8vo (142 x 87mm.), ff. [19], Black Letter, title within a typographical border, side-notes, ILLUSTRATION: woodcut initial, BINDING: eighteenth-century vellum-backed marbled boards, *lacking final blank, spine slightly defective, a few small stains*

FIRST EDITION. RARE: two copies are recorded, in the British Library and Lambeth Palace. This tract denouncing the evils of dancing was published the same year as Caroso's sumptuous treatise celebrating the art.

References: ESTC S2371; cf. STC 24242.5 (title incorrectly transcribed); not in RISM, Magriel or Gregory & Bartlett

£600-800
€900-1,200

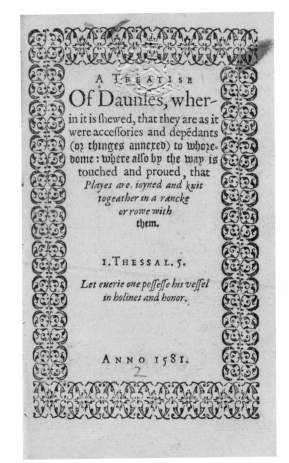

1476

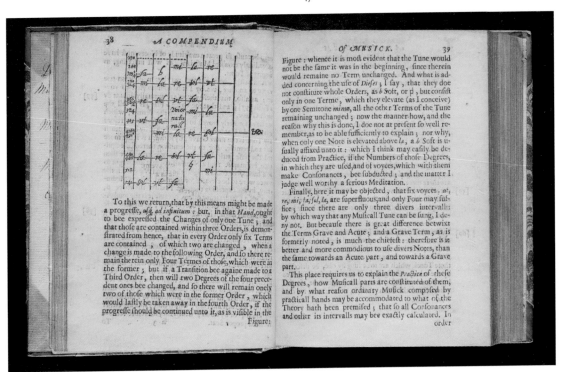

1477

1477

1477 Music—Descartes, René (1596-1650). Renatus Des-cartes Excellent Compendium of Musick: with necessary and judicious animadversions thereupon, by a person of honour [William, Viscount Brouncker]. *London: Thomas Harper for Humphrey Moseley & Thomas Heath, 1653,* [16], 94, [1 (errata)], [1 (blank)] pp., ILLUSTRATION: 3 full-page engravings, including an illustration of a lute, second title-page (p.59: "Animadversions upon the Musick-Compendium"), [Wing D1132; Gregory & Bartlett i, 73]

Butler, Charles (c. 1560-1647). The Principles of Musik. *London: John Haviland for the Author, 1636,* FIRST EDITION, [16], 135, [1 (blank)]pp., [STC 4196; Gregory & Bartlett i, 48]

Le Fèvre d'Etaples, Jacques (c. 1460-1536). Musica libris quatuor demonstrata. *Paris: Guillaume Cavellat, 1552,* ff. 44, device, [Gregory & Bartlett i, 150; RISM Écrits, p.493]

Heyden, Sebald (1499-1561). De arte canendi, ac vero signorum in cantibus usu, libri duo. *Nuremberg: Johann Petreius, 1540,* [12], 163, [1 (blank)] pp., over 60 pages of type-set music, including the last 24 pages, [Gregory & Bartlett i, 123; RISM, p.412; Adams H528]

4 works in one volume, 4to (172 x 130mm.), ILLUSTRATION: woodcut diagrams, woodcut and type-set music examples, BINDING: eighteenth-century English half calf, spine in compartments, red morocco lettering-piece, a few annotations and manuscript side-notes to the first item, *dust-marking or staining to titles, full-page woodcut (in the Butler item) and a few annotations cropped by the binder*

Sebald Heyden's work is important and rare. It deals with the art of musical composition, rather than scientific speculation and acoustics. The extensive musical extracts are from works by Josquin des Près, Ockeghem, Obrecht, Agricola, Pierre de la Rue, Isaac and Ludwig Senfl (c. 1486-1543), whom Heyden, in his preface, describes as the finest contemporary German composer ("...in musica totius Germaniae nunc principem..."). He also records important composers of the previous century, including Dufay and the Englishman John Dunstaple. Butler's *Principles of Musik* is written throughout in the author's newly devised orthography, as found in his *English Grammar* (1633). For an earlier edition of Le Fèvre d'Etaples's treatise, see lot 1113.

£3,000-4,000
€4,350-5,800

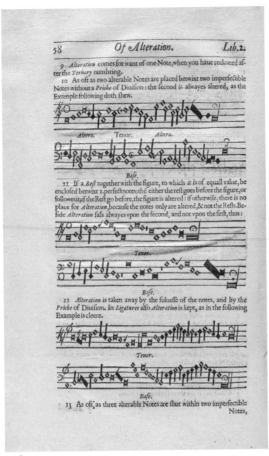

1478

1478 Music—Dowland, John (1563-1626). Andreas Ornithoparcus His Micrologus, or Introduction: containing the art of singing, digested into foure bookes... by John Douland lutenist, lute-player, and Bachelor of Musicke in both the Universities. *London: [T. Snodham] for Thomas Adams, 1609*

folio (275 x 185mm.), [8], 80 (i.e. 90), [2]pp, ILLUSTRATION: title within a typographical border, many woodcut and type-set musical examples and diagrams (2 white on black), small woodcut of "The Monacord", BINDING: eighteenth-century parchment-backed marbled boards, *tear in title without loss, some dustmarking, spine defective*

FIRST EDITION IN ENGLISH. John Dowland was England's greatest lutenist and lute-song composer. In his prefatory letter, he announces that he will shortly issue *My Observations and Directions concerning the Art of Lute-Playing*, describing the lute as, among all instruments, "the hardest to mannage with cunning and order" and promising to describe "the true nature of fingering; which skill hath as yet by no Writer been rightly expressed". This tantalizing project remained unfulfilled: although some chapters appeared in a translation of Besard's lute lessons in 1610, they may in fact be by Robert Dowland. Ornithoparcus's *Musicae activae micrologus* dates from 1517; it is a didactic work, instructing the young on practical matters, rather than scientific theory, and was widely used. This is the only edition in English.

References: RISM Écrits p.628; Gregory & Bartlett i, 201; STC 18853; Hirsch i, 444

£4,000-6,000
€5,800-8,700

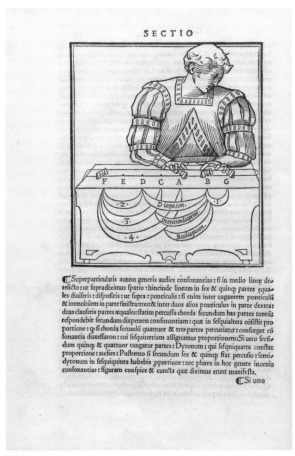

SECTIO·

F E D C A B G

·Z· Diapason ·I·

·3· Diapasondiapente

·4· Bisdiapason

⁋Superparticularis autem generis audies confonantias: fi in medio lincę deretlicto: ut fupradiximus fpatio: hincinde lineam in fex & quinc partes ęquales diuiferis: difpofitis: ut fupra: ponticulis: fi enim inter uagantem ponticulū & immobilem in parte finiftra: tres: & inter duos alios ponticulos in parte dextra: duas clauferis partes ęquales: ftatim percuffa chorda fecundum has partes tantū: refpondebit fecundum diapenten confonantiam: quę in fefquialtera cōfiftit proportione: q̄ fi chorda fecundū quattuor & tres partes percutiatur: confurget cō fonantia diateffaron: cui fefquitertiam affignamus proportionem: Si uero fecū dum quinc & quattuor tangatur partes: Dytonum: qui fefquiquarta conftat proportione: audies: Poftremo fi fecundum fex & quinc fiat percufio: femidytonum in fefquiquinta habebis pportione: nec plures in hoc genere inuenio confonantias: figuram confpice & cuncta quę diximus erunt manifefta.

⁋Si uero

1479

1479 Music—Fogliani, Lodovico (*c.* 1475-1542). Musica theorica... dilucide pertractata: in qua quamplures de harmonicis intervallis: non prius tentatae: continentur speculationes. *(Venice: Giovanni Antonio & brothers da Sabbio, July 1529)*

folio (295 x 205mm.), ff. [2], xliii, [1], last leaf a blank (here cut away), ILLUSTRATION: woodcut illustrations and tables, decorative initials, BINDING: seventeenth-century calf, gilt spine, *slight marginal worming at gutter in first few leaves*

FIRST EDITION AND A FINE LARGE, CLEAN COPY.

Fogliani, who came from Modena but spent many years in Venice, where he learned Greek, discusses in this work the nature of sound and the theory of mathematical and musical proportions. He then proceeds to deal with the division of the monochord, and his divisions, which for the smaller intervals are not the Pythagoran ones, were intended to reflect current practice. In fact Fogliano, like Gaffurio, recognized just intonation and describes it here thirty years before Zarlino, who mentions him. The six woodcuts of musicians with monochords are particularly fine.

In his short preface to the reader Fogliani urges one to rely on reason and clarity: "But I would wisht, O best of readers, demand from me carefull weighed words or painted speech, for I aim to please not by words but by reason solely".

References: Censimento 16 CNCE 42704; RISM Écrits p. 320; Sander 2837; New Grove IX, 57-58 (an account taken almost literally from Palisca); Hirsch i, 176; Gregory & Bartlett i, 91; Palisca, *Humanism in Italian Renaissance musical thought* (New Haven, CT: Yale UP, 1985), pp. 235-247

£10,000-15,000
€14,500-21,800

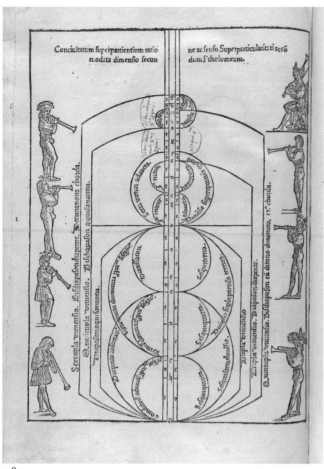

Concinitatum superpartientium ratio
modata dimensio secun

ne ac sensu Superparticularitati acco
dum Ptholomeum.

1480

1480 Music—Gaffurio, Franchino (1451-1522). De harmonia musicorum
instrumentorum opus. *(Milan: Gottardo da Ponte, 27 November 1518)*

folio (299 x 211mm.), ff. [4], C, [2], ILLUSTRATION: 2 woodcut portraits of the
author: on the title (instructing scholars) and at the end (playing an organ);
numerous woodcut diagrams (15 full-page), smaller figures, diagrams and two
musical examples, BINDING: eighteenth century English half calf, gilt spine, red
morocco lettering-piece, *some staining and soiling to the lower corners*

This copy of the second edition of one of the most famous humanist musical
treatises is copiously annotated in English in at least three sixteenth- and
seventeenth-century English hands. Some of the marginalia are purely linguistic -
translations of individual words or expressions, but there are many leaves with
detailed analysis and commentary.

The work is dedicated to Jean Grolier to whose Milanese patronage, in both
general and financial terms, fulsome tribute is paid in some elegiac couplets by
Mauro Ugerio of Mantua, printed above a small woodcut containing Grolier's
arms: "Illic fulgenti residet Grolierius Aula / Et secum doctos continet ille viros...
Hos amat: Hos refovet: placidaque amplectitur ulna: / Prevet & e largo maxima
Dona sinu...".

References: Censimento 16 CNCE 20121; Mortimer, *Harvard Italian* 204; RISM
Ecrits, p.342; Gregory & Bartlett i, 102; Hirsch i, 197; Sandal, *Editori* 338;
Sander 2989; Rosenwald 787; see C.V. Palisca, *Humanism in Italian Renaissance
musical thought, passim* for Gaffurio

£10,000-15,000
€14,500-21,800

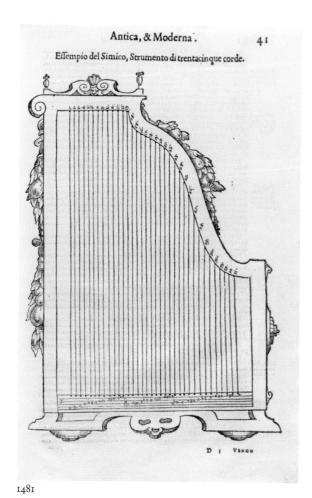

1481

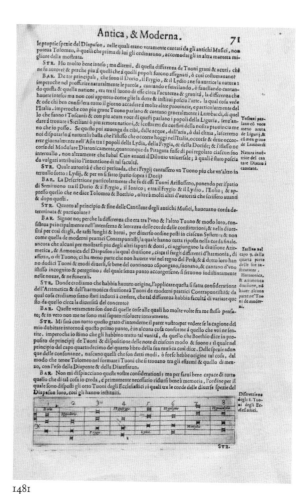

1481

1481 Music—Galilei, Vincenzo (1520s-1591). Dialogo della musica antica e moderna... in sua difesa contro Ioseffo Zerlino. *Florence: Filippo Giunti, 1602*

folio (306 x 202mm.), [1], [3 (blank)], 149, [1 (blank)], [9,] [1 (blank)] pp.,
ILLUSTRATION: 2 engraved musical tables on pp.71 & 78, woodcuts (3 full-page),
including 5 illustrations of ancient lyres (2 with music notation), tables and
diagrams, folding diagram attached to p.120, type-set musical examples, device,
BINDING: eighteenth-century half calf, early ownership inscription on title ("A moy
[G]uenebaud"), some contemporary corrections to the musical examples, *a few
stains, browning on title*

Vincenzo Galilei's *Dialogo della musica* is here printed from the 1581 edition with
a new title page. Vincenzo commends ancient music for its simple and noble
declamation of poetry, contrasting it with the complex polyphonic techniques of
"modern" music, as promulgated by Zarlino. His erroneous claim that Ancient
Greek tragedy was sung throughout influenced Italian musical thought in general
and the development of opera and monody in particular. The volume contains two
early examples of engraved musical notation.

Vincenzo Galilei was the father of Galileo.

References: RISM Écrits, p.344; BL STC Italian XVIIc., p.373; cf. Cinti 6

£2,500-3,000
€3,650-4,350

1482

1482 Music—Glarean, Heinrich (1488-1563) [Henricus Loritus, *Glareanus*]
Dodekachordon. *(Basel: Henric Petri, 27 September 1547)*

folio (305 x 200mm.), [20], 370, [6]pp., ILLUSTRATION: woodcut diagrams, extensive type-set music etc., BINDING: contemporary vellum, *clean tear in a2*

FIRST EDITION OF THIS IMPORTANT WORK OF MUSICAL THEORY AND PRACTICE, and a fine crisp copy.

The work is divided into three books. Book I discusses the basis of music, consonance and dissonance, and solmization. Book II discusses the eight modes known in the Middle Ages, to which two parts are added (Ionian and Hypoionian), one ending on C and the other on A. Thus Glarean was the first theorist to recognize modern major and minor modes, proudly displayed on the title. Many liturgical musical examples are given in this book, and also setting of various Horatian odes, including (pp. 189-190) Ode I.5 *Quis multa gracilis...*, famously translated by Milton, and the subject of a charming anthology edited by Sir Ronald Storrs. Book III discusses polyphonic music with a time signature and contains extensive musical examples, including complete movements by Josquin des Prez, Ockeghem, and others, and forms a veritable musical anthology. Glarean's commentaries on these pieces shows an advanced appreciation of the profundity and emotional appeal of a great master such as Josquin.

The work was influential in both theoretical and practical terms. Using the twelve modes or 'toni' as they termed them, both Andrea and Giovanni Gabrieli wrote extensively for brass consort, and these are works which are still very popular today. It was published in epitomized form in 1557, and a short section purely on modes was published in Hamburg in 1635.

References: RISM Écrits p. 366; Hirsch i, 226; Gregory & Bartlett i, 109; Davidsson 39; New Grove IX, 365-367 and bibliographies there cited, particularly the article by Iain Fenlon

£10,000-15,000
€14,500-21,800

1483

1483 Music—Greeting, Thomas (d. 1682). The Pleasant Companion: or, new lessons and instructions for the flagelet... the second edition, with large additions. *London: for John Playford, 1673*

oblong 8vo (97 x 159mm.), ff. [8], [28 (engraved music)], ILLUSTRATION: engraved frontispiece of a musician playing the flageolet, engraved and type-set music within the text ('Instructions for the Flagelet'), woodcut musical diagrams, BINDING: contemporary sheep, *tear to E1 in the engraved music, top edges trimmed within engraved plates (including frontispiece), some head-lines cropped, small tears to lower cover*

RARE: NOT IN BUC, WING OR THE ESTC. Only two other copies of this edition, in Washington and Stockholm, appear to survive.

There are 59 musical pieces on 56 pages ('Lessons for the Flagilett'): the composers of the pieces are named as Matthew Locke, Pelham Humphrys, John Banister, Jeffery Banister, "Mr Babtista" (probably G.B Draghi), Will Aylworth, Robert Smith, Louis Grabu and Clayton. The flageolet music is engraved in tablature, where the six holes of the instrument are represented by a six-line stave, dots indicating when the holes are to be closed.

There is some confusion about editions of this work: the earliest to survive is that of 1672 (a single exemplar in Cambridge), containing the first forty-six pieces. Neither the 1672 nor the present edition is mentioned in the ESTC or Wing: the earliest there is the 1675 edition and, in the British Library, 1678. However, Pepys records buying a copy on 16 April 1668 for one shilling, and it is listed in *The Term Catalogues* at this price on 20 November 1671. Pepys mentioned Thomas Greeting several times throughout 1667, having played music with him and having employed him to teach his wife Elizabeth.

References: RISM G3802; RISM Recueils 1673⁵

£3,000-4,000
€4,350-5,800

1484 Music—Grassineau, James (?1715-1767). A Musical Dictionary; being a collection of terms and characters, as well ancient as modern; including the historical, theoretical, and practical parts of music. *London: C. Jephson for J. Wilcox, 1740*

8vo (202 x 120mm.), xii, 347, [1]pp., ILLUSTRATION: 4 engraved plates containing music, many woodcut music examples and diagrams, BINDING: contemporary mottled calf gilt, spine in compartments, *joint splitting at head, tiny tear to last leaf*

FIRST EDITION. This is the earliest substantial dictionary of music in English. Earlier works had provided only telegraphic definitions of terms. Facing the title, there are commendations by Dr Pepusch (to whom Grassineau acted as amanuensis), Maurice Greene and J.E. Galliard.

References: Gregory & Bartlett i, 113; RISM Écrits p.375

£250-300
€400-450

1485 Music—Holder, William (1616-1698). A treatise of the natural grounds, and principles of harmony. *London: J. Heptinstall, for the author, and sold by John Carr, 1694*

8vo (190 x 110mm.), [10], 204pp., errata leaf, manuscript addition on p.111, ILLUSTRATION: 2 engraved plates of music, one folding, woodcut diagrams and notation in the text, BINDING: contemporary calf, *occasional browning, binding rubbed*

FIRST EDITION. A fellow of the Royal Society, Holder wrote widely: as well as the present book on harmony, he published treatises on calendrics and the teaching of speech to deaf-mutes. He was married to Sir Christopher Wren's sister, and, according to the *DNB* "had a considerable share in [his] education".

"Holder's originality in his Treatise lies in his explanation of the physics and acoustics of music, making a link with Galileo's isochronism theory of the pendulum... Its preoccupation with the physical basis of music is typical of the growing spirit of scientific enquiry of the period and of the Age of Reason that brought the arts as well as the sciences within the scope of such enquiry" (New Grove).

References: Gregory and Bartlett ii, 125; RISM Écrits p.420; Wing H2389

£600-800
€900-1,200

1486 Music—[Menestrier, Claude-François (1631-1705)] Des Répresentations en musique anciennes et modernes. *Paris: René Guignard, 1681*

12mo (157 x 87mm.), [24], 333, [3]pp., BINDING: contemporary calf, spine gilt, *some light foxing, covers worn, top joint spitting*

FIRST EDITION, *Des Répresentations* is a history of dramatic music covering ancient tragedy, Renaissance fêtes and Baroque opera. Menestrier outlines the aesthetics and describes actual performances, including those of his contemporary, J.B. Lully.

References: Gregory & Bartlett i, 178; RISM Écrits p.570

£600-800
€900-1,200

1487 Music—Meibom, Marcus (1630-1711). Antiquae Musicae auctores septem. Graece et latine. *Amsterdam: Louis Elzevir, 1652*

2 volumes in one, 4to (209 x 160mm.), [48], 132, [4 (misbound)], [4], 68, [4], 60, 8, 80, [4], 40, [4], and 36; [8], 363, [1 (blank)] pp., parallel Greek and Latin text, 2 titles in red and black, type-set musical examples, ILLUSTRATION: Minerva device on titles, small woodcut diagrams, 4 folding tables (3 printed in red and black), BINDING: late seventeenth-century English panelled calf, *tear to first folding table, occasional staining and dust-marking, joints & corners rubbed*

FIRST EDITION, dedicated to Queen Christina of Sweden. This volume contains seven Greek texts on music (with parallel Latin translations), including by Aristoxenus (fourth century BC), Cleonides (here attributed to Euclid) and Gaudentius (both second century BC), Nicomachus (second century AD), Alypius, and Bacchius (both fourth century AD). The second volume contains the *De Musica* of Aristides Quintilianus (second century AD), together with a Latin version by Martianus Capella. Aristoxenus is the most important Greek music theorist, the basis for most of the others collected here: among them, Cleonides, Gaudentius and Bacchius all help fill in gaps in the transmission of Aristoxenus's text. Alypius's *Introduction* is our main guide for deciphering the surviving framents of Greek musical notation. For Aristoxenus, see also lot 1474.

References: RISM Écrits p.568; Gregory & Bartlett i, 177; Willems 1148

£500-600
€750-900

1488 Music—Mengoli, Pietro (1626-1686). Speculationi di musica. *Bologna: heirs of V. Benacci, 1670*

4to (204 x 136mm.), [22], 295, [1 (blank)] pp., 2 folding printed tables at p.64 and p.292, BINDING: eighteenth-century mottled calf, spine gilt in compartments, green morocco lettering-piece, mottled edges, *lacking half-title*

In his "proemio" the author tells us that as a singer from the age of ten, he had been fascinated by music, and had spent fourteen years on writing an account of music which he finished about 1658. He used this as the basis for his lectures in the schools and he made copies for distribution. He explained in this work, he says, many things discussed by Zarlino and Galileo. His conversations with Ercole Zani led him to proceed further and to consult Galeazzo Manzi, professor of anatomy at Bologna, on the anatomy of the ear. There are twenty-five "speculationi", covering aural anatomy, intervals, chords, contemporary modulations and the passions of the soul.

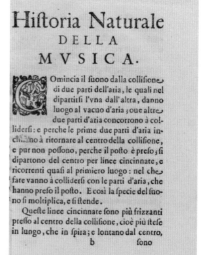

In his *Anno* of 1673 (paragraph 11 of the "Protesta dell'autore"; see lot 1366) Mengoli writes that he held long conversations with Ercole Zani, after his return from abroad, and has caused to be reprinted certain leaves of the original edition suitably corrected, which "I will give free to those who possess copies earlier in date than the present, if they have the grace to ask me, so that they may be bound in their rightful place".

References: RISM Écrits p.570; Riccardi ii, 151; Gregory & Bartlett i, 178

£800-1,000
€1,200-1,450

1488

1489 Music—Mersenne, Marin (1588-1648). Harmonie universelle, contenant la théorie et la pratique de la musique, où il est traité de la nature des sons, & des mouvements des consonances... de la voix, des chants, & de toutes sortes d'Instrumens [Seconde partie de l'Harmonie universelle]. *Paris: Sébastien Cramoisy, (part 2: Pierre Ballard), 1636-1637*

10 parts in one volume, folio (350 x 213mm.), [1 (title, laid down)], [12], [1 (engraving)], [1 (blank)], [1 (title of part: "Traitez de la Nature des sons")], [1 (blank)], [6], 228, 36, [1 (loose: "Advertissement au Lecteur")], [1 (blank)], [1 ("Traitez de la voix et des chants")], [1 (blank)], [6], 180, [1 ("Traitez des Consonances [etc]")], [1 (blank)], [10], 282 (last 2 leaves misbound); [1 (second title by Ballard: "Seconde Partie")], [1 (blank)]; [2], 283-442; [1 ("Traité des Instrumens a chordes")], [1 (blank)], [6], 412, 79, [1 (blank)], 68, 28, [44]pp., irregular paginations and foliations, cancel-leaves in I and M of "Traitez de la voix", ILLUSTRATION: engraved device on title, additional title with engraving of Orpheus by H. Le Roy, Ballard's device on title to part 2, 21 further engravings and many woodcuts in the text, mainly of musical instruments (a few full-page with engraved music), including a vignette portrait of Jacques Mauduit, many woodcut diagrams (one on a folding sheet), extensive type-set and woodcut music and tablature, BINDING: contemporary calf, title label to spine, raised bands, *title laid down with tears slightly affecting the text (verso obscured), lacking one engraved diagram (see below), a few woodcuts and one engraving cropped at leading edges by the binder, one trimmed to plate, some browning, a very few tears and paper-flaws, some worming in the gutter, front cover detached with first few leaves working loose, new liners*

FIRST EDITION IN FRENCH, RARE AT AUCTION: while the smaller Latin compendium (so called by the author) is not uncommon at auction, we have not traced any copy of the French edition of Mersenne's celebrated treatise during the past ten years.

Mersenne's *Harmonie universelle* is one of the fundamental works in the history of music theory and of the greatest importance for the early Baroque era. It is particularly valuable for around a hundred illustrations of musical instruments, including many from Mersenne's own time (in volumes [6] and [7], see below). Some of the plates include musical notation: the first examples of engraved music in France.

The French edition is composed of ten parts (including indices), each signed separately, some with separate titles and prefaces (see below). At the beginning of the fifth part there is a title-page for the "Seconde partie de l'Harmonie universelle", with the imprint of Pierre Ballard and dated 1637. Mersenne's numbering of the various sections and books is somewhat inconsistent and, in addition, revised leaves and short sections are found inserted. In some copies, the volumes are bound differently (see Gregory & Bartlett). The Hirsch copy has an engraved diagram on a folding sheet in part [4] (also found in Mersenne's own annotated copy in the Bibliothèque Nationale); it is lacking here, as in the two other copies in the British Library. The present copy comprises the following parts:

[1] "Traitez de la nature des sons", in three books: "De la nature et des proprietez du son" (pp.1-84); "Des mouvements de toutes sortes de corps" (pp.85-156); "Du mouvement, de la tension... des corps Harmoniques" [etc], (157-228)
[2] "Traité de Mechanique" (pp.1-36)
[3] "Traitez de la voix et des chants", in two books: "De la voix" (pp.1-88); "Des chants" (89-180)
[4] "Traitez des consonances, des dissonances...[etc]", in six books: "Des consonances" (pp.1-112); "Des dissonances" (113-140), "Des genres... & des Modes de la Musique" (141-196); "De la composition de musique" (197-282)

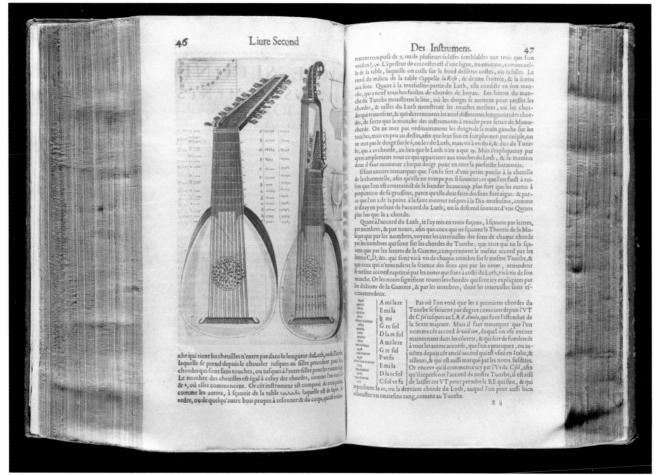

1489

[5] "Seconde partie" begins: "De la composition de musique" (283-330); "De l'art de bien chanter" (331-442)

[6] "Traité des instrumens a chordes", in six books, of which the last two treat of wind instruments and organs (pp.1-412)

[7] "Livre septiesme des instrumens de percussion" (pp.1-79)

[8] "Livre VIII. De l'utilité de l'harmonie", (pp.1-68)

[9] "Nouvelles observations physiques et mathematiques" (pp.1-28)

[10] "Table de propositions... de l'harmonie universelle" and "Table [des matières]"

References: Hirsch i, 404; Gregory & Bartlett i, 179-180; RISM Écrits p.573; Davidsson 66

£10,000-15,000
€14,500-21,800

1489

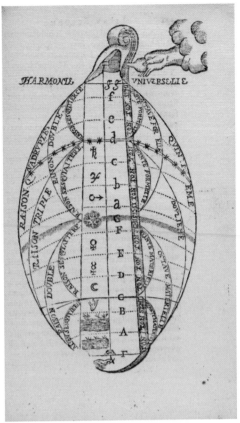

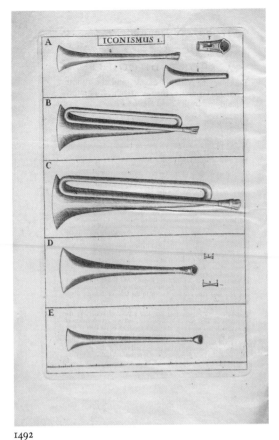

1490   1492

1490 Music—[Mersenne, Marin] Traité de l'harmonie universelle. Où est contenu la musique théorique & pratique des anciens & modernes, avec les causes de ses effets. Enrichie de raisons prises de la philosophie, & des mathematiques. Par le sieur de Sermes. *Paris: Guillaume Baudry, 1627*

FIRST EDITION, 8vo (170 x 109mm.), [32], 304, [4], [1 (title for 'Livre second'), [1 (blank)], [18], 305-487, [3]pp., device on title, ILLUSTRATION: full-page woodcuts of the Guidonian hand and the "Harmonie universelle", 6 pages of woodcut music, woodcut musical diagrams and tables, pp.[368]-370 irregularly paginated, BINDING: contemporary mottled calf, spine gilt in compartments, red morocco lettering-piece, *first woodcut trimmed by the binder, some staining, joints splitting*

References: RISM Écrits p.574; Gregory & Bartlett i, 180

£600-800
€900-1,200

1491 Music—Mersenne, Marin. Les préludes de l'harmonie universelle, ou questions curieuses. *Paris: Henry Guenon, 1634*

8vo (173 x 105mm.), ff. [7], 224pp., ILLUSTRATION: woodcut astrological diagrams, BINDING: early vellum-backed boards, *some foxing*

FIRST EDITION. Mersenne discusses the various qualities required in the perfect musician (including his horoscope, temperament, learning, and sense of hearing), and considers aspects of Greek theory (the enharmonic and chromatic genres, chords, tetrachords and the effects of music on the passions).

References: Gregory & Bartlett i, 180: RISM Écrits p.573

£600-800
€900-1,200

1492 Music—Morland, *Sir* **Samuel (1625-1695).** Tuba Stentoro-Phonica, an instrument of excellent use as well at sea as at land; Invented, and variously experimented in the Year 1670. *London: W. Godbid for M. Pitt, 1671*

folio (293 x 292mm.), [2], 14pp., title and D1 verso printed in red and black, ILLUSTRATION: 5 full-page engravings of trumpets and acoustical phenomena (repeated), BINDING: calf-backed marbled boards, *without the portrait, some browning, small paper-flaw in C2*

FIRST EDITION. Morland's Tuba Stentoro-Phonica or "speaking trumpet" was an early megaphone, which he claimed permitted conversation at a distance of three-quarters of a mile. On the title, Morland advertises "speaking trumpets" of all sizes sold by Simon Beal.

References: RISM Écrits p.597 (3 copies); Wing M2783; Gregory & Bartlett ii, 75

£800-1,000
€1,200-1,450

1493 Music—[North, Francis (1637-1685), *1st Baron Guilford*] A Philosophical Essay of Musick directed to a Friend. *London: for John Martyn, 1677*, 25 (i.e. 35), [1 (blank)], [1 ('mistakes')], [1 (blank)], [1 ('A Scheme whereby the Symmetry of the Pulses ranged in Musical proportions appear')] pp., ILLUSTRATION: engraved folding plate

Salmon, Thomas (1648-1706). The Theory of Musick reduced to Arithmetical and Geometrical Proportions [extracted from the *Philosophical Transactions of the Royal Society* (1705)], 4 leaves, cut from the periodical publication, irregularly paginated, folding table

2 works in one volume, 4to (210 x 160mm.), BINDING: eighteenth-century vellum-backed boards, manuscript title to spine, *tear to engraved plate in the first work, first leaf of the second cut down*; sold not subject to return

Francis North describes a modern theory of harmony and keys, showing how chords function in relation to their root (or fundamental note) within a particular tonality. This copy includes an errata-leaf, not present in two of the copies in the British Library. North became Lord Chancellor of England in 1682 and was a keen amateur musician: he is known to have played music with Purcell. For Thomas Salmon, see M. Tilmouth, 'Salmon', in New Grove XXII, 171, and lots 1496 and 1497.

References: RISM Écrits p.621; Gregory & Bartlett i, 116; Wing G2216

£300-400
€450-600

1494

1494 Music—Morley, Thomas (1557/8-1602). A Plaine and Easie Introduction to Practicall Musicke, set downe in forme of a dialogue. *London: Peter Short, 1597*

folio (291 x 200mm.), [6], 183, [35]pp., dedicatory epistle to William Byrd, verses by Anthony Holborne, extensive type-set music, including a motet printed in red and black, ILLUSTRATION: elaborate historiated woodcut title-border (McKerrow & Ferguson 99), some woodcut music and diagrams, BINDING: eighteenth-century calf gilt, *title shaved at top, some wormholes, some wear to the first few leaves, staining to margins*

FIRST EDITION. Morley's *Plaine and Easie Introduction* is the most famous musical treatise in the English language. Morley was a famous composer in his own right and emphasizes practical musical matters rather than scientific theory. When the pupil is presented with an obscure tabular mnemonic from Gaffurio, he protests to his master: "Heere is a Table in deede contayining more than I ever meane to beate my brayns about. As for musick, the principal thing we seek in it, is to delight the eare... therefore proceede to the rest of your musicke". The printed music includes whole pieces printed in "table format": that is to say, in a version of choirbook format where the separate parts are laid out on a double-page, so that the players can sit round the volume opened on a table. Morley's work, which sold for four shillings, was very popular: this is a good copy of a book that is often found well-used.

References: RISM Écrits p.598; STC 18133; ESTC S111843; Gregory & Bartlett i, 188; Hirsch i, 416; Steele 161

£4,000-5,000
€5,800-7,300

1494

1495

1495 Music—Purcell, Henry (1659-1695). Orpheus Britannicus. A collection of all the Choicest Songs for One, Two, and Three Voices. *London: J. Heptinstall for Henry Playford, 1698*, vi, 248pp.

Ibid. Orpheus Britannicus... The Second Book, which renders the First Compleat. *London: William Pearson for Henry Playford, 1702*, [iv], ii, [ii], 176pp.

2 volumes, folio (315 x 200mm.), dedications, epistles, verses, advertisement and index, type-set music, titles in red and black, ILLUSTRATION: engraved frontispiece portrait by White after Closterman to each volume, BINDING: contemporary panelled calf (volume 2: contemporary calf), spines gilt in compartments, *3 small tears near hinge (Aa2 & Bb1 in volume 1, F1 in volume 2), some browning in volume 1 (stain to last leaf), bindings worn but sound*

FIRST EDITIONS. These two important publications contain many first printings of Purcell's secular songs. Of particular interest is "Ah Belinda" from *Dido & Aeneas*: this is the earliest musical source for the opera, as no autograph or other contemporary manuscript or edition survives.

References: Day & Murrie 166 & 200; RISM P5979 & P5983; BUC p.859; Hoboken XVI, 210 & 211

Provenance: engraved booklabels of Thomas Parker (1704)

£1,200-1,800
€1,750-2,650

1496 Music—Salmon, Thomas (1648-1706). An Essay to the advancement of musick, by casting away the perplexity of different cliffs. And uniting all sorts of musick. *London: J. Macock for John Carr, 1672*

8vo (167 x 105mm.), [14], 92, [2]pp., ILLUSTRATION: 5 folding plates of engraved music, 7 engraved musical examples in the text, BINDING: contemporary calf, spine gilt, *lacking engraved additional title and half-title, one plate cropped at head, others trimmed, worn with the front cover detached*

FIRST EDITION. Salmon here proposes simplifying musical notation, thereby provoking an intense musical pamphlet war with Matthew Locke and John Playford.

References: RISM Écrits p.749; Wing S417; Gregory & Bartlett i, 242

£200-300
€300-450

1497 Music—Salmon, Thomas. A Proposal to Perform Musick, in perfect and mathematical proportions. *London: for John Lawrence, 1688*

4to (229 x 176mm.), [12], 42, [2]pp., advertisement, ILLUSTRATION: title in a woodcut border, 4 folding engraved tables, BINDING: eighteenth-century vellum-backed boards, *some staining towards the end, binding weak*

FIRST EDITION. Salmon's proposals are for music to be performed using just intonation, rather than equal temperament. Salmon persuaded some viol players to fret their instruments accordingly. The main disadvantage of just intonation is that it severely restricts modulation (away from the home key), and was most famously abandoned altogether by J.S. Bach in his "Well-Tempered Clavier".

References: RISM Écrits p.749; Gregory & Bartlett i, 243

£200-250
€300-400

1498 Music—Simpson, Christopher (*c.* 1602-1669). A Compendium of Practical Musick... together with lessons for viols, &c, the third edition. *London: M.C. for Henry Brome, 1678*

8vo (180 x 110mm), ff. [8], 192pp., extensive type-set music (including for 2 viols in table-format), some engraved and woodcut musical examples and tablature, ILLUSTRATION: frontispiece portrait by W. Faithorne, BINDING: contemporary calf, some figured basses and musical annotations in manuscript, *light overall browing, extremities very worn*

References: Gregory & Bartlett i, 254; RISM Écrits p.786; Wing S3811

£200-300
€300-450

1499 Music—Smith, Robert (1689-1768). Harmonics, or the philosophy of musical sounds. *Cambridge: J. Bentham for W. Thurlbourn & T. Merrill etc, 1749*

FIRST EDITION, 4to (223 x 140mm), xv, [i], 292, [14]pp., ILLUSTRATION: 25 folding engraved plates, 3 folding tables attached to M1, N2 and Q6, BINDING: contemporary calf, 2-line border and spine gilt in compartments

References: RISM Écrits p.788; Gregory & Bartlett i, 255

£300-400
€450-600

1500 Music—Tosi, Pier Francesco (1654-1732). Observations on the Florid Song... translated into English by Mr. Galliard... to which are added, explanatory annotations and examples in musick. *London: for J. Wilcox, 1742*

12mo (165 x 95mm.), xviii, [2], 184 pp., ILLUSTRATION: 6 folding plates of engraved musical examples, BINDING: contemporary calf gilt, border, spine in compartments, *plates cropped by the binder*

FIRST ENGLISH EDITION. The translation is by the composer John Ernest Galliard (1666 or 1687-1747), who added important additional matter deriving from his own first-hand knowledge of the great Italian castrato singers of the early eighteenth century. Together with Tosi's original (1723), it is a fundamental treatise on the Italian *bel canto* tradition.

References: Gregory & Bartlett i, 272; RISM Écrits, p.839

£250-300
€400-450

1501 Musschenbroek, Peter van (1692-1761). Physicae experimentales, et geometricae, de magnete, tuborum capillarium vitreorumque speculorum attractione, magnitudine terrae... dissertationes, ut et Ephemerides meteorologicae Ultrajectinae. *Leiden: Samuel Luchtmans, 1729*

FIRST EDITION, 4to (247 x 191mm.), [10], 685pp., title printed in red and black, folding printed table at p.536, folding engraved table of ephemerides at p.672, ILLUSTRATION: engraved portrait of Musschenbroek, 28 numbered folding engraved plates, BINDING: contemporary mottled calf, spine gilt in compartments, *binding slightly rubbed*

FIRST EDITION. The portrait of Musschenbroek does not appear to be present in most copies.

References: Wheeler Gift 268

£800-1,000
€1,200-1,450

1501

1502 Musschenbroek, Peter van. Tentamina experimentorum naturalium captorum in Academia del Cimento. *Leiden: J. & H. Verbeek, 1731*

4to (245 x 194mm.), [16], xlviii, [12], 193; 192, [14]pp., title printed in red and black, folding printed table at p.165, ILLUSTRATION: 32 folding engraved plates, BINDING: contemporary calf, *some light browning*

One of the best-known apparatuses first described in this work is the pyrometer, as named by Musschenbroek.

References: Wheeler Gift 276

£200-300
€300-450

1503 Musschenbroek, Peter van. Essai de physique... Avec une description de nouvelles sortes de machines pneumatiques, et un recueil d'expériences par Mr. J[ean] v. M[usschenbroek]. Traduit du hollandais par Mr. Pierre Massuet. *Leiden: Samuel Luchtmans, 1739*

2 volumes in one, 4to (243 x 196mm.), xxv, [3], 502; [2], 501 [i.e. 503]-914, [32]; 63, 8pp., 2 title-pages printed in red and black, ILLUSTRATION: 34 folding engraved plates (including one map), BINDING: contemporary mottled calf gilt, *lacking a portrait, some plates very slightly trimmed*

A translation of *Beginsels der natuurkunde*, published in 1736. The last eight pages contain a priced catalogue of instruments made by Jan van Musschenbroek, Peter's brother, who succeeded their father Johan in the family business of brass foundry and instrument-making.

While the present copy lacks the portrait, the Shirburn copy of Musschenbroek's *Physicae experimentales* (see lot 1501) contains a portrait not normally found in that edition.

References: Wellcome IV, p.206; Blake p.318

£250-300
€400-450

1504 Musschenbroek, Peter van. The Elements of natural philosophy... Translated from the Latin by John Colson. *London: for J. Nourse, 1744*

2 volumes in one, 8vo (207 x 123mm.), xiii, [3], 334; [4], 328pp., ILLUSTRATION: 26 folding engraved plates, BINDING: contemporary calf, spine gilt in compartments

£200-300
€300-450

1505 Mydorge, Claude (1585-1647). Examen du livre des recreations mathematiques, et de ses problemes en geometrie, mechanique, optique, & catoptrique. Ou sont aussi discutées & restablies plusieurs experiences physiques y proposees. *Paris: Rolet Boutonné, 1630*

part 1 only (of 3), 8vo (176 x 111mm.), [16], 280pp., ILLUSTRATION: woodcut initials and headpieces, engraved illustrations, BINDING: contemporary vellum gilt, flat spine gilt, gilt edges, *slight staining on upper cover*

FIRST EDITION. *Les recréations mathématiques* was by Jean Leurechon.

£700-1,000
€1,050-1,450

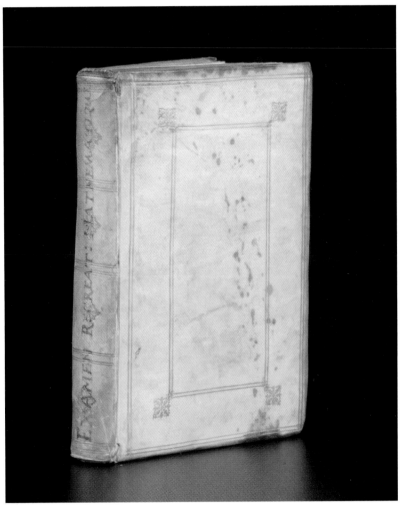

1505

1506 Mydorge, Claude. Examen du livre des recreations mathematiques, et de ses problemes en geometrie, mechanique, optique, & catoptrique (Nottes sur les recreations mathematiques... par D.H.P.E.M. [Didier Henrion]). *Paris: Rolet Boutonné, 1638*

4 parts in one volume, 8vo (172 x 106mm.), [16], 280; 63, [5], 67-106, [10], [2 (blank)]; 39, [1 (blank)] pp., ILLUSTRATION: woodcut initials and headpieces, woodcut illustrations, BINDING: contemporary vellum, *paper flaw on N1 (affecting a few letters), binding very slightly soiled*

£600-800
€900-1,200

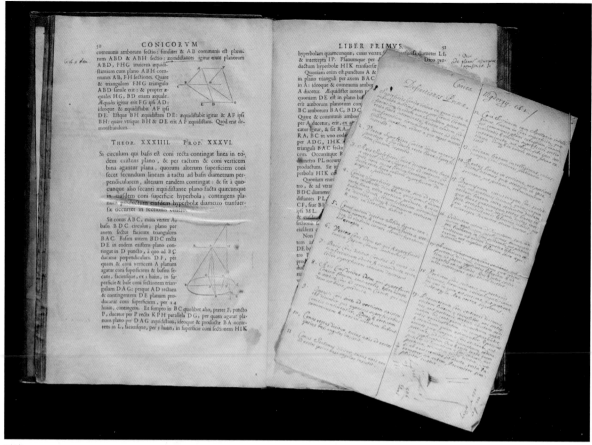

1507

1507 Mydorge, Claude. Prodromi catoptricorum et dioptricorum: sive conicorum operis ad abdita radii reflexi et refracti mysteria praevij & facem praeferentis. Libri quatuor priores. D.A.L.G. *Paris: J. Dedin, 1639*

folio (337 x 220mm.), [6], 308, [2]pp., ILLUSTRATION: woodcut diagrams in text, BINDING: contemporary English calf, spine gilt, *without 4 pages of preliminaries and the errata leaf (signed D.A.L.G.) at end, upper cover loose*

FIRST EDITION. Mydorge continued the work of Apollonius on conics, and his work contains a great many problems here published for the first time. He introduced the word 'parameter' for the first time of a conic section (a word much abused in today's parlance), and in his solutions (in particular his method of deforming figures) had considerable influence upon later geometricians and mathematicians, Newton amongst them.

The missing leaves were clearly never present in this copy which has been copiously annotated by two hands in books I and IV (and a little in book II) with calculations and drawings. There are also 2 leaves of manuscript notes loosely inserted, one of the 'Definitiones' of Book I, and one of four propositions/theorems. Some other annotations are by Jones.

In 1671 John Collins wrote "they complaine in france (as we doe here) that their Booksellers will not undertake to print mathematicall Bookes there, thence it came to pass that the four latter books of Mydorge were never printed, as the former had not been unless Sir Charles Cavendish… had given 50 crownes as a Dowry with it…" (Collins to Gregory, 14 March 1671/2 in Newton, *Correspondence* 47). The manuscript of the remaining four books was reputedly brought to England, and there lost.

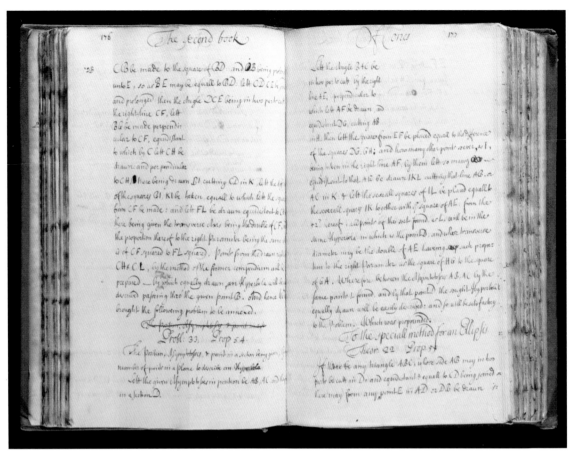

1508

Sir Charles Cavendish (?1595-1654) seems to have developed contacts with foreign mathematicians and by the summer of 1631 was corresponding with Mydorge, who dedicated this work to him. 1631 also saw the publication of Oughtred's *Clavis*, which Oughtred tells us Sir Charles had encouraged him to publish. Mersenne's *Harmonicorum libri* of 1636 was dedicated by the publisher to Sir Charles, and Hobbes seems to have brought a manuscript of Galileo's *Mecanica* as a present from Mersenne, which Payne translated. An exile from England after the Battle of Marston Moor, in March 1651 he returned to England where in February 1654 he died.

Only in some copies is the dedication present.

Provenance: B. Walker, inscription on title

£3,000-4,000
€4,350-5,800

1508 Mydorge, Claude. [Conica I-IV. English] The first (-fourth) book of Cones of Claudius Mydorgius a patrician of Paris. *[London, c. 1700]*

folio (300 x 180mm.), 523pp., MANUSCRIPT ON PAPER (watermark of the City of London Arms, akin to Heawood 461, dated 1713), written in English in a single scribal hand, brown ink, 24 lines to a full page plus headline, pp.1-110 book I, pp.111-199 book II, pp.200-408 book III, pp.409-523 book IV, ILLUSTRATION: book I has a small number of diagrams pasted to the edges of leaves, in the other books spaces have been left for diagrams which have not been supplied, BINDING: contemporary reversed calf

The translation is anonymous, but is made from the Latin edition published in 1644.

£5,000-6,000
€7,300-8,700

1509 Myl, Abraham van der (1563-1637). De origine animalium, et migratione populorum. *Geneva: Pierre Columes, 1667*, [2], 68pp., ILLUSTRATION: woodcut device on title-page, woodcut initials

[Kirchmaier, Georg Caspar (1635-1700)] De diluvii universalitate dissertatio prolusoria. *Geneva: Pierre Columes, 1667*, [6], 109, [1 (blank)] pp., ILLUSTRATION: woodcut device on title-page, woodcut initials

2 works in one volume, 12mo (141 x 80mm.), BINDING: contemporary sheep, spine gilt in compartments, *slight browning, binding rubbed*

FIRST EDITIONS. A treatise on the diversity of animal species between the Old World and the New World, together with one on the habitation of America after but not before the Great Flood.

References: JCB 667/100; Sabin 48982; *1st work:* Krivatsy 8232; Palau 169293

£500-700
€750-1,050

1510 Napier, John (1550-1617), *Baron Merchiston.* A description of the admirable table oe [*sic*] logarithmes: with a declaration of the most plentiful, easy, and speedy use thereof in both kindes of trigonometrie, as also in all mathematicall calculations. Invented and published in Latin... and translated into English by... Edward Wright. With an addition of an instrumentall table to finde the part proportionall, invented by the translator, and described in the end of the booke by Henry Brigs... *London: Nicholas Okey, 1616*

12mo (145 x 80mm.), [22], 89, [91], 8pp., ILLUSTRATION: woodcut initials and headpieces, woodcut diagrams, folding engraved plate, 3 folding manuscript tables inserted at end, BINDING: contemporary calf, spine gilt in compartments, *a few headlines shaved, upper cover detached*

A translation of *Mirifici logarithmorum canonis descriptio* (see Macclesfield Science D-H, lot 887, and the footnote there). Henry Briggs was the first Savilian professor of mathematics at Oxford, and a close friend of the translator, Edward Wright (1558-1615).

"The table is to one place less than the Canon of 1614, but the logarithms of the sines for each minute from 89º-90º are given in full, the last figure being marked off by a point. This is, I believe, the earliest instance of the decimal point being used in a printed book" (Macdonald, pp.145-146).

References: STC 18351; Macdonald, *Napier*, pp.144-146

£1,000-1,500
€1,450-2,200

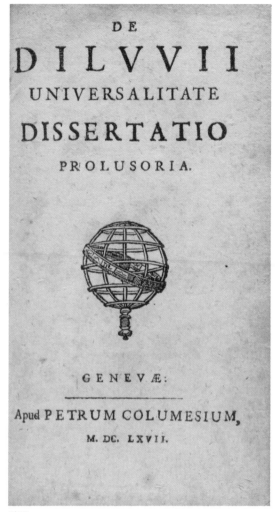

DE
DILVVII
UNIVERSALITATE
DISSERTATIO
PROLUSORIA.

GENEVÆ:

Apud PETRUM COLUMESIUM,
M. DC. LXVII.

1509

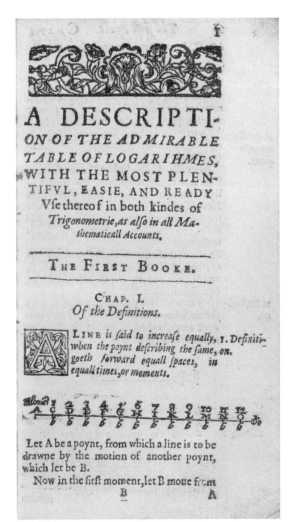

1510

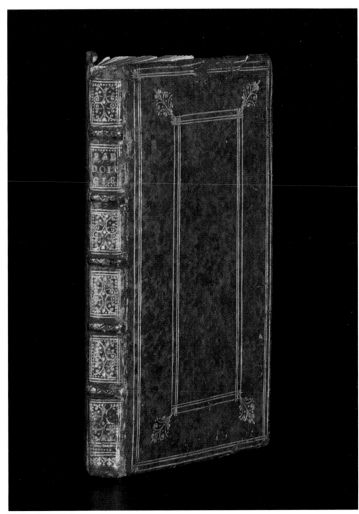

1511

1511 Napier, John, *Baron Merchiston.* Rabdologiae seu numerationis per virgulas libri duo: cum appendice de expeditissimo multiplicationis promptuario. Quibus accessit & arithmeticae localis liber unus. *Leiden: Petrus Rammasenius, 1628*

12mo (144 x 80mm.), [12], 139, [9 (blank)] pp., ILLUSTRATION: woodcut initials and diagrams, 9 folding plates (woodcut and letterpress), BINDING: contemporary mottled calf gilt, spine gilt in compartments, *binding very slightly rubbed*

Originally published in 1617, this is the third edition of Napier's *Rabdologiae*, essentially the same as the second edition of 1626 but with a new title-page.

"A set of ten rods of wood or ivory ("*Napier's bones*") constituted one of the earliest forms of mechanized calculation. With these Napier tried to do away with the tediousness of calculating and coined the term "*Rabdologia*" as numeration by little rods" (Dibner, p.51).

References: cf. Norman 1574; Dibner 107 (1st edition)

£1,000-1,500
€1,450-2,200

1512 Nautonier, Guillaume de (1557-1620). Mecometrie de laymant cest a dire la maniere de mesurer les longitudes par le moyen de l'eymant. Par laquelle est enseigné, un tres certain moyen, au paravant inconnu, de trouver les longitudes geographiques de tous lieux aussi facilement comme la latitude... Oeuvre necessaire aux admiraux (part 2: Premier livre de la mecometrie arithmetique de l'eymant; part 3: The mecographie of ye loadstone. Tat is to say ane description of the lenthes or longitudes, quhikis ar son be ye obseruations of ye loadstone: this moyen is verie certain, and neulie fond ond and schauis phou meikil ye nidil or guideymant, goir a side or fleis from ye lyn meridional... necessaire for ye admirals, cosmographes... skippers, geometriens or architectes). *Venes and Toulouse: Raimond Colomies & Antoine de Courteneuve, for the author, 1603-1604*

3 parts in one volume, folio (310 x 195mm.), part 1: [50], 1-128, [4], 129-208, [4], 209-292, [8], 245-252, 305-327 [=328, 1 page omitted]; part 2: [8], 32; part 3: [2], 9-16, 16, 195 [i.e. 268]pp., folding table at p. 244 of part 1 'Les noms des vents de marine selons leur ordre dont on se peut aider pour un anemoscope', small printed slip with 6 lines text loosely inserted at p.215, ILLUSTRATION: titles to parts 1 & 3 within engraved frames with inset views and town plans of France beneath a battle scene with Henri of Navarre on horseback on first title, and views of St Helena, Ascension Island and other islands on third title, 2 full-page engravings at p. 245 in part 1 printed on inner forme of a bifolium, with a small slip pasted to first blank recto, 'Ceste feuille soit estre mises apres la rose des vents, & devant la page 245', woodcut vignette on second title, numerous woodcut diagrams etc., some full-page, woodcut head-pieces and initials, BINDING: English binding of brown calf *c.* 1700, spine gilt, *engraved border on title of part 3 shaved at head, binding rubbed*

A FINE COPY OF A RARE BOOK PRINTED AT VENES (TARN) IN THE AUTHOR'S HOUSE AND AT HIS COST. The first part, in French, is dedicated to Henri IV; the second part, also in French, to James I of England (27 March 1604); and the third part, in Scottish, to James Montgomery, serving in the French king's army (1 June 1603). Versions of the text are also recorded in Spanish (copies at Auch, Toulouse and Bordeaux) and Dutch (copy at Albi). The author also published at Castres in 1657 a *De artificiosa memoria* (see *Rép. bibl. xviie siècle* xxiii, p. 55).

The make-up of this book is complex. The first part contains six subdivisions, numbers 2 to 6 each with a separate title-page and preliminary material: the preliminary matter for subdivisions 2, 3 and 5 is not included in the pagination, while that for parts 4 and 6 is. The pagination of the present copy appears to correspond to that in the National Library of Scotland.

References: STC 18415 (L, London RINA, Paris BNF, Folger, and Yale only); *English Maritime Books* 2636; *Rép. bibl. xviie siècle* vi, pp. 229-230, and his article in *Revue du Tarn* (1977), 101-116; Houzeau & Lancaster 10321-10323

£15,000-20,000
€21,800-29,000

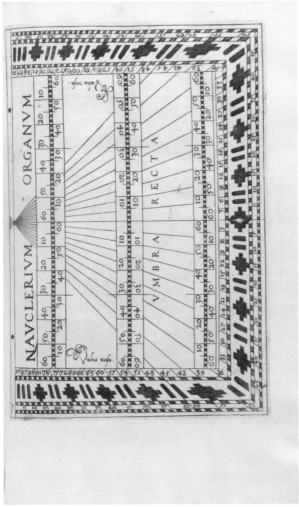

1512

1512

1513 Neve, Richard (*fl.* 1702-1716?). Baroscopologia, or, a discourse of the baroscope, or quicksilver weather-glass [etc.]. *London: W. Keble, 1708*

8vo (140 x 90mm.), [2], 44, [2 (adverts)] pp., BINDING: eighteenth-century vellum-backed marbled paper boards

£800-1,200
€1,200-1,750

1514 Neve, Richard. Mathematicks made plain, in the solution of variety of useful propositions... all perform'd by that excellent line of numbers, commonly call'd Gunter's-Line. Being a necessary companion for gentlemen, military officers, engineers, architects... *London: W. Pearson for G. Conyers, J. Sprint and T. Ballard, 1708*

12mo (161 x 93mm.), [12], 276, [1]pp., BINDING: contemporary speckled calf, spine gilt in compartments, morocco lettering-piece, red speckled edges, *extremities slightly rubbed*

FIRST EDITION. Neve also wrote books on architecture, building, chemistry and mechanics.

References: Taylor, *Tudor & Stuart* 581 (giving publication date as 1707)

£300-400
€450-600

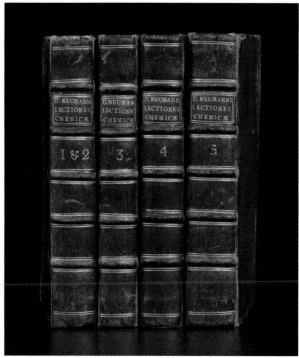
1515

1515 Neumann, Caspar (1683-1737). Lectiones publicae von vier subjectis pharmaceuticis, nehmlich vom Succino, Opio, Caryophyllis aromaticis, und Castoreo. *Berlin: Ambrosius Haude, 1730*, [20], 226pp., ILLUSTRATION: woodcut initials, head- and tailpieces

Ibid. Lectiones chymicae von Salibus alkalino-fixis und von Camphora. *Berlin: widow of Gotthard Schlechtiger, 1727*, [8], 164pp., ILLUSTRATION: woodcut initials, head- and tailpieces

Ibid. Lectiones publicae von vier subjectis chimicis, nehmlich vom Salpeter, Schwesel, Spiess-Glas und Eisen. *Berlin: Johann Gottfried Michaelis, 1732*, [16], 440pp., ILLUSTRATION: woodcut initials, head- and tailpieces

Ibid. Lectiones publicae von vier subjectis diaeteticis...vom Thee, Caffee, Bier, und Wein... *Leipzig: Gottlob Benjamin Fromman, 1735*, [28], 468pp., ILLUSTRATION: woodcut initials, head- and tailpieces

Ibid. Lectiones publicae von vier subjectis pharmaceutico-chemicis, nehmlich vom gemeinem Salmtze, Weinstein, Salmiac und der Ameise... *Leipzig: Gottlob Benjamin Frommann, 1737*, [8], 379, [1]pp., ILLUSTRATION: woodcut initials, head- and tailpieces, *Ee3 torn and repaired in margin*

5 works in 4 volumes, 4to (206 x 161mm.), BINDING: uniform contemporary calf gilt, spines gilt in compartments with red morocco lettering-pieces, contemporary English annotations, *occasional slight browning, extremities slightly rubbed*

Neumann apprenticed as an apothecary and worked in Berlin, London, Paris and Holland. He was a member of the Royal Society and of the Berlin Academy of Sciences. He was appointed court pharmacist in Berlin in 1719 and then professor of practical chemistry at the Medical-Surgical college there. Many of his papers were first published in the *Philosophical Transactions* of the Royal Society, and these volumes of lectures were published in English in 1759.

References: Ferguson II, p.137; Krivatsy p.323; Partington II, 702-706

£3,000-4,000
€4,350-5,800

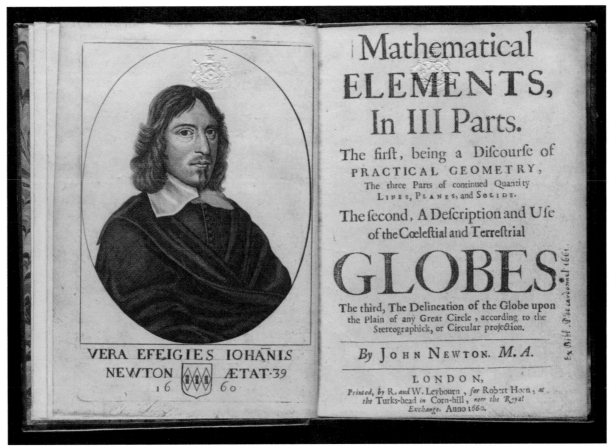

1516

1516 Newton, John (1621-1678). Mathematical elements in three parts... Practical geometry... a description and use of the... globes... The delineation of the globe upon the plain of any great circle, according to the stereographick, or circular projection. *London: R. & W. Leybourn for R. Horn, 1660*

4to (185 x 125mm.), [4], 218, [2]pp., ILLUSTRATION: engraved portrait of Newton dated 1660, engraved slide rule on p.[viii], with advert on previous recto for Anthony Thompson as maker, 6 engraved plates for part 1, 4 for part 2 and 4 for part 3, BINDING: eighteenth-century mottled calf, spine gilt in compartments, red edges

A handsome copy of an uncommon book, first published in 1657 (one copy only recorded, at Castle Ashby). This is probably a reissue of the sheets of the 1657 edition. The advertisements on the last leaf comprise the Post-Script advertising "blank charts... made in imperial paper, both for plain and for Mercators sailing", available from Horn, and books sold by him.

References: Wing N1066

Provenance: P. de Cardonnel, inscription on title-page dated 1661 (see lot 1406)

£2,000-3,000
€2,900-4,350

Arithmetica Universalis;

SIVE

DE COMPOSITIONE

ET

RESOLUTIONE

ARITHMETICA

LIBER.

Cui accessit

HALLEIANA

*Æquationum Radices Arithmeticé
inveniendi methodus.*

In Usum Juventutis Academicæ.

CANTABRIGIÆ

TYPIS ACADEMICIS.

LONDINI, Impensis *Benj. Tooke* Bibliopolæ juxta Medii Templi Portam in vico
vulgo vocato *Fleetstreet.* A. D. MDCCVII.

1517

[1]

Universal Arithmetick;

OR, A

TREATISE

OF

Arithmetical COMPOSITION
and RESOLUTION.

OMPUTATION is either perform'd by
Numbers, as in Vulgar Arithmetick, or by
Species, as usual among Algebraists. They are
both built on the same Foundations, and aim
at the same End, *viz. Arithmetick* Definitely and Particularly, *Algebra* Indefinitely and
Universally; so that almost all Expressions
that are found out by this Computation, and particularly Conclusions, may be call'd *Theorems.* But *Algebra* is particularly
excellent in this, that whereas in *Arithmetick* Questions are
only resolv'd by proceeding from given Quantities to the
Quantities sought, *Algebra* proceeds, in a retrograde Order,

B   from

1518

ARITHMETICÆ UNIVERSALIS;

SIVE

DE

COMPOSITIONE

ET

RESOLUTIONE

ARITHMETICA

LIBER.

Auctore IS. NEWTON, Eq. Aur.

LUGDUNI BATAVORUM,

Apud JOH. ET HERM. VERBEEK, Bibliopolæ

MDCCXXXII.

1519

Arithmetica Universalis:

SIVE

DE COMPOSITIONE

ET

RESOLUTIONE

ARITHMETICA

LIBER.

EDITIO SECUNDA,

*In qua multa immutantur & emendantur,
nonnulla adduntur.*

LONDINI;

Impensis BENJ. & SAM. TOOKE, Bibliopolarum;
juxta Medii Templi Portam, in Vico vulgo vocato
Fleetstreet. M.DCC.XXII.

1520

1517 Newton, *Sir* **Isaac (1642-1727).** Arithmetica universalis; sive de compositione et resolutione arithmetica liber. Cui accessit Halleiana aequationum radices arithmetice inveniendi methodus [edited by William Whiston]. *Cambridge: typis academicis; London: for B. Tooke, 1707*

8vo (192 x 112mm.), [8], 343pp., half-title, ILLUSTRATION: woodcut diagrams, BINDING: contemporary panelled calf, spine gilt, *slightly rubbed*

FIRST EDITION, edited by Whiston from the manuscript of Newton's Lucasian lectures which were on deposit in Cambridge. Newton liked nothing about the book, and even threatened to buy up the whole edition, as well as complaining about the running titles, but when he republished it himself, the changes he made were primarily the reordering of his own manuscript, and not what Whiston had done. (The printer's copy for this 1707 edition, of which 1000 copies were printed, is in Cambridge University Library.) The piece by Halley occupied pp. 327 to the end, and is reprinted from the *Philosophical Transactions*.

References: Babson 199; Wallis 377; McKenzie pp.278-279; Newton, *Mathematical Papers* V

£1,500-2,000
€2,200-2,900

1518 [Newton, *Sir* **Isaac]** [Arithmetica universalis] Universal arithmetick: or, a treatise of arithmetical composition and resolution. To which is added, Dr. Halley's method of finding the roots of aequations arithmetically. Translated... by the late Mr. Raphson, and revised and corrected by Mr. Cunn. *London: J. Senex, W. Taylor, T. Warner, and J. Osborn, 1720*

FIRST EDITION IN ENGLISH, 8vo (195 x 115mm.), [4], iv, 272pp., half-title, ILLUSTRATION: 8 numbered engraved folding plates, all printed on extensions, small slip with manuscript diagram at p.230, BINDING: contemporary mottled calf, gilt spine, red edges

References: Babson 201; Wallis 283

£500-600
€750-900

1519 Newton, *Sir* **Isaac.** Arithmetica universalis; sive de compositione et resolutione arithmetica liber [with works by Halley, Colson, A. de Moivre, MacLaurin and Campbell, all reprinted from *Philosophical Transactions*, and translated into Latin by J.P. Bernard, edited by W.J.S. van s' Gravesande]. *Leiden: J. & H. Verbeek, 1732*

4to (246 x 185mm.), [8], 344pp., title-page printed in red and black, ILLUSTRATION: engraved device on title-page, 13 folding engraved plates, BINDING: contemporary calf, *a little rubbed*

References: Babson 204; Wallis 279

£800-1,000
€1,200-1,450

1520 Newton, *Sir* **Isaac.** Arithmetica universalis: sive de compositione et resolutione arithmetica liber. Editio secunda, in qua multa immutantur & emendantur, nonnulla adduntur. *London: for B. & S. Tooke, 1722*

8vo (200 x 120mm.), [2], 322pp., title-leaf printed on heavier paper, ILLUSTRATION: woodcut figures, BINDING: contemporary mottled calf, blue edges, *joints very worn*

Revised by Newton himself, who already by September 1720 was "fort avancé", this second edition of his Lucasian lectures incoporates up-to-the-minute revisions. The cancelled leaf U6, which in this copy has almost the air of being a page proof, is a vivid testimony to this (cf. *Mathematical Papers* V, p.469 note 686). The section by Halley which had been included in the 1707 edition edited by Whiston (see lot 1517) is here omitted.

The running-titles throughout the 1707 edition which had so vexed Newton were simply ALGEBRAE and ELEMENTA on facing versos and rectos. In this edition the running-titles change according to the text up to p.75 and thereafter the versos have *Resolutio Quaestionum* and the rectos ARITHMETICARUM (to p.97), *Resolutio Quaestionum* GEOMETRICARUM (p.99-239), AEQUATIONUM NATURA (pp.240-241), AEQUATIONUM and NATURA on facing versos and rectos (pp.242-249), AEQUATIONUM NATURA on p.250, and thereafter they change again in accordance with the text. The book is therefore much easier to find one's way around. In addition there is a greater use of italic in this edition.

Benjamin Tooke, the London publisher and printer (he was Queen's printer), had eight books published at the Cambridge Press, all of them by Whiston, between 1702 and 1712. There are two London printer's ornaments used in this volume (pp.283 & 289, and nowhere else), but we know that the woodcuts for the illustrations in the 1707 edition were delivered to Cambridge, possibly from London (6d. was paid for the parcel; McKenzie, p.278). So far as one can tell, the woodcuts are identical, and we must assume they had been reclaimed by Tooke. Unfortunately, we have no letters from Newton about the printing history of this volume.

At p.56 is a small slip with a note on extraction referring to Albert Girard's work of 1629, which was in Jones' collection, and at p.316 is inserted a leaf of early eighteenth-century manuscript with the figure and text as appearing in the cancellans ("pag. 316 lin. 12 lege"). Jones has also numbered the problemata in ink with the numbers they bore in the 1707 edition.

References: Babson 200; Wallis 278

£1,500-2,000
€2,200-2,900
See illustration on p. 276

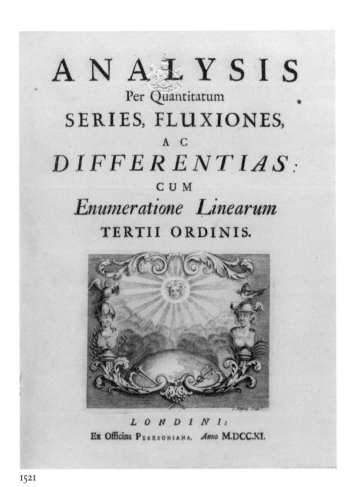

ANALYSIS
Per Quantitatum
SERIES, FLUXIONES,
A C
DIFFERENTIAS:
CUM
Enumeratione Linearum
TERTII ORDINIS.

LONDINI:
Ex Officina PEARSONIANA. *Anno* M.DCC.XI.

1521

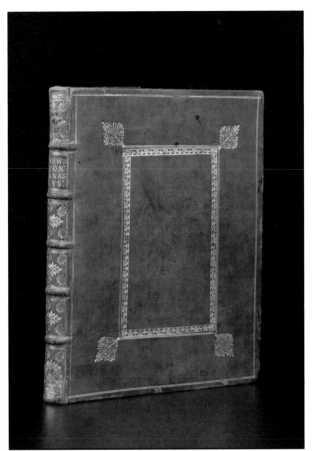

1521

To the R.t Hon:ble S.r Tho.s Parker
Kn.t
Lord Chief Justice of England,

This Book is most Humbly Presented

By

W.m Jones.

1521

1521 Newton, *Sir* **Isaac.** Analysis per quantitatum series, fluxiones, ac differentias: cum enumeratione linearum tertii ordinis [and other works, edited with a preface by William Jones]. *London: ex officina Pearsoniana, 1711*

4to (232 x 175mm.), [14], 101pp., ILLUSTRATION: woodcut typographical ornaments, woodcut figures in the text, engraved vignettes and initials, engraved table on p.62 and 2 double-page engraved tables inserted between pp. 62 & 63, all engraved by John Senex, engraved vignettes and initials (see below), BINDING: contemporary panelled calf, gilt panel on covers within a gilt double fillet, spine gilt, *slightly rubbed, worn at head of spine*

FIRST EDITION AND PRESENTATION COPY FROM JONES TO SIR THOMAS PARKER, LORD CHIEF JUSTICE OF ENGLAND. A remarkable association copy. As the editors of Newton *Correspondence* remark: "without mentioning Leibniz or the calculus dispute, Jones in eleven short pages presented powerful evidence of Newton's mathematical originality as far back as 1665. For the first time the testimony of Newton's earliest communications... was set before the public, thus anticipating the fuller documentation attempted in the *Commercium epistolicum*" (*Correspondence* V, p. 95 note 7).

When Jones published *De analysi* with no indication of Newton's authorship other than in the preface, he made use of the papers he had obtained in 1708, with Newton's agreement, and added, as well as *De quadratura, Enumeratio linearum tertii ordinis*, and *Methodus differentialis*, fragments of four letters to Oldenburg, Wallis and Collins. In this preface he attempted to give a very brief history of Newton's mathematical evolution. Jones also penned for Thomas Birch a fuller English account of Newton's mathematics, which remains unpublished (the autograph is CUL Add. 3960.2; see *Mathematical Papers* VIII, 22 n.34) and is dismissed by Professor Whiteside as 'unscholarly' and 'a mere historical curiosity', but which does have some interest.

The book itself is handsomely printed and makes use of a number of engraved vignettes, that on the title-page signed J. Nutting. This vignette has at the side the figures of Athene and Hermes, with the insignia of the trumpet (of Fame) and the *caduceus* of Hermes, and at the centre the sun with Newton's face shining upon the globe of the earth with his rays. There is a tail-piece used three times, once with a motto.

De quadratura was first published with *Opticks* in 1704. The *Methodus differentialis* was printed in 1711 from Jones's transcription of Newton's own autograph, which does not survive (*Mathematical Papers* VIII, 236 n.1), but some fragments of a 'preliminary augmentation of 1676 parent text' are printed by Whiteside from the originals in CUL (dating from just before 1710). Whiteside also prints the full text of Jones's transcription (*Mathematical Papers* VIII, 244 onwards).

Jones's edition of these texts earned him the fellowship of the Royal Society and praise both at home and abroad. On the home front Roger Cotes wrote on 15 February 1711 congratulating him, and it was to Jones that Cotes, who was editing the second edition of *Principia*, sent the text of the Index to it (completed April 1713). Cotes wrote on 3 May 1713 delighted that Jones had approved the index but stating "that it was not design'd to be of any use to such readers as your self, but to those of ordinary capacity".

References: Babson 207; Wallis 293

£30,000-40,000
€43,500-58,000
See illustrations on previous page

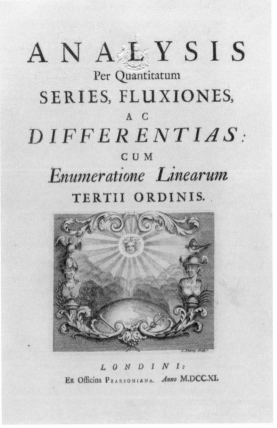

1522

1522

1522 Newton, *Sir* **Isaac.** Analysis per quantitatum series, fluxiones, ac differentias: cum enumeratione linearum tertii ordinis [and other works, edited with a preface by William Jones]. *London: ex officina Pearsoniana, 1711*

4to (230 x 190mm.), [14], 101, [3]pp., last leaf blank, manuscript errata leaf (by Jones) pasted on, mezzotint portrait after Kneller inserted, ILLUSTRATION: 1 engraved table on p. 62 and 2 double-page engraved tables, all engraved by John Senex, 77 numbered small engraved figures, with a further unnumbered at p. 97, a few small woodcut figures, handsome engraved head- and tailpieces and one initial (T), engraved by Joseph Nutting, woodcut headpieces etc., BINDING: contemporary English red morocco, gilt panel on covers with gilt fleuron corner-pieces, within a double gilt fillet, gilt spine lettered in gilt, elaborate decorated paper liners, gilt edges, *upper joint cracking*

FIRST EDITION AND THE EDITOR'S OWN COPY. There is one leaf of manuscript by Jones at p. 64: 'Mr Newton in the Introduction to the Tract De Quadratura Curvarum has shewed that if any indeterminate quantity increase or flow uniformly or in proportion to time, & its fluxion or velocity of increasing be represented by an unit, & its moment of velocity generated in a moment of time be called 0... [ending] And the same thing is to be understood of the series mentioned in the 10th proposition of the second book of the Principia Philosophiae. But the second and third moments are not there considered nor have any thing to do with the method there proposed of solving problems by converging series. The method of fluxions is different from that of converging series, & both methods together make up one general method according to Mr Newton'. This seems to relate to the second paragraph of the scholium on p. 64.

A hitherto unnoticed autograph manuscript by Newton, found in this book, is described in the next lot.

References: Babson 207; Wallis 293

£25,000-35,000
€36,200-51,000

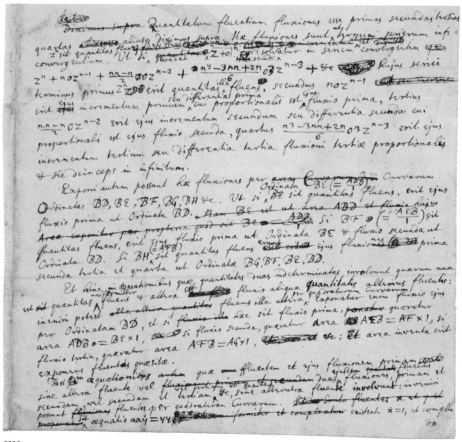

1523

1523 Newton, *Sir* **Isaac.** AUTOGRAPH MANUSCRIPT of part of the *De quadratura curvarum*. [*c. 1670s*]

folio (290 x 188mm.), 1 leaf written in ink on both sides, paper with frequent deletions and revisions, paper unwatermarked, loose in folder

An autograph from this late period of the master's activity, still showing, as always, changes and corrections. This single leaf was found in the copy of the 1711 *Analysis* given by Jones to the first Earl of Macclesfield (see lot 1522).

The text begins (deletions and changes not printed): In his Tabulis series curvarum cujusque formae utrinque in infinitum continuari potest (top of p.63 in the printed text) and consists of 3 initial paragraphs, which constitute the first section of p.63. The section prop. XI. Theor. VIII is omitted (i.e. the remainder of p.63) and the text resumes with the corollary on p.64 ('unde curvae quarum ordinatae sunt...') followed by the Scholium in 11 paragraphs (pp.64-66 of the printed text). The latter begins: 'Quantitatum fluentium fluxiones esse primas secundas tertias quartas aliasque diximus supra, Hae fluxiones sunt ut termini serierum...'. The text is as the printed text, but in the paragraph beginning 'Aequationes quae tres incognitas quantitates involvunt aliquando reduci possunt...' some five lines of text have been crossed out and (in part) rewritten.

Newton began work on this subject in the mid-1670s. In the mid-1680s various details came into the public domain as Newton had shown his materials to the Scottish mathematician John Craige, who had not remained reticent on his return to Scotland.

References: Wallis 293; Newton, *Mathematical papers* VIII, 1981

 # £25,000-35,000
€36,200-51,000

1524 Newton, *Sir* Isaac. Philosophiae naturalis principia mathematica. Editio secunda auctior et emendatior (edited with a preface by Roger Cotes). *Cambridge: Cambridge University Press, 1713*

4to (245 x 188mm.), [28], 484, [8]pp., ILLUSTRATION: woodcut diagrams, engraved device on title-page, BINDING: nineteenth-century half calf by Hatton of Manchester, *old repair to base of title-leaf*

Second edition of the *Principia* but in many ways as important as the first. Newton's revisions are of great importance, and above all this second edition contains the "Scholium generale" which is completely new.

Newton's constant revisions, begun in 1687, carried on without stop, but it was not until 1708 that the idea of a "reprint", to be produced at Cambridge, was considered. Newton's corrections had circulated in manuscript, transcribed by him into copies of the 1687 edition and in some cases transcribed by associates, with others deriving directly or indirectly from Newton's own copies; Fatio de Duillier had indeed sent them to Huygens, whence they came to Leibnitz, and in 1701 Johann Groening printed them in his *Historia cycloeidis* published in Hamburg, which contains Huygens's *Annotata posthuma in Isaaci Newtoni* (see Appendix IV, "The dissemination of Newton's manuscript corrections and annotations to E1" in Koyré & Cohen). Fatio, whose own copy is in the Bodleian, had actually proposed a new edition in folio, and from his work on the 1687 edition, we can see how he would have introduced running heads and postils and other improvements to the use of the book. But essentially nothing was done and the price of the first edition rose considerably (as had happened with Hobbes' *Leviathan* a good few years earlier).

The Cambridge Press had recently been reinvigorated (in the mid 1690s), and, whilst not alone, the great classical scholar Richard Bentley played a very important role in this. Bentley had been chaplain to Bishop Stillingfleet and in 1692 had been chosen to give the Boyle Lectures, in which he tried to reconcile religion and the new science. From that date onwards, Bentley's star was in the ascendant, and in 1700 he was created Master of Trinity College. As the late Don McKenzie puts it, "almost alone among critics he perceived the implications for the classics of the natural scientists search for demonstrable authority... The *sine qua non*, the necessary instrument, for such a programme [of re-doing the work of the past], was a learned Press" (McKenzie, p. 9).

In the years 1696 to 1713 some 274 items, books and ephemera, were produced at the press, ranging from large works of scholarship to book labels. These included various classical texts, including Joshua Barnes's edition of Homer, Kuster's huge edition of the Suda (1705, produced in large number of copies) and Bentley's Horace, some patristic and theological works, and a few scientific works by Flamsteed, Whiston and Newton.

In 1708 Bentley had a specimen of *Principia* printed, of which no copy survives, but the type was kept standing. Bentley wrote to Newton on 10 June 1708 mentioning this specimen and saying that the revision "is expected here with great impatience, & the prospect of it has already lowered ye price of ye former edition above half of what it once was" (*Correspondence* IV, 742), at the same time discussing the typography of the "proof sheet" and the changes he has introduced such as a running title, and the use of Genoese paper (this was highly prized, and was particularly good for taking illustrations).

The work went forward very slowly and in May 1709 the Trinity mathematician Roger Cotes became editor, and went to see Newton in London. Newton was, as Halley had found out, slow and needed to be pushed, and he was of course by this time a public figure in London with many tasks to hand. Cotes's contribution is well shown in two manuscripts, one at Trinity (R.16.38) which contains Cotes's letters during the printing, and another volume which was in the Portsmouth Collection, most of which relate to the later period of production (all printed in *Correspondence*). In April 1710 the printing was half completed and Cotes informed Newton that he had ventured to make some changes, and indeed what are shown in the critical edition of *Principia* as "variae lectiones" are as often as not from the pen of Cotes or Bentley, and not from Newton. We do not however know exactly how many changes, or what changes, were introduced by Cotes. We know from other sources that Newton could be extremely fussy about how he wrote something, but one might imagine that Bentley, one of the greatest Latinists of all time, may well have had some polishing to do.

Newton sent Cotes the manuscript of the "Scholium generale" to Cotes on 2 March 1712/13. Later in the month (28 March 1713), Newton wrote to Cotes asking him to make two changes. He asked him to add "Et haec de Deo: de quo utique ex phaenomenis disserere, ad Philosophiam experimentalem pertinet". Cotes copied this out *litteratim*, but changed "phaenomenis" to "Phaenomenis". In the printed book this appears as "Et haec de Deo; de quo... ad *Philosophiam Experimentalem* pertinet". (The word "experimentalis" has an interesting history; in the third edition it was famously changed to "naturalis"). The second change was connected with the word "hypothesis". Newton had originally written: "Rationem vero harum gravitates proprietatum ex phaenomenis nondum potui deducere, & hypotheses non fingo. Quicquid enim ex phaenomenis non deducitur, hypothesis vocanda est...". He wished to change this to: "Quicquid enim ex phaenomenis non deducitur Hypothesis vocanda est, et ejusmodi hypotheses... in Philosophia experimentali locum non habent...". Cotes wrote out the new sentences in the margin but he made various accidental changes, and most importantly omitted the word "ejusmodi", which did not appear in the printed text, where, as a matter of fact, various other accidental changes, from whatever source, were made.

What we have therefore in this second edition is a splendid example of how a book was produced in the hand press period with a text with: (a) authorial revision, largely quantifiable: (b) editorial revision, to a small extent quantifiable but not necessarily attributable to one hand; (c) the interaction of printing-house practice to a degree which cannot be determined. What we do not have - and this is of course true of something like the Shakespeare Folio - is a text which we can confidently state to be "ex manu autoris". The text of first edition, set from Humphrey Newton's fair copy (M, a manuscript now in the Royal Society) was itself, as we see, eminently mutable. Texts do not remain fixed, and it is not for nothing that the first three editions of *Principia* are called the "substantive editions", each of them having its own position in the evolution of the text, which properly does not attain its full form until the third edition of 1726.

Seven hundred copies of the book were printed, some distributed to foreign dignitaries and savants (for the copy sent to France to the abbé Bignon who thanked Newton in a letter, see Sotheby's New York, 4 December 2004, lot 512) and the rest put on sale. Many institutions received copies very quickly: Eton College, for example, was given a copy by Thomas Horne in 1713.

References: Babson 12; Wallis 8; Todd E2 (in Koyré and Cohen II); for the history of the publication see McKenzie I, pp. 330-336, no. 239

Provenance: Richard Bentley; possibly given by him to William Jones

£10,000-15,000
€14,500-21,800

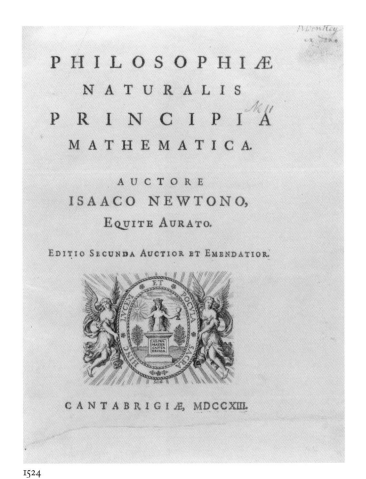

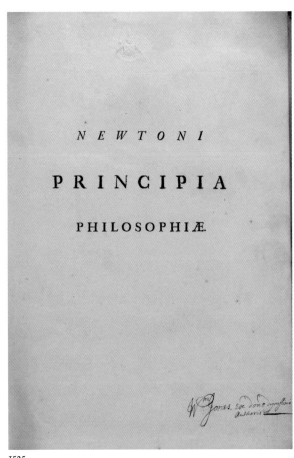

1524   1525

1525 Newton, *Sir* **Isaac.** Philosophiae naturalis principia mathematica... *Editio tertia aucta et emendata* [edited by H. Pemberton]. *London: [W. Bowyer for] W. & J. Innys, 1726*

4to (327 x 225mm.), ONE OF 50 LARGE PAPER COPIES, [32], 530, [6]pp., title printed in red and black, ILLUSTRATION: half-title with mezzotint portrait by Vertue, proof *avant la lettre* pasted to verso, BINDING: contemporary russia leather, gilt border on covers, spine with 7 raised bands, gilt in 7 compartments, black morocco lettering-piece, gilt edges, *without the Innys advertisement leaves at the end and the Licence of 25 March*

PRESENTATION COPY ON LARGE PAPER FROM THE AUTHOR TO WILLIAM JONES, inscribed on the half-title "Wm Jones ex dono dignissimi authoris". Fifty copies of this impression on Writing Super Royal paper were printed, watermark a fleur-de-lis within a crown (Heawood 1803). The complete edition consisted of 1250 copies.

Pemberton's role in the work is discussed by Koyré and Cohen II, appendix VI (pp.827-47).

References: Babson 13; Wallis 10; Todd E3; see the census of copies of the 1687 and 1726 editions by Macomber in *PBSA* xlvii (1953), with a census of copies of this impression on pp.292-300; *Bowyer Ledgers* 1202

£20,000-30,000
€29,000-43,500

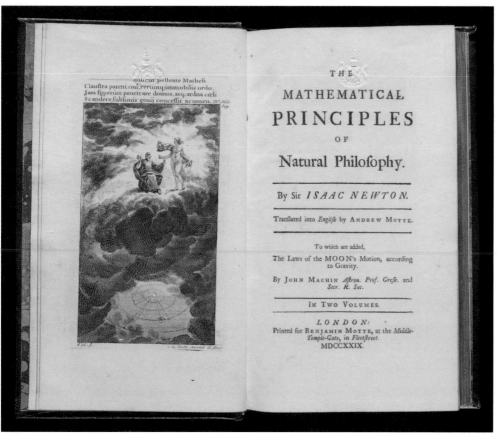

1526

1526 Newton, *Sir* **Isaac.** [Principia] The mathematical principles of natural philosophy... Translated... by Andrew Motte. To which are added, the lawes of the moon's motion, according to gravity. By John Machin... In two volumes. *London: for B. Motte, 1729*

2 volumes, 8vo (227 x 130mm.), [38], 320; [2], 393, [13], with printed table at p. 377; viii, 71, [1]pp., errata for both volumes at end of volume 2, thick paper copy, ILLUSTRATION: engraved frontispieces in both volumes by Motte, 25 folding engraved plates in volume I, 19 & 3 in volume II, numbered in 3 sequences, engraved head-pieces by Motte, BINDING: contemporary black morocco, gilt border on covers, spines gilt, red morocco lettering-pieces, red edges, *binding a little rubbed and scuffed*

FIRST EDITION IN ENGLISH. Andrew Motte (1696-1734) was the son of the well-known printer Benjamin Motte, and very briefly a lecturer on geometry at Gresham College. This translation, which is based on the 1726 Pemberton edition of the Latin text, is a handsome work, dedicated to Sir Hans Sloane as President of the Royal Society, and was revised later in the eighteenth century by Thorp.

The frontispiece to volume I shows the apotheosis of Newton, and quotes four lines from Halley's liminary verses to the original edition of *Principia*; that to volume II shows a pendulum and has two references to the text, one in the scholium generale.

References: Babson 20; Wallis 23; I.B. Cohen, 'Pemberton's translation of Newton's *Principia*, with notes on Motte's translation', *Isis* 54 (1963), 319-51; M. Feingold, *Isaac Newton and the Making of Modern Culture* (New York, 2004), p.144

£3,000-5,000
€4,350-7,300

1527 Newton, *Sir* **Isaac.** Philosophiae naturalis principia mathematica... perpetuis commentariis [largely by Jean Louis Calandrini] illustrata, communi studio PP. Thomae Le Seur & Francisci Jacquier. *Geneva: Barrillot & sons, 1739-1742*

3 parts in 2 volumes, 4to (244 x 180mm.), xxxv, [1], 548; [8], 422; [8], xxvii (Introductio ad tertium librum), 374, viii [actually 6], 375-703pp., titles printed in red and black, half-titles in part 1 and 2 but not in part 3, ILLUSTRATION: numerous woodcut figures etc., BINDING: eighteenth-century English polished calf, gilt spines, morocco lettering-pieces, red edges, *?lacking one leaf from preliminaries of book 3 continuation, small hole at foot of spine of first volume*

This edition, taken from the third edition of *Principia*, was edited by two Minim fathers, Thomas le Seur (1703-1770) and François Jacquier (1711-1788), both known for their work at St Peter's, Rome (*Pareri di tre mattematici* and *Riflessioni*, both published in 1742, on the cracks in the fabric), but the extensive notes are actually by Calandrini (1703-1758), professor of philosophy at Geneva.

The 'Introductio ad tertium librum', according to Wallis, forms part of the 1760 Geneva edition, although it is sometimes found in copies of this edition.

References: Wallis 13; Babson 30

£2,000-3,000
€2,900-4,350

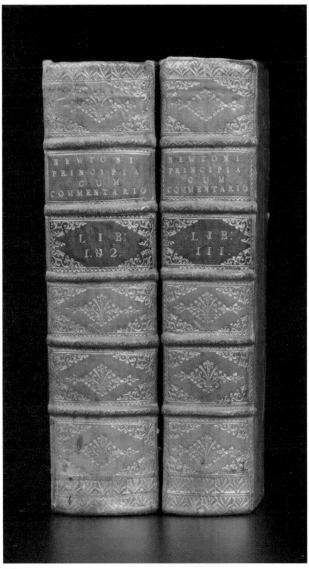

1527

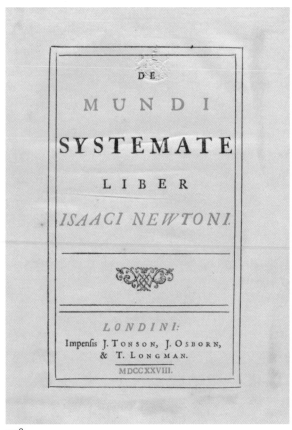

1528

1528 Newton, *Sir* **Isaac.** De mundi systemate liber. *London: [printed for] J. Tonson, J. Osborn & T. Longman, 1728*

4to (237 x 180mm.), iv, 108pp., ILLUSTRATION: inserted mezzotint portrait, 2 folding engraved plates at end, BINDING: contemporary sprinkled calf, red edges, *slightly rubbed*

LARGE PAPER COPY of an earlier version of book III of Newton's *Principia*.

References: Wallis 19; Babson 16

£2,000-3,000
€2,900-4,350

1529 Newton, *Sir* **Isaac.** A treatise of the system of the world… Translated into English. The second edition, wherein are interspersed some alterations and improvements. *London: for F. Fayram, 1731*

8vo (200 x 125mm.), [16], 152pp., first leaf with note to reader, ILLUSTRATION: 2 engraved plates (pp. 6 & 29), diagrams in text, BINDING: contemporary English mottled calf, gilt spine, green silk marker, red edges, *label chipped*

First printed in 1728, as a translation of *De systemate mundi* (an earlier version of *Principia* III; see lot 1528), which was possibly edited by Conduitt, this second edition contains marginal references to the 1729 English translation of *Principia*.

References: Wallis 31; see Cohen, pp. 109 onwards

Provenance: WILLIAM JONES'S COPY with two manuscript diagrams loosely inserted at pp. 6 & 81.

£1,000-1,500
€1,450-2,200

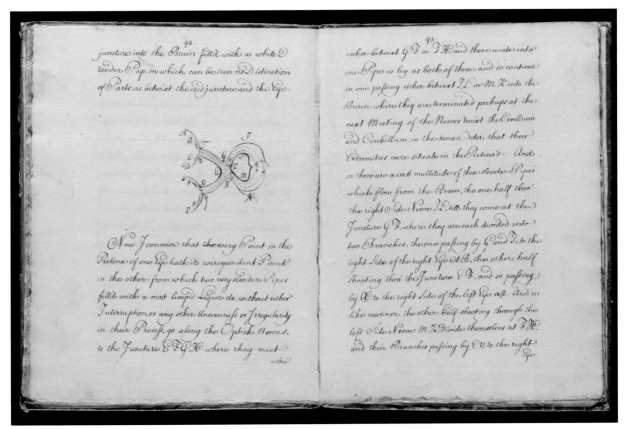

junaine into the Brain fill'd with a white
tender Pap, in which can be seen no Distinction
of Parts, as betwixt the said juncture and the Eye.

either betwixt GF or FH and there unite into
one Pipe as big as both of them, and so continue
in one passing either betwixt IL or MZ into the
Brain, where they are terminated perhaps at the
next Meeting of the Nerves twixt the Cerebrum
and Cerebellum, in the same Order that their
Extremities were situate in the Retina's. And
so there are a vast multitude of these slender Pipes
which flow from the Brain, the one half thro'
the right Side Nerve IL, till they come at the
Juncture GF, where they are each divided into
two Branches, the one passing by G and I, to the
right Side of the right Eye AB, the other half
shooting thro' the Juncture FH, and so passing
by H to the right Side of the left Eye aß. And in
like manner, the other half shooting through the
left Side Nerve MZ, divide themselves at FH,
and their Branches passing by FV to the right
Eye

Now I conceive that the every Point in the
Retina of one Eye hath its correspondent Point
in the other: from which two very slender Pipes
fill'd with a most limpid Liquor do, without either
Interruption, or any other Unevenness or Irregularity
in their Process, go along the Optick Nerves.
to the Juncture EFGH where they meet

1531

1530 Newton, *Sir* **Isaac.** Optical lectures read in the publick schools of the University of Cambridge, Anno Domini, 1669... Never before printed. Translated into English out of the original Latin. *London: Francis Fayram, 1728*

8vo (200 x 115mm.), xi, [1], 212pp., ILLUSTRATION: 13 numbered engraved folding plates with 62 figures, BINDING: eighteenth-century polished calf, gilt spine, red morocco lettering-piece

A handsome copy printed on thick paper. This is an anonymous incomplete translation of Book I of *Lectiones opticae.*

References: Wallis 190; Babson 154

£1,500-2,000
€2,200-2,900

1531 Newton, *Sir* **Isaac.** Manuscript copy of his tract "Of Colours". *[London, early eighteenth century]*

4to (243 x 190mm.) 54pp., (scribal note on lower paste-down "at 1½ᵈ p[er] page 6ˢ.9ᵈ"), written in a neat professional hand on paper (watermark, coat of arms akin to Heawood 452-473, *c.* 1683-1729), ILLUSTRATION: ink-drawn diagrams, BINDING: contemporary vellum-backed marbled boards

£1,000-1,500
€1,450-2,200

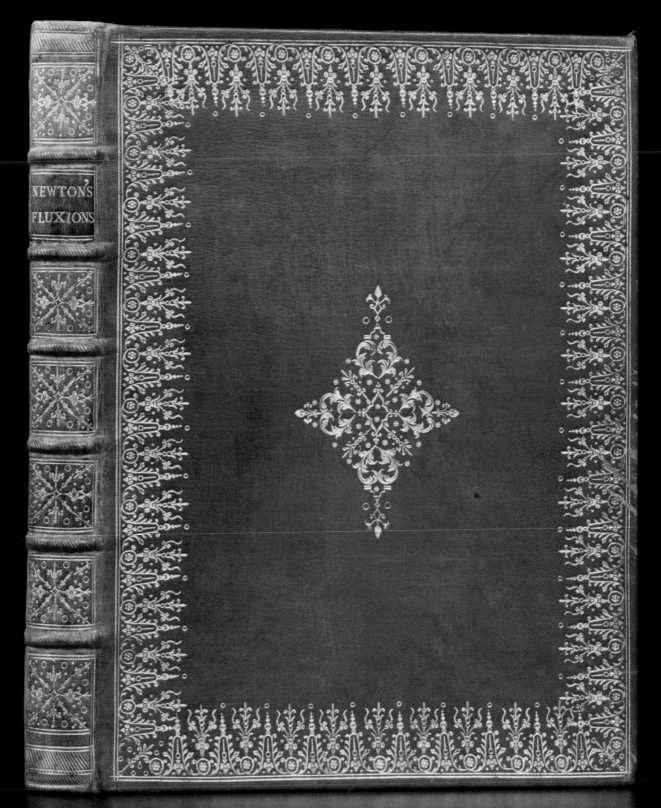

1532 Newton, *Sir* **Isaac.** The method of fluxions and infinite series; with its application to the geometry of curve-lines… To which is subjoin'd a perpetual comment… Translated… by John Colson, [etc.]. *London: H. Woodfall and sold by John Nourse, 1736*

4to (290 x 220mm.), iv, ix-xiv, 339pp., BINDING: contemporary English red morocco gilt in the Harleian style, gilt central cartouche on covers with broad dentelle within a double fillet, spine gilt in seven compartments, one with green morocco lettering-piece, gilt turn-ins, gilt edges

THE LARGE PAPER DEDICATION COPY TO WILLIAM JONES, who has made the odd correction. This translation was made from a manuscript copy of the Latin in Jones's possession.

References: Babson 171; Wallis 232

£6,000-8,000
€8,700-11,600

1533 Newton, *Sir* **Isaac.** La methode des fluxions [translated by Georges Louis Le Clerc]. *Paris: De Bure l'aîné, 1740*

FIRST AND ONLY EDITION IN FRENCH, 4to (260 x 190mm.), xxx, [4] (errata and privilege), 148pp., title printed in red and black, ILLUSTRATION: woodcut figures etc., BINDING: contemporary French mottled calf, spine gilt

References: Babson 173; Wallis 236

£1,000-1,500
€1,450-2,200

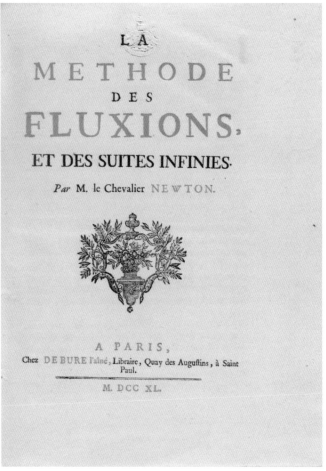

1533

1534 Newton, *Sir* **Isaac—Stirling, James (1692-1770).** Lineae tertii ordinis Neutonianae, sive illustratio tractatus D. Neutoni de enumeratione linearum tertii ordinis, cui subjungitur, solutio trium problematum. *Oxford: at the Sheldonian Theatre, 1717*

8vo (192 x 117mm.), [4], 128, 19pp., ILLUSTRATION: engraving on title of the Sheldonian Theatre, woodcut diagrams, BINDING: contemporary mottled calf gilt, spine gilt in compartments, manuscript amendments to the text, *without the 8-page list of subscribers, binding slightly rubbed*

FIRST EDITION. By 1695 Newton had identified 72 cubic curves. Stirling announced another four in this addition to Newton's *Enumeratio linearum tertii ordinis.* The last two were discovered in the 1730s by François Nicole and Nicolas Bernoulli.

References: Wallis 301

£300-500
€450-750

1535 Newton, *Sir* **Isaac—Stewart, John (d. 1766),** *Professor at Aberdeen.* Sir Isaac Newton's two treatises of the quadrature of curves, and analysis by equations of an infinite number of terms, explained. *London: J. Bettenham, at the expence of the Society for the Encouragement of Learning; and sold by John Nourse and John Whiston, 1745*

4to (265 x 195mm.), xxxii, 479, [5]pp., last 2 leaves with errata etc., ILLUSTRATION: woodcut figures in text, tail-piece at end designed by William Kent and engraved by Virtue, BINDING: contemporary black morocco, gilt fillet on covers, spine gilt, red morocco lettering-piece, red edges

FIRST EDITION of Stewart's translation and commentary, and a very handsome copy. The Society for the Encouragement of Learning existed to enable authors to be rewarded for their labours. Unfortunately in this case they did not succeed: the book, of which 350 copies had been printed, was in large part remaindered two years later.

References: Babson 210; Wallis 303

£1,500-2,500
€2,200-3,650

1536 Newton, *Sir* **Isaac—Whiston, William (1667-1752).** [Praelectiones physico-mathematicae] Sir Isaac Newton's mathematick philosophy more easily demonstrated: with Dr Halley's account of comets illustrated. Being forty lectures read in the publick schools at Cambridge. *London: J. Senex & W. Taylor, 1716*

8vo (195 x 115mm.), [4], 443, [1]pp., half-title with advertisements on verso, ILLUSTRATION: 9 folding engraved plates by Senex, all printed on extensions, small slip with manuscript diagram at p.230, BINDING: contemporary English calf, spine gilt, *upper joint split*

The first appearance in English of extensive selections from the *Principia.*

References: Babson 127; Wallis 168

£400-500
€600-750

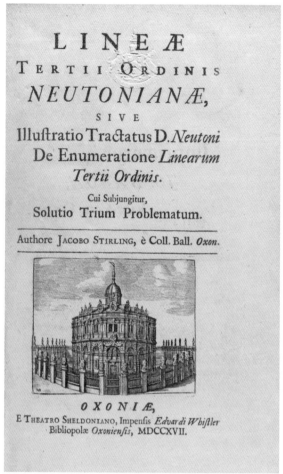

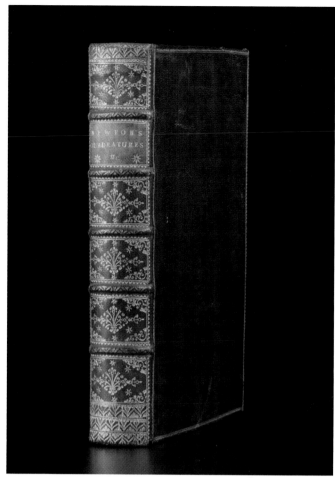

1534

1535

1537 Newton, John (1621-1678). Astronomia Britannica, exhibiting the doctrine of the sphere, and theory of the planets decimally by trigonometry and by tables. Fitted for the meridian of London, according to the Copernican systeme as illustrated by Bullialdus, and the easie way of calculation, latly published by Doctor [Seth] Ward. *London: R. & W. Leybourn for the author, and are to be sold by Thomas Pierrepoint, 1657*

4to (200 x 150mm.), [12], 168; 156pp., R3 in part 1 a cancel (?) with stub, errata slip pasted after p.156 of part 2, title-page ruled in red, ILLUSTRATION: woodcut figures in text and attached to p.136 in part 1 a woodcut diagram lettered in manuscript Fig. A and described on p.137, BINDING: contemporary calf, *the first 2 leaves heavily browned and friable at edges, small paper flaw in T1, spine worn*

References: Wing N1053

Provenance: William Jones, signature on title-page

£1,000-1,500
€1,450-2,200

1538 Newton, John. Geometrical trigonometry, or, The explanation of such geometrical problems as are most useful & necessary, either for the construction of the canons of triangles, or for the solution of them. Together with the proportions themselves suteable unto every case both in plain and spherical triangles, those in spherical being deduced from the Lord Nepeirs catholick or universal proposition. *London: for George Hurlock and Thomas Pierrepont, 1659*

12mo (126 x 70mm.), [8], 136pp., ILLUSTRATION: woodcut initials and diagrams, BINDING: contemporary sheep, *a few leaves shaved, slightly damp-stained at foot, binding slightly rubbed*

FIRST EDITION. Newton was a Royalist who supported himself before the Restoration by teaching mathematics and publishing textbooks.

References: Wing M1059

£300-400
€450-600

1539 Newton, John. Institutio Mathematica: or a mathematical institution. Shewing the construction and use of the naturall and artificiall sines, tangents, and secants, in decimal numbers, and also of the table of logarithms, in the general solution of any triangle... *London: R. & W. Leybourn for George Hurlock and Robert Boydel, 1654*, 12mo (123 x 72mm.), [8], 420pp., ILLUSTRATION: woodcut initials and headpieces, woodcut diagrams, 3 woodcut plates (2 folding), *?lacking one plate, one plate loose*

Ibid. Tabulae mathematicae: or, Tables of the naturall sines, tangents and secants, and the logarithms of the sines and tangents to every degree and hundredth part of a degree in the quadrant... *London: R. & W. Leybourn for George Hurlock and Robert Boydel, 1654*, 12mo (124 x 73mm.), A-P^{12}, Q^{10} plus errata leaf, folding letterpress table, *lacking all after Q10 except errata*

together 2 volumes, BINDINGS: contemporary calf, flat spines gilt, *bindings rubbed, joints cracking*

FIRST EDITIONS. The second volume seems complete but ESTC specifies signatures A-T^{12} with final errata leaf.

References: Wing M1061 & M1071; Taylor, *Tudor & Stuart* 219 & 220

Provenance: Euclid Speidell, inscriptions on title-page and last leaf of first work, dated 1659 (for another work from his library, see Macclesfield Science A-C, lot 558).

£400-600
€600-900

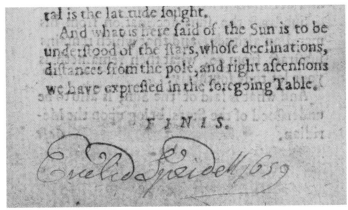

1539

1540 Newton, John. Cosmographia, or a view of the terrestrial and coelestial globes, in a brief explanation of the principles of plain and solid geometry, applied to surveying and gauging of a cask... *London: printed for T. Passinger, 1679*

8vo (175 x 110mm.), [16], 510, [14]pp., first leaf with imprimatur, pp.[511-512] (L11) a catalogue of fixed stars, followed by Contents and final leaves with adverts for books sold by Passinger, ILLUSTRATION: 3 engraved plates at pp. 42, 45, 75, with figures numbered 1-33, and a further 11 plates bound variously, all on stubs and folding, BINDING: contemporary calf

At the end of the Passinger adverts is a long advertisement from a mathematical school: "At Cherry Garden Stairs on Rotherhith Wall, are taught the mathematical sciences... by James Atkinson" (see Taylor, *Tudor & Stuart*, p.254).

References: Wing N1055

£700-1,000
€1,050-1,450

1541 Nierop, Dirck Rembrantsz van (1610-1682). Nederduytsche astronomia, das is: Onderwijs van den loop des hemels, leerende het vinden der plaetsen en bewegingen der vaste sterren son en maen: als oock haer eclipsen... Hier by gevoeght een aen-hangh, dienende tot naeder verklaeringhe over den loop des hemels... Ende nu met den tweeden druck, overghesien, vertbetert... by den zelfden autheur, als oock een gedruckten planeet-wyser. *Amsterdam: Gerrit van Goedesbergh, 1658*

3 parts in one, 4to (235 x 175mm.), [12], 105 [*sic*=207 (pp. 199-200 repeated)], [1]; 65; 112, [2]pp., Black Letter, last leaf of part 3 with errata on recto, ILLUSTRATION: additional engraved title-page, large folding engraved plate at p.200 (Planeet-Wyser), engraved illustration on p.11 (part 1), woodcut illustrations in text, BINDING: eighteenth-century calf, gilt spine, *small hole in leather on upper cover*

FIRST EDITION, AND A HANDSOME COPY. Nierop, a humble cobbler and a staunch advocate of Copernican ideas, which he defends in this work, is said to have visited Descartes, who was greatly impressed by him.

The additional engraved title has a portrait of the author at centre flanked by Hipparchus (as if in a Rembrandt painting), Ptolemy, Copernicus, King Alfonso, Tycho Brahe and Johannes Phocylides [van Holwards] (1618-1651) the Dutch astronomer. One imagines that the book must have been acquired by Collins, who seems to have had a strong interest in Dutch publications.

References: J. Smit, *Dirck Rembrandts van Nierop: het leven en werk van een beroemd sterrenkundige, meester in de wiskonst en een uitmuntend onderwijzer voor schippers en stuurleden* (2 dln, Winkel, 1992)

£2,000-2,500
€2,900-3,650
See illustration on next page

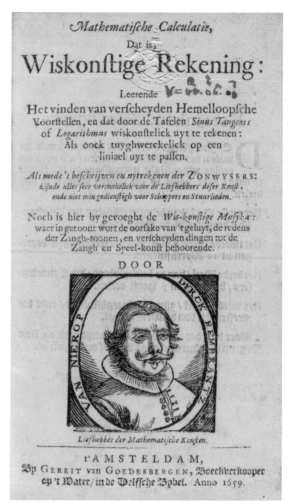

1541

1542

1542 Nierop, Dirck Rembrantsz van. Mathematische calculatie, dat is, wiskonstige rekening: leerende het vinden van verscheyden hemelloopsche voorstellen, en dat door de tafelen sinus tangents of logarithmus wiskonstelick uyt te rekenen... Noch is hier by gevoeght de wis-konstige musyka: waer in getoont wort de oorsake van 't geluyt, de redens der zangh-toonen, en verscheyden dingen tot de zangh en speel-konst behoorende. *Amsterdam: Gerrit van Goedesberge, 1659*

2 parts in one, 8vo (175 x 100mm.), 167pp., 2 folding tables at pp.12/13; 70pp., ILLUSTRATION: woodcut portrait of the author on title-page, woodcut diagrams, 2 folding engraved plates in part 2, BINDING: eighteenth-century sprinkled calf, gilt spine, red morocco lettering-piece, red edges

This volume contains another of Nierop's popular works, the second part dealing with music. Nierop was much influenced by Vredeman's *Isagoge musicae* (1618), and his annotated copy of this is still in existence. The *Tweede deel op de wiskonstige rekening* was published in 1680.

£1,000-1,500
€1,450-2,200

1543 Nieuwentyt, Bernard (1654-1718). Analysis infinitorum, seu curvilineorum proprietates ex polygonorum natura deductae. *Amsterdam: Joannes Wolters, 1695*, [16], 304pp., title in red and black, ILLUSTRATION: engraved device on title-page, woodcut initials, head- and tailpieces, 20 folding engraved plates, *lacking one plate*

Ibid. Considerationes circa analyseos ad quantitates infinite parvas applicatae principia, & calculi differentialis usum in resolventis problematibus geometricis. *Amsterdam: Joannes Wolters, 1694*, 48pp., ILLUSTRATION: woodcut device on title-page, folding engraved plate

Ibid. Considerationes secundae circa calculi differentialis principia, et responsio ad... G.G. Leibnitium. *Amsterdam: Joannes Wolters, 1696*, [4], 42pp., ILLUSTRATION: woodcut vignette on title-page, folding engraved plate

3 works in one volume, 4to (171 x 108mm.), BINDING: contemporary panelled calf, spine gilt in compartments, morocco lettering-piece, *binding slightly rubbed*

ALL FIRST EDITIONS. "Nieuwentijt's was the first comprehensive book on 'analysis infinitorum'. By L. Euler's *Introductio in analysin infinitorum*, analysis became the name of a mathematical discipline. To this field Nieuwentijt contributed little more than the name. What is surprising, however, is the erudite scholarship of a small-town physician who, except for limited university study, does not seem to have cultivated many learned colleagues. Nieuwentijt's work reveals his full aquaintance with the mathematics of his period and a remarkable self-reliance" (*DSB* X, p.120).

£500-700
€750-1,050

1544 Noble, Edward (d. 1786). The elements of linear perspective demonstrated by geometrical principles, and applied to the most general and concise modes of practice: with an introduction, containing so much of the elements of geometry as will render the whole rationale of perspective intelligible, without any other previous mathematical knowledge. *London: T. Davies, 1771*

8vo (215 x 126mm.), [7], iv-cxvi (i.e. cxv), [1], 298pp., ILLUSTRATION: 51 engraved plates (2 folding), BINDING: contemporary mottled calf, spine gilt in compartments, red morocco lettering-piece, red speckled edges

FIRST EDITION. According to the *ODNB*, Noble was also a journeyman bookseller.

Provenance: eighteenth-century armorial bookplate, "Militar. collection of the Hon. Lt. Genl. G.L. Parker"

£300-400
€450-600

1545 Norwood, Richard (1590-1675). Trigonometrie: or, the doctrine of triangles... The eight [*sic*] edition... (The Chiliades or the logarithms). *London: R.W. for W. Fisher, T. Passinger, and R. Smith, 1685*

2 parts in one, 4to (195 x 145mm.), [6], 165 [*sic*=173], [1]pp., ff. [90], last page with adverts of mathematical and similar works published by Fisher, Passinger, and Smith, ILLUSTRATION: woodcut diagrams, BINDING: eighteenth-century panelled calf, gilt spine

First published in 1631 and recorded in eight actual editions up to 1685. Norwood, the surveyor of Bermuda, where he died, was also the author of *The Seaman's Practice*, which was enormously popular.

References: Wing N1388

£400-600
€600-900

1546 Nottnagel, Christoph. Institutionum mathematicarum pars I [all published]. *Wittenberg: Johann Röhner, 1645*

12mo (152 x 91mm.), [12], 984, [2]pp., ILLUSTRATION: woodcut diagrams in text, BINDING: contemporary calf, *paper browned, binding worn*

£300-400
€450-600

1547 Nuis, Henrik Jaspar. 't Gebruik van het rectangulum catholicum geometrico-astronomicum, ofte regthoekig algemein meet-en-sterkundig plat, verstrekkende voor een proportional-passer, meetkundig astrolabium, algemeine Zonnewyzer, en verscheiden andere werktuigen. *Zwolle: Gerard Tydeman, 1686*

4to (194 x 151mm.), [32], 362pp., ILLUSTRATION: woodcut initials, 2 folding engraved plates, woodcut diagrams, woodcut plate, BINDING: contemporary vellum, *boards slightly warped, binding soiled*

£400-500
€600-750

1548 Nuñez, Pedro (1502-1578). Libro de algebra en arithmetica y geometria. *Antwerp: heirs of Arnold Birckman, 1567*

8vo (161 x 99mm.), ff. [16], 341 [*recte* 339], [1 (blank)], ILLUSTRATION: woodcut device on title, woodcut diagrams in text, woodcut initials, BINDING: early seventeenth-century red morocco gilt, double line border, flat spine gilt in compartments with small fleuron in each, gilt edges, *foremargin of a5 repaired*

FIRST EDITION. Born in Portugal, Nuñez studied at Salamanca before moving to Lisbon in 1524 or 1525. On 16 November 1529 he was appointed royal cosmographer, and later to the chairs of moral philosophy, logic and metaphysics at the University of Lisbon. In 1544 he was appointed professor of mathematics at Coimbra, where he taught, amongst others, Clavius. The preface to this work is written in Portuguese; the edition was divided between the heirs of Birckman and the heirs of Johann Steelsius.

References: Palau 196753; Peeters-Fontainas 845; *Belgica typographica* 2225

£1,000-1,500
€1,450-2,200

1549 Octoul, Etienne (1589-1655). Inventa astronomica. Primae mundi epochae a priori constructae eodem tempore. Conceptae, quo Ludovicus XIV… conceptus: nataeque, quo natus, [etc.]. *Avignon: Jacques Bramereau, 1643*

4to (248 x 180mm.), [24], 92pp., ILLUSTRATION: engraved frontispiece, full-page engraved plates on pp. 38 and 70 (pp. 37 and 38 with no printed text), BINDING: contemporary French red Turkey leather, the covers with a semé of fleurs-de-lys within a gilt border, spine gilt with fleurs-de-lys etc., gilt edges

An attempt to establish the age of the world.

£2,000-3,000
€2,900-4,350

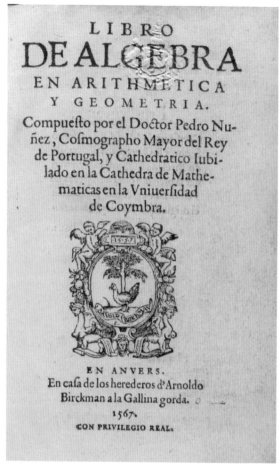

1548

1549

1550 Odierna, Giovanni Battista (1597-1660).

Opuscoli… 1. Il nunzio della terra. 2. La Nuova pendente. 3. L'Occhio della mosca. 4. Il Sole del microcosmo. *Palermo: Decio Cirillo, 1644*, [8], 32; 24; 24; 48pp., ILLUSTRATION: woodcut coat-of-arms of dedicatee on title-page

Ibid. Archimede redivivo con la stadera del momento… dove non solamente s'insegna il modo di scoprir le frodi nella falsificatione dell'oro, e dell'argento, ma si notifica l'uso delli pesi, e delle misure civili preso diverse nationi del mondo, e di questo Regno di Sicilia. *Palermo, 1644*, [8], 72pp., ILLUSTRATION: woodcut coat-of-arms of dedicatee on title-page

2 works in one volume, 4to (205 x 140mm.), BINDING: seventeenth-century calf, gilt spine

References: Riccardi ii, 215

£1,000-1,500
€1,450-2,200

1550

1551 Odierna, Giovanni Battista. Menologiae Iovis compendium seu ephemerides Medicaeorum (Canonum ac tabellarum astronomicarum series, index & usus...). *Palermo: apud Cirillos, 1656*

4to (220 x 170mm.), [20], 3-71; 79, [1]pp., half-title reading: "Medicaeorum ephemerides... cum suis introductionibus in tres partes distinctis", ILLUSTRATION: numerous woodcut illustrations (black on white) and figures, woodcut initials etc., BINDING: eighteenth-century sprinkled calf, gilt, red edges

FIRST EDITION of the first published ephemerides of the Galilean satellites, based on an improved theory of the motion of Jupiter's moons by the contribution of three types of periodic disturbances, analogous to contemporary planetary theory.

Odierna (Hodierna) was a Sicilian from Ragusa in Sicily, and a priest. Having little formal education, he took up the study of astronomy, and although well away from the centre of such studies, he made many observations and wrote and published several works.

In 1646 and 1653, Odierna observed Saturn and created drawings showing the planet with its ring quite correctly, and in 1656 he briefly corresponded with Huygens. His *Protei caelestis vertigines seu Saturni systema*, published in 1657, is among his best known publications.

In 1652, he had observed eclipses and in *De admirandis phasibus in sole et luna visis* (1656) he discusses the appearance of the sun and the moon, sunspots and eclipses.

His *De systemate orbis cometici; deque admirandis coeli characteribus* is a remarkable work, which was ignored until it was recovered by Serio in 1985. Odierna thought there were profound differences between comets and nebulae: because of the motion and changing appearance of comets, he thought them to be made up of a more terrestrial matter, while nebulae should be made up of stars, and thus "Lux Primogenita". In the first part he follows Galileo's ideas on comets. In the second, more interesting, part, he describes and lists 40 nebulae he had observed, with finder charts and some sketches, which Odierna classifies according to their resolvability into stars in Luminosae (star clusters to the naked eye), Nebulae (appearing nebulous to the unaided eye, but are resolved in his telescope) and Occultae (not resolved in his telescope). About 25 of them could be identified with real deepsky objects (mostly open clusters), the others are either asterisms or insufficiently described for identification. He never completed his proposed celestial atlas *Il Cielo Stellato Diviso in 100 Mappe*.

For other works by Odierna see Macclesfield Science A-C, lots 215 and 237.

References: Riccardi ii, 214; Mario Pavone, *La vita e le opere di Giovan Battista Hodierna* (Ragusa: Didattica Libri Eirene Editrice, 1986); G.F. Serio, L. Indorato and P. Nastasi, "G.B. Hodierna's Observations of Nebulae and his Cosmology", *Journal for the History of Astronomy* XVI (1985), 1-36

£1,500-2,000
€2,200-2,900

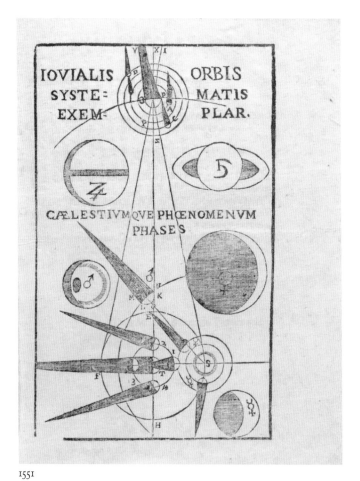

1551

1552

1552 Omerique, Antonio Hugo de (1634-1698). Analysis geometrica sive nova, et vera methodus resolvendi tam problemata geometrica, quam arithmeticas quaestiones. Pars prima de planis. *Cadiz: Christophorus de Requena, 1698*

4to (211 x 144mm.), [24], 440pp., ILLUSTRATION: engraved frontispiece, woodcut initials and headpieces, woodcut diagrams, BINDING: contemporary panelled calf, spine gilt in compartments, morocco lettering-piece, red speckled edges, *extremities slightly rubbed*

FIRST EDITION. Only the first part was published. Newton commented on this work of Omerique's (see Wallis 4.4).

References: BL STC Spanish XVIIc. O26; not in Palau

£1,000-1,500
€1,450-2,200

1553 [Oppel, Friedrich Wilhelm von (1720-1769)] Analysis triangulorum (Appendix varia promiscue tractans). *Dresden & Leipzig: J.G.I. Breitkopf for G.D. Walther, 1746*

folio (270 x 175mm.), [4], 98, [2]pp., last leaf with errata, ILLUSTRATION: 13 folding engraved plates, BINDING: eighteenth-century polished calf, spine gilt in compartments, *a few leaves slightly foxed*

Oppel was one of the founders of the Mining Academy at Freiburg (where there is a prize named after him), and director of mining, and himself a collector of minerals, books and other objects.

£700-1,000
€1,050-1,450

1554 Optical Tracts—Euclid. [Optica] La prospettiva... tradotta dal R.P.M. Egnatio Danti... Insieme con la prospettiva di Eliodoro Larisseo cavata della Libreria Vaticana, e tradotta dal medesimo nuovamente data in luce. *Florence: Giunti, 1573*, [8], 110pp. only, ILLUSTRATION: woodcut diagrams, [Steck VIII.6], *without the Greek text*

Ibid. [Optica] Euclidis optica & catoptrica... Eadem latine reddita per Ioannem Penam. *Paris: A. Wechel, 1557*, [10], 48; [4], 64pp., last leaf of preliminaries in part 1 with errata, ILLUSTRATION: woodcut diagrams, [Steck VIII.2]

[Pecham, John (d. 1292), *Archbishop of Canterbury*] Perspectiva... correcta, et figuris illustrata, per Pascasium Hamellium. *Paris: Gilles Gourbin, 1556*, ff. [4], 43, [1], [*]4 and L4 blank, [Vagnetti Db8], *without final blank*

Tagliani, Giuseppe (d. 1658). Orologi riflessi per mezo di un picciolo specchio parallelo, o perpendicolare all'orizonte. *Macerata: Filippo Camacci, 1648*, [6], 48pp., title printed in red and black, ILLUSTRATION: woodcut figures, [Riccardi ii, 481-2]

[De focis curvarum; De speculis Archimedeis] *[c. 1720]*, [4], 36pp., dedicated to Ernest August of Saxony, *lacking title-leaf*

5 works in one volume, 4to (211 x 144mm.), BINDING: eighteenth-century polished calf, spine gilt in compartments, red morocco lettering-piece, red edges

£800-1,000
€1,200-1,450

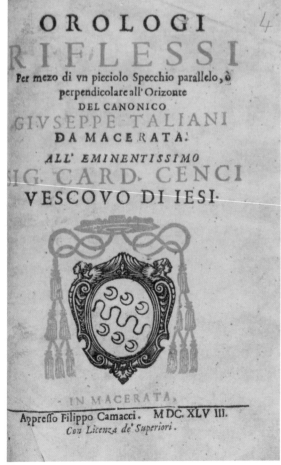

1554

1555 Optical Tracts—Maurolico, Francesco (1494-1575). Theoremata de lumine, et umbra, ad perspectivam, & radiorum incidentiam facienta. Diaphanorum partes, seu libri tres... Problemata ad perspectivam & iridem pertinentia. His accesserunt Christophori Clavii... notae, asteriscis inter authoris demonstrationes distinctae. Adscriptis ad marginem fundamentis, quibus omnia innituntur. *Lyon: B. Vincent, 1613*, [8], 94pp., ILLUSTRATION: woodcut figures, [Vagnetti Aa1; Riccardi ii, 142; E. Rosen, "The editions of Maurolico's mathematical works", *Scripta mathematica* xxiv (1959), pp.67ff], *without the final blank leaf, small worm hole in first three leaves, quire A cropped close with loss of some catchwords*

Dominis, Marco Antonio de (1566-1624), *Archbishop of Spalatro*. De radiis visus et lucis in vitris perspectivis et iride tractatus... per Ioannem Bartolum in lucem editus... *Venice: T. Baglioni, 1611*, [8], 78, [2]pp., errata on last leaf, ILLUSTRATION: woodcut figures (see Macclesfield Science D-H, lot 839, for a discussion of this work)

[Cooper, Robert (d. 1733)] Propositions concerning optic-glasses, with their natural reasons, drawn from experiments. *Oxford: at the Theater, 1679*, [4], 46pp., ILLUSTRATION: engraved vignette on title-page, woodcut figures, [Wing W409; Madan 3208]

Borel, Pierre (1620?-1671). De vero telescopii inventore, cum brevi omnium conspiciliorum historia... Centuria observationum microcospicarum. *The Hague: A. Vlacq, 1655-1656*, 2 parts (with 3 paginations), [8], 67; 63; 45, [3]pp., ILLUSTRATION: 2 engraved portraits of Jansen and Lipperhey, folding engraved plate of the moon at p.38, engraving of the Bear on p.41, woodcut diagrams and illustrations

4 works in one volume, 4to (195 x 140mm.), BINDING: eighteenth-century calf, spine gilt in compartments, red morocco lettering-piece, red edges, *upper joint a little worn*

Maurolico: The second edition of the "best optical book of the Renaissance" and the first to contain "an adequate geometrical theory of the camera obscura" (Lindberg). It was written in the second quarter of the sixteenth century, but remained unpublished until Clavius published it in Naples in 1611. Clavius had visited Maurolico in 1574 (when Maurolico seems to have been teaching at the Jesuit College in Messina) and was given a manuscript of *Photiscmi de lumine et umbra* and of *Diaphana*.

Cooper: Seen through the press by Obadiah Walker of University College, Oxford, who was a Delegate of the Press, it is highly unlikely that this work is by him, although he is credited with it by some. Abraham Woodhead (who died in 1678) may perhaps have left the book amongst his papers at his death, which was then unearthed by Walker, who then published it. Anthony Wood however says definitely that it is by Robert Cooper. He was of Pembroke College and contributed to Pitt's Atlas. He died in 1733 as Archdeacon of Dorset. Five hundred copies of this pamphlet were printed on "fine Genoa paper, perhaps to take the diagrams well" (Madan).

Borel: Borel was a Parisian doctor born in Castres and trained at Montpellier, who is chiefly famous for his *Bibliotheca chimica* (1654), an important bibliography of alchemy, and a book owned by and used extensively by Newton.

£4,000-6,000
€5,800-8,700
See illustration on next page

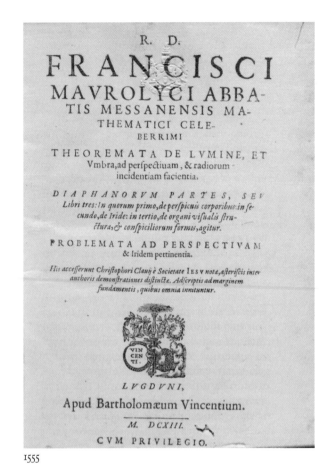

1555

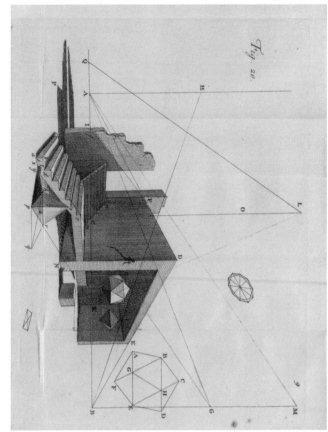

1557

1556 Optics and antiquities—[Berkeley, George (1685-1753), *Bishop of Cloyne*] The theory of vision, or visual language, shewing the immediate presence and providence of a deity, vindicated and explained. By the author of Alciphron, or, the Minute Philosopher. *London: J. Tonson, 1733*, FIRST EDITION, 64pp.

Robins, Benjamin (1707-1751). Remarks on Mr Euler's Treatise of motion, Dr Smith's compleat System of opticks, and Dr Jurin's Essay upon distinct and indistinct vision. *London: J. Nourse, 1739*, FIRST EDITION, vi, 112pp., ILLUSTRATION: woodcut diagrams

[Defoe, Daniel (1661-1731)] An essay upon References: or, an enquiry into the antiquity and original of letters; proving that the two tables, written by the finger of God in Mount Sinai, was the first writing in the world. *London: Tho. Bowles, John Clark and John Bowles, 1726*, FIRST EDITION, [2], 127, [1 (blank)] pp., [Furbank & Owens 227]

[Ward, John (1679-1758)] De asse et partibus eius commentarius. *London: [S. Buckley?], 1719*, FIRST EDITION, LXXIV pp., ILLUSTRATION: engraved illustrations, *engravings shaved*

4 works in one volume, 8vo (188 x 113mm.), BINDING: eighteenth-century sprinkled calf, spine gilt in compartments, red morocco lettering-piece, red edges

For Berkeley's views on fluxions and *The Analyst* see Macclesfield Science D-H, lot 796; for the reception and discussion of Newton's *Opticks*, see Rupert A. Hall, *All was light* (Oxford, 1993)

£800-1,000
€1,200-1,450

1557 Optics and Dialling—Taylor, Brook (1685-1731). New principles of linear perspective... *London: [W. Bowyer for] R. Knaplock, 1719*, [14], 74pp., ILLUSTRATION: 12 folding etched plates with 25 figures, [BAL RIBA 3258]

Wells, Edward (1667-1727). [The young gentleman's chronology, astronomy and dialling] The young gentleman's dialling... (Dialling part only). *London: J. Knapton, 1712*, [8], 56pp., ILLUSTRATION: 9 folding engraved plates with numerous figures

Ibid. [The young gentleman's course of mathematics... in three volumes] The young gentleman's opticks... (Opticks part only). *London: J. Knapton, 1713*, [4], 83-171, [1]pp., ILLUSTRATION: engraved plates

3 works in one volume, 8vo (185 x 105mm.), BINDING: eighteenth-century sprinkled calf, spine gilt in compartments, red morocco lettering piece, red edges, *boards slightly warped*

FIRST EDITION of this pamphlet by Brook Taylor, of which Bowyer printed 500 copies (*Bowyer Ledgers* 533). It was reprinted in 1835 but this 1719 edition is not common. Edward Wells was a hugely productive writer on divinity, geography and many other subjects, most of whose works are, as Hearne put it, inaccurate.

£800-1,000
€1,200-1,450

1558 Orta, Garcia de. Aromatum, et simplicium aliquot medicamentorum apud Indos nascentium historia: primum quidem Lusitanica lingua... conscripta... nunc vero Latino sermone in epitomen contracta, & iconibus ad vivum expressis, locupletioribusque annotatiunculis illustrata a Carolo Clusio... Tertia editio. *Antwerp: Christopher Plantin, 1579*, 217, [7]pp., ILLUSTRATION: woodcut device on title-page, woodcut initials and illustrations

Monardes, Nicolas (*c.* 1512-1588). Simplicium medicamentorum ex novo orbe delatorum, quorum in medicina usus est, historia, Hispanico sermone descripta... Latio deinde donata, & annotationibus, iconibusque affabre depictis illustrata a Carolo Clusio... Altera editio. *Antwerp: Christopher Plantin, 1579*, 84, [4]pp., ILLUSTRATION: woodcut device on title-page, woodcut initials and illustrations

L'Écluse, Charles de (1526-1609). Aliquot notae in Garciae aromatum historiam. *Antwerp: Christopher Plantin, 1582*, 43, [1]pp., ILLUSTRATION: woodcut device on title-page, woodcut initials and illustrations

Acosta, Cristobal (*c.* 1515-*c.* 1592). Aromatum et medicamentorum in Orientali India nascentium liber: plurimum lucis adferens iis quae a Doctore Garcia de Orta... scripta sunt... Caroli Clusii... opera ex Hispanico sermone latinus factus, in epitomen contractus, et quibusdam notis illustratus. *Antwerp: Christopher Plantin, 1579*, 88pp., ILLUSTRATION: woodcut device on title-page, woodcut initials and illustration

4 works in one volume, 8vo (169 x 109mm.), BINDING: later vellum-backed blue boards, *small tear in spine, boards a little soiled*

References: Krivatsy 3416, 3217 & 1065; Wellcome 4657, 4395 (1st 2 works); Voet 1840, 1711, 1010 & 1038

Provenance: T. Lynford, inscription on title-page

£700-1,000
€1,050-1,450

1558

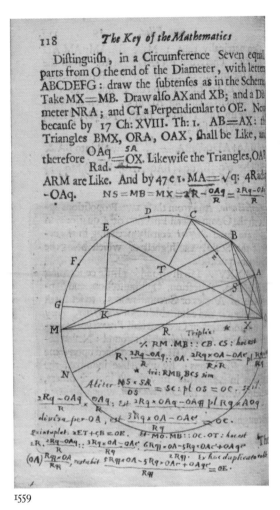

1559

1561

1559 Oughtred, William (1575-1660). [Clavis] The key of the mathematicks new forged and filed: together with a treatise of the resolution of all kinds of affected aequations in numbers. With the rule of compound usury... And a most easie art of delineating all manner of plaine sun-dyalls. *London: T. Harper for R. Whitaker, 1647*

8vo (145 x 88mm.), [14 (including engraved portrait)], 174, [2 (blank)] pp., ILLUSTRATION: engraved portrait of the author, engraved diagrams in text, small engraved slip pasted to p.11, 9 folding engraved plates at end, one with annotated manuscript drawing by Oughtred on verso, another with volvelle, BINDING: contemporary calf gilt, spine gilt later in compartments, later red morocco lettering-piece, *extremities slightly rubbed*

THE AUTHOR'S OWN COPY WITH HIS ANNOTATIONS AND CORRECTIONS. These take the form of minute changes and reworking in the body of the text, and on the front fly-leaves, some with crossings out, a small slip inserted at p.13, some brief notes on chronology also on the front flyleaf and more detailed notes on weights on the end fly-leaves.

The *Clavis* was published in 1631 and was reprinted several times between 1647 and 1700 in Latin (mostly in Oxford). This is the first English edition, and is printed by the same two men as the Latin editions of 1647 and 1648.

References: Wing O582

£4,000-6,000
€5,800-8,700

1559

1560 Oughtred, William. Key of the mathematicks. Newly translated from the best edition with notes... Recommended by Mr. E. Halley. *London: John Salusbury, 1694*

8vo (160 x 95mm.), [4], 208pp., BINDING: contemporary sheep, gilt spine, *extremities slightly rubbed*

Halley writes in his preface that the previous English translation of *Clavis* by Wood had been made from an edition which had "since been much improved and augmented and besides, the concise brevity of the author is such, as in many places to need an explication, to render it intelligible to the less knowing in mathematical matters. This translation is new and from the fullest edition...". Halley's recommendation makes no mention of the fact that he is the translator. Newton thought very highly of Oughtred.

References: Wing O583

Provenance: Francis Say, Trinity College, Cambridge, inscription on flyleaf dated 1709, with note on price (2s.9d.)

£300-400
€450-600

1561 Oughtred, William. Trigonometrie, or, the manner of calculating the sides and angles of triangles, by the mathematical canon, demonstrated [the dedication to William Backhouse signed by the translator Richard Stokes] (Canones sinuum, tangentium, secantium: et logarithmorum pro sinubus et tangentibus; Chiliades logarithmorum). *London: R. & W. Leybourn for T. Johnson (J. Moxon for T. Johnson), 1657*

4to (185 x 140mm.), 2 parts, [8 (including portrait)], 40; 234, [10]pp., ILLUSTRATION: engraved portrait of the author by Faithorne with verses by Stokes, BINDING: contemporary calf, *without pp.235-244, upper cover detached*

Printed and published in the same year and by the same team as the original Latin edition: "Why this English edition should so soon follow the Latine, the Stationer is able to give a better account then I, though it may be pleaded that many ingenious men and much addicted to these studies, are yet not qualified to read them in Latine, but are content to have no more Languages than they have tongues...". The second part printed by Moxon was also used in the Latin edition; copies seem to vary at the end as to the number of pages. All the logarithms called for (- 10,000) are present in this copy.

Inserted into this copy are 10 pages (2 bifolia and a single leaf) of authorial manuscript in a neat minuscule hand, WRITTEN IN LATIN BY OUGHTRED (we are grateful to Dr F Wilmoth for her help with this). These constitute the Latin text of chapters 2 and part of 3 of the *Trigonometria* and can be followed clearly in the Latin or English text. The first bifolium is headed "Cap. 2um Triangulorum planorum calculus", and is in three sections: "De triangulo planorectangulo", "De triangulo plano obliquangulo" (with paragraphs numbered consecutively 1-6), "Datis tribus lateribus invenire anulum quemlibet" (numbered 7, and occupying more than a page and a half), followed by two paragraphs with no headings, numbered 8-9. The single leaf has 10, "Datis tribus angulis inevire satus quodlibet", followed by paragraph 11 (covering the rest of the page and the verso), which begins: "Si vero in Triangulo obliquangulo sphaerico termini dati non se habeant modo aliquot praedicto".

The second bifolium begins in the middle of a paragraph: "super diametrum zeta xi centro mu describatur...". This has three lemmata after which three solutions are given, concluding with: "Atque in haec est prima demonstratio per lem. 1, 2, 3 quam nobilissimi Domini Caroli Cavendish hortatu misi in Galliam an. Dom. 1632". This is followed by further sections numbered 8 ("Datus duobus angulis cum latere interjacenti invenire reliquos duos angulos") and 9 ("Datis tribus lateribus invenire angulum quemlibet...") which carries on over the page. On the verso of the leaf are some further calculations about triangles, ending with the catchword "Ergo".

References: Wing O590

£1,000-1,500
€1,450-2,200

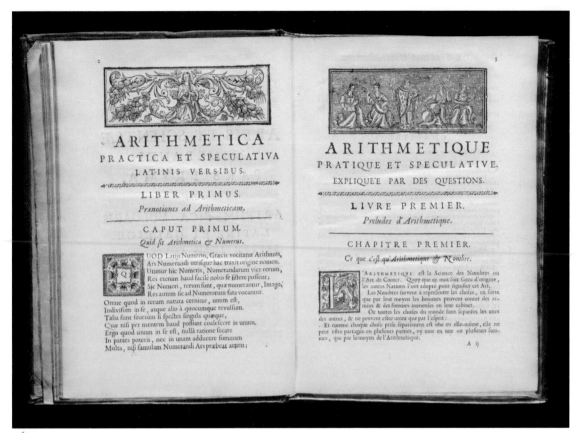

1562

1562 [Ouvrard, René (1624-1694)] L'art et la science des nombres en François et en Latin: ou l'arithmétique pratique et speculative en vers latins expliquée par des questions. Divisée en deux parties. *Paris: Lambert Roulland and Christophe Ballard, 1677*

4to (231 x 163mm.), [30], 122, [2], 123-337, [7]pp., ILLUSTRATION: woodcut initials, head- and tailpieces, 2 pages containing woodcut music, BINDING: contemporary mottled calf, spine gilt in compartments, *last leaf torn and repaired with slight loss, binding slightly rubbed*

FIRST EDITION. Ouvrard is chiefly known for his writings on musical theory. He was *maître de musique* at Sainte Chapelle in Paris from 1663 to 1679.

References: Wellcome IV, p.276

£400-500
€600-750

1563 Owen, Edward (*fl.* 1754). Observations on the earths, rocks, stones and minerals, for some miles about Bristol, and on the nature of the Hot-Well, and the virtues of its water. *London: W. Johnston, 1754*

FIRST EDITION, 12mo (164 x 95mm.), [12], 250pp., title-page printed in red and black, ILLUSTRATION: engraved frontispiece, woodcut initials, head- and tailpieces, 2 engraved plates, BINDING: contemporary mottled calf gilt, spine gilt in compartments, morocco lettering-piece, *upper cover scraped, extremities slightly rubbed*

References: Wellcome IV, p.277; Challinor 30

£300-400
€450-600

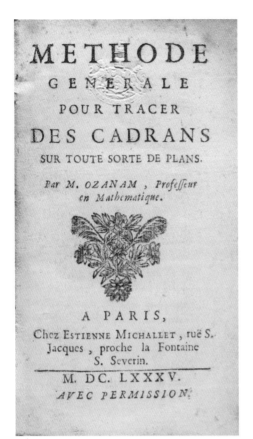

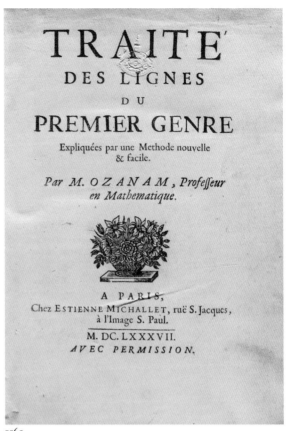

1564

1565

1564 Ozanam, Jacques (1640-1717). Méthode générale pour tracer des cadrans sur toute sorte de plans. *Paris: Estienne Michallet, 1685*

12mo (160 x 89mm.), [4], 161, [5]pp., ILLUSTRATION: woodcut vignette on title-page, woodcut initial and headpiece, 12 folding engraved plates, BINDING: contemporary calf, spine gilt in compartments, *binding rubbed, head of spine chipped*

Originally published in 1673, this was Ozanam's first published work.

£300-400
€450-600

1565 Ozanam, Jacques. Traité des lignes du premier genre expliquées par une methode nouvelle et facile. *Paris: Estienne Michallet, 1687*, 151, [1 (blank)] pp., ILLUSTRATION: woodcut vignette on title-page, woodcut initials, head- and tailpieces, 14 engraved plates

Ibid. Traité des lieux geometriques, expliques par une methode courte et facile. *Paris: Estienne Michallet, 1687*, 59, [1 (blank)] pp., ILLUSTRATION: woodcut vignette on title-page, woodcut initials, head- and tailpieces, 12 engraved plates

Ibid. Traité de la construction des équations. Pour la solution des problèmes [in]déterminez. *Paris: Estienne Michallet, 1687*, [4], 92pp., ILLUSTRATION: woodcut vignette on title-page, woodcut initials, head- and tailpieces, 9 engraved plates

3 works in one volume, 4to (251 x 182mm.), BINDING: contemporary vellum, flat spine gilt, morocco lettering-piece, *boards slightly warped*

ALL FIRST EDITIONS. The last word in the title of the last work has been partially erased.

£400-500
€600-750

1566 Ozanam, Jacques. La geometrie pratique, contenant la trigonometrie theorique & pratique, la longimetrie, la planimetrie, & la stereometrie. Par de nouvelles demonstrations tres-courtes & tres-faciles, & de nouveaux abregez pour mesurer exactement les plans & les solides. Seconde edition reveuë, corrigée & augmentée. *Paris: the author and Estienne Michallet, 1689*

12mo (164 x 92mm.), [4], 301, [11]pp., ILLUSTRATION: woodcut initials, head- and tailpieces, woodcut diagrams, BINDING: contemporary sheep, spine gilt in compartments, *binding rubbed, upper joint cracked*

Originally published in 1684.

£300-400
€450-600

1567 Ozanam, Jacques. L'usage du compas de proportion: expliqué & demontré d'une maniere courte & facile, & augmenté d'un traité de la division des champs. *The Hague: Henry van Bulderen, 1691*

12mo (152 x 88mm.), 216pp., ILLUSTRATION: woodcut device on title-page, folding engraved plate, woodcut diagrams, BINDING: contemporary calf, spine gilt in compartments, *binding slightly rubbed*

Originally printed in Paris in 1688 and regularly reissued.

£300-400
€450-600

1568 Ozanam, Jacques. Dictionaire mathématique, ou idée générale des mathématiques. *Amsterdam: Huguetan, 1691*

4to (243 x 183mm.), [14], 739pp., title printed in red and black, ILLUSTRATION: engraved frontispiece, engraved vignette on title, 24 engraved plates (a few folding), woodcut illustrations and diagrams in text, head- and tail-pieces and initials, BINDING: contemporary calf, *small rust-hole in Yyy4 with slight loss, some light browning, binding rubbed*

A reprint of the first edition, published in the same year by Michallet in Paris. The dictionary is divided into sections dealing with subjects such as arithmetic, algebra, geometry, cosmography, astronomy, navigation, optics, perspective, mechanics, hydrostatics, architecture, fortification and music.

References: Houzeau & Lancaster 9334

£300-400
€450-600

1569 Ozanam, Jacques. Nouveaux elemens d'algebre, ou Principes generaux, pour resoudre toutes sortes de problemes de mathematique. Premiere (-seconde) partie. *Amsterdam: George Gallet, 1702*

FIRST EDITION, 8vo (190 x 120mm.), [14], 272, [14], 273-668pp., title-pages in red and black, ILLUSTRATION: engraved frontispiece, woodcut initials, head- and tailpieces, woodcut diagrams, BINDING: contemporary blind-tooled speckled calf, spine gilt in compartments, morocco lettering-piece, *extremities slightly rubbed, upper joint cracking at head and foot*

£200-300
€300-450

1570 Ozanam, Jacques. Cursus mathematicus: or, a compleat course of the mathematicks... Now done into English, with additions and corrections by several hands (volumes 4 & 5: by J.T. Desaguliers). *London: for John Nicholson and sold by John Morphew (volumes 4 & 5: Oxford: L. Lichfield for John Nicholson and sold by John Morphew), 1712*

5 volumes, 8vo (195 x 118mm.), [6], x, 80, 288; [24], 92, 156, [284]; [16], 215, [1 (blank)], [14], 204, [8]; [30], 185, [7], 72, [8]; [16], 166, [18], 131, [11]pp., half-title in volume 1, ILLUSTRATION: 205 engraved plates, BINDING: contemporary speckled calf (volume 4: contemporary panelled calf), spines gilt in compartments, *slight worming in lower margins of last few plates of volume 5, occasional light browning, spines rubbed, lacking 4 spine-labels*

FIRST EDITION IN ENGLISH. Ozanam's *Cours de mathématiques*, first published in 1693, contains sections on algebra and Euclid's *Elements*, arithmetic, trigonometry, geometry, fortification, mechanics, perspective, geography and dialling. John Theophilus Desaguliers, whose name is mentioned on the title-pages of volumes 4 and 5, published his translation of Ozanam's treatise on fortification separately in 1711 (the treatise here forms the second part of volume 3, with its original title-page).

£400-500
€600-750

1571 Ozanam, Jacques. Recréations mathématiques et physiques... Nouvelle édition... augmentée. Tome premier (-quatrieme). *Paris: Claude Jombert, 1725*

4 volumes, 8vo (195 x 118mm.), [16], 460, [20]; [6], 462, [14]; [2], 482, [14]; [8], 446, [4]pp., ILLUSTRATION: woodcut initials, head- and tailpieces, woodcut digrams, 32+55+30+17 engraved plates (some folding), BINDING: contemporary mottled calf gilt, spines gilt in compartments, morocco lettering-pieces, red edges, *E5 in vol.3 torn in margin with slight loss, extremities slightly rubbed*

1571

Originally published in 1694 and reprinted regularly. "Ozanam's *Recréations* may be regarded as the forerunner of modern books on mathematical recreations. He drew heavily on the works of Bachet de Méziriac, Mydorge, Leurechon, and Daniel Schwenter; his own contributions were somewhat less significant, for he was not a particularly creative mathematician" (*DSB* X, p.264).

£400-600
€600-900

END OF SALE

Adams	H.M. Adams, *Catalogue of books printed on the continent of Europe, 1501-1600, in Cambridge libraries* (Cambridge, 1967)
Babson	*A Descriptive Catalogue of the Grace K. Babson Collection of the Works of Sir Isaac Newton* (New York, 1950)
BAL RIBA	*Catalogue of the British Architectural Library Early Imprints Collection* (London, 1994-2003)
Belgica Typographica	E. Cockx-Indestege and G. Glorieux, *Belgica Typographica 1541-1600* (Nieuwkoop, 1968-1980)
Berlin Catalogue	*Katalog der Ornamentstich-Sammlung der Staatlichen Kunstbibliothek Berlin* (Berlin, 1939)
Bigmore & Wyman	E.C. Bigmore and C.W.H. Wyman, *A Bibliography of Printing*, second edition (New York, 1945)
BL STC German XVIIc.	*Catalogue of Books printed in the German-speaking countries... from 1601 to 1700 now in the British Library* (London, 1994)
BL STC Italian XVIIc.	*Catalogue of Seventeenth Century Italian Books in the British Library* (London, 1986)
BL STC Spanish XVIIc.	*A Short Title Catalogue of Spanish and Portuguese Books in the Library of the British Museum* (London, 1974)
Blake	J.B.Blake, *A short title catalogue of eighteenth century printed books in the National Library of Medicine* (Bethseda, 1979)
BMC	*Catalogue of Books printed in the XVth Century now in the British Museum* (London, 1963-1971)
Bonacini	C. Bonacini, *Bibliografia delle arti scrittorie e della calligrafia* (Florence, 1653)
Bowyer Ledgers	K. Madsen and J. Lancaster, editors, *The Bowyer Ledgers* (London, 1991)
British Optical Association	J.H. Sutcliffe, *British Optical Association Library and Museum Catalogue* (London, 1932)
Bruun	P.C.V. Bruun, *Bibliotheca Danica. Systematisk Fortegnelse over den Danske Literatur fra 1482 til 1830, efter Samlingerne i det Store Kongelige Bibliothek i Kjobenhavn* (reprint, Copenhagen, 1961)
BUC	*The British Union Catalogue of Early Music printed before the year 1801* (London, 1957)
Burmeister	K.H. Burmeister, *Georg Joachim Rhetikus, 1514-1574: eine Bio-Bibliographie* (Wiesbaden, 1968)
Caillet	A. Caillet, *Manuel bibliographique des sciences psychiques ou occultes* (Paris, 1912)
Carter, *OUP*	H. Carter, *A History of the Oxford University Press* (Oxford, 1975)
Caspar	M. Caspar, *Bibliographia Kepleriana* (Munich, 1936)
Censimento 16	*Censimento delle edizioni italiane del XVI secolo*, http://edit16.iccu.sbn.it
Challinor	J. Challinor, *The History of British Geology: A bibliographical study* (Newton Abbot, 1971)
Cicognara	L. Cicognara, *Catalogo ragionato dei libri d'arte e d'antichità* (Leipzig, 1931)
Cinti	D. Cinti, *Biblioteca Galileiana* (Florence, 1957)
Cockle	M. Cockle, *A Bibliography of English Military Books up to 1642 and of Contemporary Foreign Works* (London, 1900)
Cohen	I.B. Cohen, *Introduction to Newton's 'Principia'* (London, 1971)
Cole	N.B. Eales, *The Cole Library of Early Medicine and Zoology: Catalogue of books and pamphlets part I, 1472 to 1800* (Reading, 1969)
Cole, *Chemical Literature*	W.A. Cole, *Chemical Literature 1700-1860* (London, 1988)
Conlon	P.M. Conlon, *Prélude au siècle des lumières en France... 1680 à 1715* (Geneva, 1970-1975)
Davidsson	A. Davidsson, *Catalogue critique et descriptif des ouvrages théoriques sur la musique imprimés au XVIe et au XVIIe siècles et conservés dans les bibliothèques suédoises* (Uppsala, 1953)
Day & Murrie	C.L. Day and E.B. Murrie, *English song-books, 1651-1702: a bibliography with a first-line index of songs* (Oxford, 1940)
Dibner	B. Dibner, *Heralds of Science as Represented by Two Hundred Epochal Books and Pamphlets Selected from the Burndy Library* (Norwalk, 1955)
DSB	C.C. Gillispie (editor), *Dictionary of Scientific Biography* (New York, 1970-1980)
Dünnhaupt	G. Dünnhaupt, *Bibliographisches Handbuch der Barockliteratur... des siebzehnten Jahrhunderts* (Stuttgart, 1980-1981)
Duveen	D.I. Duveen, *Bibliotheca alchemica et chemica* (London, 1949)
Duveen & Klickstein, *Lavoisier*	D.I. Duveen and H.S. Klickstein, *A bibliography of the works of Antoine Laurent Lavoisier, 1743-1794* (London, 1954)

Eimas	R. Eimas, *Heirs of Hippocrates... a Catalogue of Historic Books in the Hardin Library for the Health Science, the University of Iowa*, third edition (Iowa City, 1990)
English Maritime Books	T.R. Adams and D.W. Waters, *English maritime books printed before 1801* (Providence, 1995)
ESTC	*English Short Title Catalogue* (on-line edition)
Evans	C. Evans, *American Bibliography* (Chicago, 1903)
Ferguson	J. Ferguson, *Bibliotheca chemica. The Collection of the late James Young* (Glasgow, 1906)
Fowler	L.H. Fowler and E. Baer, *The Fowler Architectural Collection of the Johns Hopkins University* (Baltimore, 1961)
Foxon	D.F. Foxon, *English Verse 1701-1750: a catalogue of separately printed poems* (London, 1925)
Fulton	J.F. Fulton, *A Bibliography of the Honourable Robert Boyle,* second edition (Oxford, 1961)
Furbank & Owens	P.N. Furbank and W.R. Owens, *A Critical Bibliography of Daniel Defoe* (London, 1998)
Garrison-Morton	L.T. Morton, *A Medical Bibliography*, fifth edition (Aldershot, 1991)
Goff	F.R. Goff, *Incunabula in American Libraries, a third census* (New York, 1964)
Goldsmiths	M. Canney and D. Knott, *Catalogue of the Goldsmiths' Library of Economic Literature* (Cambridge, 1970)
Grafton, *Scaliger*	A. Grafton, *Joseph Scaliger* (Oxford, 1993)
Gregory & Bartlett	J. Gregory and H. Bartlett, *Catalogue of Early Books on Music (before 1800)* (New York, 1969)
GW	*Gesamtkatalog der Wiegendrucke* (Leipzig 1925-)
H	L. Hain, *Repertorium bibliographicum in quo libri omnes ab arte typographica inventa usque ad annum MD...* (Stuttgart and Paris, 1826-1838)
Harris	E. Harris, *British Architectural Books and Writers 1556-1785* (Cambridge, 1990)
Harrison	J. Harrison, *The Library of Isaac Newton* (Cambridge, 1978)
Heal	A. Heal, *The English writing-masters and their copy-books 1570-1800: a biographical dictionary & a bibliography* (Cambridge, 1931)
Heath, *Greek Mathematics*	T.L. Heath, *A History of Greek Mathematics* (Oxford, 1921)
Heawood	E. Heawood, *Watermarks Mainly of the 17th and 18th Centuries* (Hilversum, 1950)
Hirsch	K. Meyer and P. Hirsch, *Katalog der Musikbibliothek Paul Hirsch* (Berlin, 1928)
Hoboken	*Katalog der Sammlung Anthony van Hoboken in der Sammlung der Österreichischen Nationalbibliothek,* Band 16: 'Drucke des 17. bis 19. Jahrhunderts von Albrechsberger bis Zumsteeg' (Tutzing, 1998)
Horblit	H.D. Horblit, *One Hundred Books Famous in Science. Based on an Exhibition Held at the Grolier Club* (New York, 1964)
Houzeau & Lancaster	J. C. Houzeau and A. Lancaster, *Bibliographie générale de l'astronomie* (London, 1964)
Hunt	J. Quinby and A. Stevenson, *Catalogue of Botanical Books in the Collection of Rachel McMasters Miller Hunt* (Pittsburgh, 1958-1961)
Huygens, *Oeuvres*	C. Huygens, *Oeuvres Complètes* (The Hague, 1988-1950)
IA	*Index Aureliensis. Catalogus librorum sedecimo saeculo impressorum* (Geneva, 1965-)
Ingamells	J. Ingamells, *A dictionary of British and Irish travellers in Italy, 1701-1800* (London, 1997)
Isaac	F. Isaac, *English and Scottish printing types 1535-58; 1552-58* (London, 1932)
JCB	*Catalogue of the John Carter Brown Library in Brown University* (New York, 1961-1965)
Kepler, *Gesammelte Werke*	J. Kepler, *Gesammelte Werke* (Munich, 1937-1990)
Keynes, *Hooke*	G. Keynes, *A Bibliography of Dr Roebrt Hooke* (Oxford, 1960)
Klebs	A.C. Klebs, *Incunabula scientifica et medica* (Bruges, 1938)
Koyré & Cohen	*Isaac Newton's Principia. The third edition (1726) edited by A Koyré & I.B Cohen* (Harvard, 1972)
Kress	*The Kress Library of Business and Economics Catalogue* (Boston, 1940-1967)
Krivatsy	P. Krivatsy, *A Catalogue of Seventeenth Century Printed Books in the National Library of Medicine* (Bethesda, Maryland, 1989)

Landwehr, *Romeyn de Hooghe*	J. Landwehr, *Romeyn de Hooghe 1645-1708 as Book Illustrator* (1970)
Linde, *Schachlitteratur*	A.V.D. Linde, *Das Erste Jartausend der Schachlitteratur (850-1880)* (Berlin, 1881)
Lipperheide	F.J. von Lipperheide, *Katalog der Kostumbibliothek* (New York, 1963)
MacDonald, *Napier*	W.R. MacDonald, *The construction of the wonderful canon of logarithms by John Napier translated from the Latin into English with notes and a catalogue of the various editions of Napier's works* (Edinburgh, 1889)
Machiels	J. Machiels, *Catalogus van de boeken gedrukt voor 1600 aanwezig op de Centrale Bibliotheek van de Rijksuniversiteit Gent* (Ghent, 1979)
Madan	F. Madan, *Oxford Books: A bibliography of printed works relating to the University and City of Oxford or printed or published there* (Oxford, 1895-1931)
Magriel	P.D. Magriel, *A Bibliography of Dancing* (New York, 1936)
McKenzie	D.F. McKenzie, *The Cambridge University Press 1696-1712: a bibliographical study* (Cambridge, 1966)
McKerrow	R.B. Mckerrow, *Printers' and publishers' devices in England and Scotland 1485-1640* (Chiswick, 1913)
Merrill	B.L. Merrill, *Athanasius Kirchner (1602-1680), jesuit scholar: an exhibition of his works in the Harold B. Lee Library* (Provo, Utah, 1989)
Michel	S. Michel and P.-H. Michel, *Répertoire des ouvrages imprimés en langue italienne au xviie siècle conservés dans les bibliothèques de France* (Paris, 1972-1984)
Millard	D. Wiebenson and C. Baines, *The Mark J. Millard Architectural Collection, volume I: French books sixteenth through nineteenth centuries* (Washington, 1993)
Moreau	B. Moreau, *Inventaire chronologique des éditions parisiennes du XVIe siècle* (Paris, 1972-)
Mortimer, *Harvard French*	R. Mortimer, *Harvard College Library... French 16th Century Books* (Cambridge, Massachusetts, 1964)
Mortimer, *Harvard Italian*	R. Mortimer, *Harvard College Library... Italian 16th Century Books* (Cambridge, Massachusetts, 1974)
New Grove	*The New Grove Dictionary of Music and Musicians* (London, 1981)
Newton, *Correspondence*	Sir I. Newton, *Correspondence*, edited by H. Turnbull (Cambridge, 1959-1977)
Newton, *Mathematical Papers*	Sir I. Newton, *Mathematical Papers*, edited by D.T. Whiteside (Cambridge, 1967-1981)
Nichols, *Anecdotes*	J. Nichols, *Anecdotes, biographical and literary, of the late Mr. William Bowyer, printer: compiled for private use* (London, 1778)
Nielsen, *Dansk Bibliografi 1551-1600*	L. Nielsen, *Dansk Bibliografi 1551-1600* (Copenhagen, 1931-1933)
Nissen *ZBI*	C. Nissen, *Die zoologische Buchillustration* (Stuttgart, 1969)
NK	W. Nijhoff and M.E. Kronenberg, *Nederlandsche Bibliographie van 1500 tot 1540* ('S-Gravenhage, 1923)
Norman	D.H. Hook and J.M. Norman, *The Haskell F. Norman Library of Science & Medicine* (San Francisco 1991)
ODNB	*Oxford Dictionary of National Biography* (Oxford, 2004)
Oldenburg, *Correspondence*	H. Oldenburg, *Correspondence*, edited by A.R. and M.R. Hall (Madison, 1965-1986)
Palau	A. Palau y Dulcet, *Manual del librero hispano-americano* (Barcelona & Oxford, 1948-1977)
Partington	J.R. Partington, *A History of Chemistry* (London, 1961-1970)
Peeters-Fontainas	J. Peeters-Fontainas, *Bibliographie des impressions espagnoles des Pays-Bas méridionaux* (Nieuwkoop, 1965)
Pennington	R. Pennington, *A descriptive catalogue of the etched work of Wenceslaus Hollar 1607-1677* (Cambridge, 1982)
PMM	*Printing and the Mind of Man: A descriptive catalogue* (London, 1967)
Poggendorff	J.C. Poggendorff, *Biographisch-literarisches Handwörterbuch zur Geschichte der exacten Wissenschaften* (Leipzig, 1863-1898)
Polain	L. Polain, *Catalogue des livres imprimés au quinzième siècle des bibliothèques de Belgique* (Bruxelles: Société des Bibliophiles & Iconophiles de Belgique, 1932)
Pritzel	G.A. Pritzel, *Thesaurus literaturae botanicae omnium gentium* (Leipzig, 1871-1877)

Ravier   E. Ravier, *Bibliographie des oeuvres de Leibniz* (Paris, 1937)

Redgrave   G. Redgrave, *Erhard Ratdolt and his work at Venice* (London, 1894)

Renouard   A.A. Renouard, *Annales de l'imprimerie des Alde*, third edition (Paris, 1834)

Renouard, *Estienne*   A.A. Renouard, *Annales de l'imprimerie des Estienne*, second edition (Paris, 1843)

Renouard, *Colines*   P. Renouard, *Bibliographie des éditions de Simon de Colines 1520-1546* (Paris, 1894)

Rép. bibl. xvie siècle   L. Desgraves et al., *Répertoire bibliographique des livres imprimés en France au seizième siècle* (Baden-Baden, 1968-)

Rép. bibl. xviie siècle   L. Desgraves et al., *Répertoire bibliographique des livres imprimés en France au dix-septième siècle* (Baden-Baden, 1978-)

Riccardi   P. Riccardi, *Biblioteca matematica italiana dalle origine della stampa ai primi anni del secolo XIX* (Milan, 1952)

Rigaud, *Correspondence*   S. Rigaud, *Correspondence of Scientific Men of the Seventeenth Century* (Oxford, 1841)

RISM   *Répertoire international des sources musicales* (Kassel, 1971)

Rossetti   S. Rossetti, *Rome: A bibliography from the invention of printing through 1899* (Florence, 2001)

Sabin   J. Sabin, W. Eames and R.W.G. Vail, *A Dictionary of Books Relating to America* (New York, 1868-1936)

Sandal, *Editori*   E. Sandal, *Editori e tipografi a Milano nel cinquecento* (Baden-Baden, 1977)

Sander   M. Sander, *Le livre à figures italien depuis 1467 jusqu'à 1530* (New York, 1941)

Sarton   G. Sarton, *Introduction to the History of Science* (Baltimore, 1927-1947)

Schreiber   W.L. Schreiber, *Manuel de l'amateur de la gravure sur bois et sur métal au XVe siècle* (Leipzig, 1902)

Shaaber   M.A. Shaaber, *Check-list of Works of British Authors Printed Abroad, in languages other than English, to 1641* (New York, 1975)

Smith   D.E. Smith, *Rara arithmetica* (Boston & London, 1908)

Sommervogel   C. Sommervogel, *Bibliothèque de la Compagnie de Jesus* (Brussels and Paris, 1890-1932)

Steck   M. Steck, *Bibliographia Euclideana* (Hildesheim, 1981)

STC   A.W. Pollard and G.R. Redgrave, *A Short-Title Catalogue of Books Printed in England, Scotland, Ireland, Wales, and British America and of English Books Printed in Other Countries 1641-1700*, second edition (London, 1986-1976)

Stillwell   M.B. Stillwell, *The Awakening Interest in Science During the First Century of Printing 1450-1550* (New York, 1970)

Taylor, *Tudor & Stuart*   E.G.R. Taylor, *Mathematical Practitioners of Tudor & Stuart England* (Cambridge, 1954)

Taylor, *Hanoverian*   E.G.R. Taylor, *Mathematical Practitioners of Hanoverian England* (Cambridge, 1966)

Texas   C.W. Kallendorf and M.X. Wells, *Aldine Press books at the Harry Ransom Humanities Research Center, the University of Texas at Austin: a descriptive catalogue* (Austin, 1998)

Todd (Newton?)

UCLA   *A catalogue of the Ahmanson-Murphy Aldine Collection at UCLA* (Los Angeles, 1989-94)

Vagnetti   L. Vagnetti, *De naturali e artificiali perspectiva* (Florence, 1979)

VD16   *Verzeichnis der im deutschen Sprachbereich erschienenen Drucke des XVI. Jahrhunderts* (Stuttgart, 1983-1995)

VD17   *Verzeichnis der im deutschen Sprachraum erschienenen Drucke des XVII. Jahrhunderts*, http://www.vd17.de

Vischer   M. Vischer, *Bibliographie der Zürcher Druckschriften des 15. und 16. Jahrhunderts erarbeitet in der Zentralbibliothek, Zürich* (Baden-Baden, 1991)

Voet   L. Voet, *The Plantin Press (1555-1589)* (Amsterdam, 1980)

Von Hünersdorff, *Coffee*   R. von Hünersdorff and H.G. Hasenkamp, *Coffee: a bibliography* (London, 2002)

Waller   H. Sallander, *Bibliotheca Walleriana: the Books Illustrating the History of Medicine and Science Collected by Dr Erik Waller* (Stockholm, 1955)

Wallis   P. and R. Wallis, *Newton and Newtoniana 1672-1975, a bibliography* (Folkestone, 1977)

Wellcome   *A Catalogue of Printed Books in the Wellcome Historical Medical Library* (London, 1962-1976)

Wheeler Gift   W.D. Weaver (editor), *Catalogue of the Wheeler Gift of Books, Pamphlets and Periodicals in the Library of the American Institute of Electrical Engineers* (New York, 1909)

Willems   A. Willems, *Les Elzevier* (Brussels, 1880)

Wing   D. Wing, *Short-Title Catalogue... of English Books... 1641-1700* (New York, 1972, 1982, 1951)

Zinner   E. Zinner, *Geschichte und Bibliographie der astronomischen Literatur in Deutschland zur Zeit der Renaissance* (Stuttgart, 1964)

SOTHEBY'S AUTHENTICITY GUARANTEE FOR BOOKS AND MANUSCRIPTS

If Sotheby's sells an item which subsequently is shown to be a "counterfeit", or which in Sotheby's opinion is materially defective in text or illustration, subject to the terms below Sotheby's will set aside the sale and refund to the Buyer the total amount paid by the Buyer to Sotheby's for the item, in the currency of the original sale.

For these purposes, "counterfeit" means a lot that in Sotheby's reasonable opinion is an imitation created to deceive as to authorship, origin, date, age, period, culture or source, where the correct description of such matters is not reflected by the description in the catalogue (taking into account any Glossary of Terms).

Please note that this Guarantee does not apply if either:-
(i) the catalogue description was in accordance with the generally accepted opinions of scholars and experts at the date of the sale, or the catalogue description indicated that there was a conflict of such opinions; or
(ii) the only method of establishing at the date of the sale that the item was a counterfeit would have been by means of processes not then generally available or accepted, unreasonably expensive or impractical to use; or likely to have caused damage to the lot or likely (in Sotheby's reasonable opinion) to have caused loss of value to the lot; or
(iii) the item complained of comprises an atlas, an extra-illustrated book, a volume with fore-edged paintings, a periodical publication or a print or drawing; or
(iv) in the case of a manuscript, the lot was not described in the catalogue as complete; or
(v) the defect complained of was mentioned in the catalogue or the item complained of was sold un-named in a lot; or
(vi) the defect complained of is other than in text or illustration. (For example, without limitation, a sale will not be set aside on account of damage to bindings, stains, foxing, marginal wormholes, lack of blank leaves or other conditions not affecting the completeness of the text or illustration, lack of list of plates, inserted advertisements, cancels or any subsequently published volume, supplement, appendix or plates or error in the enumeration of the plates; or
(vii) there has been no material loss in value of the lot from its value had it been in accordance with its description.

This Guarantee is provided for a period of five (5) years (in respect of counterfeit items) or twenty-one (21) days (in respect of items materially defective in text or illustration) after the date of the relevant auction, is solely for the benefit of the Buyer and may not be transferred to any third party. To be able to claim under this Guarantee, the Buyer must:-
(i) notify Sotheby's in writing within three (3) months (for counterfeit items) or twenty one (21) days (for items materially defective in text or illustration) with the reasons why the Buyer considers the item to be counterfeit or materially defective in text or illustration, specifying the lot number and the date of the auction at which it was purchased; and
(ii) return the item to Sotheby's in the same condition as at the date of sale to the Buyer and be able to transfer good title in the item, free from any third party claims arising after the date of the sale.

Sotheby's has discretion to waive any of the above requirements. Sotheby's may require the Buyer to obtain at the Buyer's cost the reports of two independent and recognised experts in the field, mutually acceptable to Sotheby's and the Buyer. Sotheby's shall not be bound by any reports produced by the Buyer, and reserves the right to seek additional expert advice at its own expense. In the event Sotheby's decides to rescind the sale under this Guarantee, it may refund to the Buyer the reasonable costs of up to two mutually approved independent expert reports.

NOTICE REGARDING AUCTION HOUSE SETTLEMENT CERTIFICATES

General: Pursuant to the settlement agreement in *In re Auction Houses Antitrust Litigation*, Christie's and Sotheby's have issued Certificates that permit the Holder to be reimbursed for certain consignment fees that are paid when property is auctioned at Christie's or Sotheby's. The reimbursable fees are: 1) vendor's commissions, 2) risk of loss or insurance fees, and 3) illustration charges. Any Certificate Holder may use the Certificates for reimbursement if the Holder paid these charges in connection with property offered for sale in a non-internet auction conducted by Sotheby's or Christie's in the United States or United Kingdom on or after May 15, 2003.

As described below, the Certificates are freely transferable to anyone and from May 15, 2007 through May 14, 2008, Certificates may be redeemed for cash at their face value. Certificates can be redeemed only through the Certificate Administrator, EquiServe, Inc.

Certificate Expiration: All outstanding Certificates and Certificate Change that have not been redeemed will expire on May 14, 2008. The Certificate Administrator will honor only Certificates and Certificate Change that it receives on or before 5:00 pm. New York time on May 14, 2008.

Market Makers and Additional Information: The Certificate Administrator maintains contact information for parties, including secondary market makers, who are interested in buying or selling Certificates or Certificate Change. The Certificate Administrator will disseminate the names of Certificate Holders interested in exchange transactions. If you wish to be identified as interested in buying or selling Certificates or Certificate Change, please notify the Certificate Administrator in writing, including your address and telephone number, at the address below. Neither Christie's nor Sotheby's is associated with or responsible for the actions of any market makers or other third-party buyers or sellers of Certificates.

Contact Information: Information regarding the Certificates may be found at the website www.auctionsetttlement.com. For additional information on how to use, redeem, purchase, or sell Certificates, contact the Certificate Administrator at **1-877-498-8863 (which can be dialed by international callers after dialing their country's access number) or www.auctionsettlement.com. Please mail, or deliver by courier all requests for reimbursement or redemption to: Certificate Administrator for the Auction Houses Litigation P.O. Box 8907, Edison, NJ 08837, overnight mail address: 156 Fernwood Avenue, Edison, NJ 08837.**

Redemption Procedure: To receive reimbursement, Certificate Holders must provide 1) a valid Certificate(s) that has the Holder's Proper Signature, as defined below; and 2) a valid remittance statement(s) from Christie's and/or Sotheby's (each statement must show a valid consignment, the auction date, and payment of reimbursable charges). A **"Proper Signature"** is a signature before a notary public or a consular official at a U.S. Embassy or Consulate, with the official stamp or seal of the notary public or consular official. To redeem a Certificate that has been transferred from its original Holder, the Certificate must also contain the Proper Signature of that Holder. The Certificate Administrator will not redeem Certificates without a Proper Signature.

Upon receiving the documentation listed above, the Certificate Administrator will mail the Holder a check in U.S. dollars for the reimbursement amount within 10 days. If the full face value of the Certificate(s) is not used in a redemption transaction, the Certificate Administrator will issue a new Certificate for the remaining balance ("Certificate Change"). The Certificate Change may be used just as any other Certificate.

If you are planning to consign property at Sotheby's or Christie's for non-internet auctions, you do not need to inform Sotheby's or Christie's that you intend to use Certificates in connection with the transaction.

Cash Redemption: Subject to certain conditions, from May 15, 2007 until May 14, 2008, the Certificates and Certificate Change may be redeemed - without making a consignment - for the face amount of the Certificate in U.S. dollars. For a cash redemption, the Holder must follow the normal redemption procedures set forth above, but need not include any remittance statement.

Certificate Exchange Procedure: The Certificates and Certificate Change are freely transferable to anyone. The Holder may request that any Certificate or Certificate Change be re-issued in different denominations, including smaller denominations. Anyone interested in buying or selling Certificates or Certificate Change must follow the procedures stated above. Each seller must execute the transferred Certificate with a Proper Signature as defined above. The Certificate Administrator will not redeem Certificates that do not contain a Proper Signature. For your protection, the Certificate Administrator recommends that you send the completed Certificate or Certificate Change to the Certificate Administrator in connection with each transfer. The Certificate Administrator will then issue a new Certificate in the name of the transferee/purchaser. This step is not necessary to complete the transfer, but if you do not follow this step, the Certificate Administrator will not replace a lost or stolen Certificate in the name of the new Holder.

IMPORTANT NOTICES TO BUYERS

The proliferation of photocopying machines makes it impossible for Sotheby's to know whether copies of lots have been taken. We will endeavour to contact vendors about the existence of photocopies, on request.

ESTIMATES IN EUROS

As a guide to potential buyers, estimates for this sale are also shown in Euros. The estimates printed in the catalogue in Pounds Sterling have been converted at the following rate, which was current at the time of printing. These estimates may have been rounded:
£1 = €1.4469

By the date of the sale this rate is likely to have changed, and buyers are recommended to check before bidding.

During the sale Sotheby's may provide a screen to show currency conversions as bidding progresses. This is intended for guidance only and all bidding will be in Pounds Sterling. Sotheby's is not responsible for any error or omissions in the operation of the currency converter.

Payment for purchases is due in Pounds Sterling, however the equivalent amount in any other currency will be accepted at the rate prevailing on the day that payment is received in cleared funds.

Settlement is made to vendors in the currency in which the sale is conducted, or in another currency on request at the rate prevailing on the day that payment is made by Sotheby's.

SAFETY AT SOTHEBY'S

Sotheby's is concerned for your safety while you are on our premises and we endeavour to display items safely so far as is reasonably practicable. Nevertheless, should you handle any items on view at our premises, you do so at your own risk.

Some items can be large and/or heavy and can be dangerous if mishandled. Should you wish to view or inspect any items more closely please ask for assistance from a member of Sotheby's staff to ensure your safety and the safety of the property on view.

Some items on view may be labelled "PLEASE DO NOT TOUCH". Should you wish to view these items you must ask for assistance from a member of Sotheby's staff, who will be pleased to assist you.

Thank you for your co-operation.

GUIDE FOR PROSPECTIVE BUYERS

Buying at Auction
The following pages are designed to give you useful information on how to buy at auction. Sotheby's staff as listed at the front of this catalogue will be happy to assist you. However, it is important that you read the following information carefully and note that Sotheby's acts for the seller; you should refer in particular to sections 3 and 4 of the Conditions of Business set out in this catalogue.

Provenance
In certain circumstances, Sotheby's may print in the catalogue the history of ownership of a work of art if such information contributes to scholarship or is otherwise well known and assists in distinguishing the work of art. However, the identity of the seller or previous owners may not be disclosed for a variety of reasons. For example, such information may be excluded to accommodate a seller's request for confidentiality or because the identity of prior owners is unknown given the age of the work of art.

Buyer's Premium
The buyer's premium payable by the buyer of each lot is at a rate of 20% on the first £100,000 of the hammer price and at a rate of 12% on the amount by which the hammer price exceeds £100,000.

VAT
Value Added Tax (VAT) may be payable on the hammer price and/or the buyer's premium. Buyer's premium may attract a charge in lieu of VAT. Please read carefully the "VAT INFORMATION FOR BUYERS" in this catalogue.

1. Before the Auction

Catalogue Subscriptions
If you would like to take out a catalogue subscription, please ring 020 7293 6444.

Pre-sale Estimates
Pre-sale estimates are intended as a guide for prospective buyers. Any bid between the high and low pre-sale estimates would, in our opinion, offer a chance of success. However, all lots can realise prices above or below the pre-sale estimates.

It is advisable to consult us nearer the time of sale as estimates can be subject to revision. The estimates printed in the auction catalogue do not include the buyer's premium or VAT.

Pre-sale Estimates in US Dollars and Euros
Although the sale is conducted in pounds sterling, the pre-sale estimates in some catalogues are also printed in US dollars and/or Euros. The rate of exchange is the rate at the time of production of this catalogue. Therefore, you should treat the estimates in US dollars or Euros as a guide only.

Symbol Key
The following key explains the symbols you may see inside this catalogue.

○ **Guaranteed Property**
The seller of lots with this symbol has been guaranteed a minimum price from one auction or a series of auctions. If every lot in a catalogue is guaranteed, the Important Notices in the sale catalogue will so state and this symbol will not be used for each lot.

△ **Property in which Sotheby's has an ownership interest**
Lots with this symbol indicate that Sotheby's owns the lot in whole or in part or has an economic interest in the lot equivalent to an ownership interest.

□ **No Reserve**
Unless indicated by a box (□), all lots in this catalogue are offered subject to a reserve. A reserve is the confidential minimum auction price established between Sotheby's and the seller and below which a lot will not be sold. The reserve is generally set at a percentage of the low estimate and will not exceed the low estimate for the lot. If any lots in the catalogue are offered without a reserve, these lots are indicated by a box (□). If all lots in the catalogue are offered without a reserve, a Special Notice will be included to this effect and the box symbol will not be used.

Condition of Lots
Prospective buyers are encouraged to inspect the property at the pre-sale exhibitions. Solely as a convenience, Sotheby's may provide condition reports. The absence of reference to the condition of a lot in the catalogue description does not imply that the lot is free from faults or imperfections. Please refer to Condition 3 of the Conditions of Business for Buyers.

Electrical and Mechanical Goods
All electrical and mechanical goods are sold on the basis of their decorative value only and should not be assumed to be operative. It is essential that prior to any intended use, the electrical system is checked and approved by a qualified electrician.

2. Bidding in the Sale

Bidding at Auction
Bids may be executed in person by paddle during the auction, in writing prior to the sale or by telephone.

Auction speeds vary, but average between 50 and 120 lots per hour. The bidding steps are generally in increments of approximately 10% of the previous bid.

Please refer to Conditions 5 and 6 of the Conditions of Business for Buyers.

Bidding in Person
To bid in person, you will need to register for and collect a numbered paddle before the auction begins. Proof of identity will be required. If you have a Sotheby's Identification Card, it will facilitate the registration process.

Should you be the successful buyer of a lot, please ensure that your paddle can be seen by the auctioneer and that it is your number that is called out. Should there be any doubts as to price or buyer, please draw the auctioneer's attention to it immediately.

All lots sold will be invoiced to the name and address in which the paddle has been registered and cannot be transferred to other names and addresses.

Please do not mislay your paddle; in the event of loss, inform the Sales Clerk immediately. At the end of the sale, please return your paddle to the registration desk.

Absentee Bids
If you cannot attend the auction, we will be happy to execute written bids on your behalf. A bidding form can be found at the back of this catalogue. This service is free and confidential. Lots will always be bought as cheaply as is consistent with other bids, the reserves and Sotheby's commissions. In the event of identical bids, the earliest received will take precedence. Always indicate a "top limit" - the hammer price to which you would bid if you were attending the auction yourself. "Buy" and unlimited bids will not be accepted. Please refer to Condition 5 of the Conditions of Business for Buyers.

Telephoned absentee bids must be confirmed before the sale by letter or fax. Fax number for bids only: 020 7293 6255.

To ensure a satisfactory service, please ensure that we receive your bids at least 24 hours before the sale.

12/04 NBS.Book.BuyA

Bidding by Telephone

If you cannot attend the auction, it is possible to bid on the telephone on lots with a minimum low estimate of £1,000. As the number of telephone lines is limited, it is necessary to make arrangements for this service 24 hours before the sale.

We also suggest that you leave a maximum bid which we can execute on your behalf in the event we are unable to reach you by telephone. Multi-lingual staff are available to execute bids for you. Please refer to Condition 5 of the Conditions of Business for Buyers.

Employee Bidding

Sotheby's employees may bid only if the employee does not know the reserve and fully complies with Sotheby's internal rules governing employee bidding.

US Economic Sanctions

The United States maintains economic and trade sanctions against targeted foreign countries, groups and organisations. US buyers will please note that US persons are generally prohibited from selling, buying or otherwise dealing with property belonging to members, residents, nationals or the governments of these countries, organisations or groups.

3. The Auction

Conditions of Business

The auction is governed by the Conditions of Business and Authenticity Guarantee. These apply to all aspects of the relationship between Sotheby's and actual and prospective bidders and buyers. Anyone considering bidding in the auction should read them carefully. They may be amended by way of notices posted in the saleroom or by way of announcement made by the auctioneer.

Consecutive and Responsive Bidding

The auctioneer may open the bidding on any lot by placing a bid on behalf of the seller. The auctioneer may further bid on behalf of the seller, up to the amount of the reserve, by placing consecutive or responsive bids for a lot. Please refer to Condition 6 of the Conditions of Business for Buyers.

4. After the Auction

Payment

Payment is due immediately after the sale and may be made by the following methods: Sterling Cash, Sterling Banker's Draft, Sterling Travellers Cheques, Sterling Cheque, Wire Transfer in Sterling, Credit Card (Visa, Mastercard & Eurocard), Debit Card (Delta, Connect & Switch).

It is against Sotheby's general policy to accept single or multiple related payments in the form of cash or cash equivalents in excess of the local currency equivalent of US$10,000. It is Sotheby's policy to request any new clients or purchasers preferring to make a cash payment to provide verification of identity (by providing some form of government issued identification containing a photograph, such as a passport, identity card or driver's licence), confirmation of permanent address and identification of the source of the funds. Thank you for your co-operation.

Cheques and drafts should be made payable to **Sotheby's**.
Although personal and company cheques drawn in Sterling on UK banks are accepted, you are advised that property will not be released until such cheques have cleared unless you have a pre-arranged **Cheque Acceptance Facility**. Forms to facilitate this are available from cashiers.

Bank transfers should be made to:
HSBC Bank plc
129 New Bond Street
London W1A 2JA
Account name: Sotheby's Receipts. Account No. 01099833.
Sort Code: 40-05-01. Swift Code: MIDLGB22.

Please include your name, Sotheby's account number and invoice number with your instructions to your bank.

Payment by Mastercard, Visa and Eurocard will be subject to a 1.5% administrative fee. Payments exceeding £20,000 can only be made by the card holder in person. For absentee payments below £20,000 please contact cashiers on 020 7293 5220.

The Conditions of Business require buyers to pay immediately for their purchases. However, in limited circumstances and with the seller's agreement, Sotheby's may offer buyers it deems credit worthy the option of paying for their purchases on an extended payment term basis. Generally credit terms must be arranged prior to the sale. In advance of determining whether to grant the extended payment terms, Sotheby's may require credit references and proof of identity and residence.

Storage and Collection

For information concerning post sale storage and charges, please see the Warehouse, Storage and Collection Information at the back of this catalogue.

Insurance

Buyers are reminded that lots are only insured **for a maximum of five (5) days** after the day of the auction. Please refer to Condition 7 of the Conditions of Business for Buyers.

Shipping

Sotheby's Shipping Logistics can advise buyers on exporting and shipping property. Our office is open between the hours of 9.00am and 5.30pm and you can contact the Shipping advisor on the number set out in the front of this catalogue.

Purchases will be despatched as soon as possible upon clearance from the Accounts department and receipt of your written despatch instructions and of any export licence or certificates that may be required. Despatch will be arranged at the buyer's expense. Sotheby's may receive a fee for its own account from the agent arranging the despatch. Estimates and information on all methods can be provided upon request and enquiries should be marked for the attention of Sotheby's Shipping Logistics and faxed to 020 7293 5952.

Transit insurance will be arranged unless otherwise specified in writing and will be at the buyer's expense. All shipments should be unpacked and checked on delivery and any discrepancies notified to the transit insurer or shipper immediately.

A form to provide shipping instructions is printed on the reverse of the bid slip in this catalogue or on the back of your buyers invoice.

Export

The export of any lot from the UK or import into any other country may be subject to one or more export or import licences being granted. It is the buyer's responsibility to obtain any relevant export or import licence. The denial of any licence required or delay in obtaining such licence cannot justify the cancellation of the sale or any delay in making payment of the total amount due.

Sotheby's, upon request and for an administrative fee, may apply for a licence to export your lot(s) outside the UK

An **EU Licence** is necessary to export cultural goods subject to the EU Regulation on the export of cultural property (EEC No. 3911/92, Official Journal No. L395 of 31/12/92) from the European Community.

A **UK Licence** is necessary to move cultural goods valued at or above the relevant UK Licence limits from the UK.

The following is a selection of some of the categories and a guide to the limits above which either an EU or UK Licence may be required. It is not exhaustive and there are other restrictions. For export outside the European Community, an EU Licence will be required for most items over 50 years of age with a value of over £30,400. For export within the European Community, a UK Licence will be required for most items over 50 years of age with a value of over £65,000.

	UK Licence Threshold	EU Licence Threshold
Archaeological objects	Zero	Zero
Elements of artistic, historical or religious monuments	£65,000	Zero
Manuscripts, documents and archives (excluding printed matter)	Zero	Zero
Other archival material	£65,000	Zero
Architectural, scientific and engineering drawings produced by hand	Zero	£9,100
Photographic positive or negative or any assemblage of such photographs	£10,000	£9,100
Textiles (excluding carpets and tapestries)	£12,000	£30,400
Firearms more than 100 years old, Arms or Armour	£35,000	£30,400
Paintings in oil or tempera	£180,000	£91,200
Watercolours, gouaches and pastels	£65,000	£18,200
Prints, Engravings, Drawings and Mosaics	£65,000	£9,100
British Historical Portraits	£10,000	According to medium

Export to Italy

Buyers intending to export their purchases to Italy under an Italian Temporary Cultural Import Licence are advised that the Italian authorities will require evidence of export from the UK. Please contact Sotheby's Shipping Representative or your own shipping agent prior to the export for more information.

Endangered Species

Items made of or incorporating plant or animal material, such as coral, crocodile, ivory, whalebone, tortoiseshell, etc., irrespective of age or value, may require a licence or certificate prior to exportation and require additional licences or certificates upon importation to any country outside the EU. Please note that the ability to obtain an export licence or certificate does not ensure the ability to obtain an import licence or certificate in another country, and vice versa. For example, it is illegal to import elephant ivory under 100 years old into the United States. Sotheby's suggests that buyers check with their own government regarding wildlife import requirements prior to placing a bid. It is the buyer's responsibility to obtain any export or import licences and/or certificates as well as any other required documentation (see Condition 10 of the Conditions of Business for Buyers).

5. Additional Services

Financial Services

Sotheby's Financial Services makes loans to clients of Sotheby's. These include loans secured by property consigned for sale and loans secured by art collections which are not intended for sale. It is Sotheby's Financial Services' general policy to lend no more than 40% of the total of its low auction estimates for such property. It is also general policy that the minimum loan for consignor advances is £25,001 (in the US $50,000) and for secured loans is £500,000 (in the US $1,000,000). For further information please call Sotheby's Financial Services in New York at (1-212) 894 1144, or in London at (44) 20 7293 5273. This is not an offer or solicitation. The services described are subject to the laws and regulations of the jurisdiction in which any services may be provided.

Pre-sale auction estimates

Sotheby's will be pleased to give preliminary pre-sale auction estimates for your property. This service is free of charge and is available from Sotheby's experts in New Bond Street on week days between 9 am and 4.30 pm. We advise you to make an appointment with the relevant expert department. Upon request, we may also travel to your home to provide preliminary pre-sale auction estimates.

Valuations

The Valuation department provides written inventories and valuations throughout Europe for many purposes including insurance, probate and succession division, asset management and tax planning. Valuations can be tailored to suit most needs. Fees are highly competitive. For further information please contact the Valuation department on 020 7293 6422, fax 020 7293 5957.

Tax and Heritage Advice

Our Tax and Heritage department provides advice on the tax implications of sales and related legal and heritage issues. It can also assist in private treaty sales, on transfers in lieu of taxation, on the obtaining of conditional exemption from tax and on UK export issues. For further information, please contact the Tax and Heritage department on 020 7293 5082, fax 020 7293 5965.

WAREHOUSE, STORAGE AND COLLECTION INFORMATION

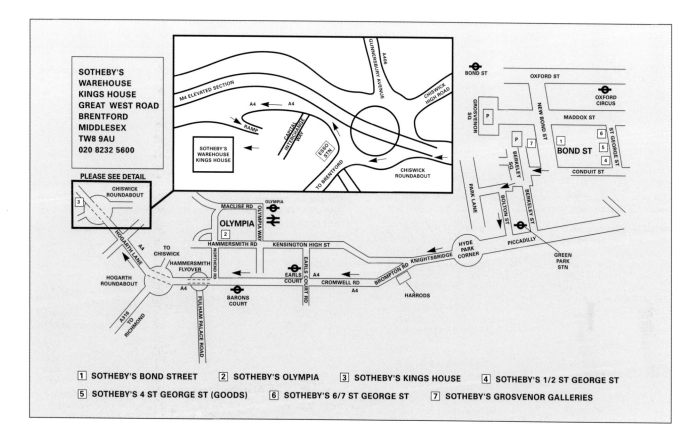

SOTHEBY'S
WAREHOUSE
KINGS HOUSE
GREAT WEST ROAD
BRENTFORD
MIDDLESEX
TW8 9AU
020 8232 5600

PLEASE SEE DETAIL

1 SOTHEBY'S BOND STREET   2 SOTHEBY'S OLYMPIA   3 SOTHEBY'S KINGS HOUSE   4 SOTHEBY'S 1/2 ST GEORGE ST
5 SOTHEBY'S 4 ST GEORGE ST (GOODS)   6 SOTHEBY'S 6/7 ST GEORGE ST   7 SOTHEBY'S GROSVENOR GALLERIES

Consignors Information

Furniture, Longcase Clocks, large Works of Art, Carpets, Rugs, Tapestries and large Musical Instruments
Consignments mentioned in the above should be delivered to Sotheby's Kings House by appointment, telephone 020 8232 5600.
Opening hours Monday to Friday 8.30am to 4.30pm, Saturdays 8.30am to 11.30am. Please arrive at least half an hour before closing.

Small items including: Pictures, Ceramics, Silver and small Works of Art, Paintings and Books, Oriental and Islamic Works of Art, Collectables, small Musical Instruments, Clocks and Watches, Wine, Stamps and Coins

Delivery in person between 9.00am and 4.30pm at 6-7 St. George Street, London, W1A 2AA.

Delivery by Courier or Shipping Agent

When instructing a Courier or Shipper to deliver items to Sotheby's, address your property to the Arrivals Department,
1-2 St. George Street, London, W1A 2AA. Consignments sent by this method must be packed appropriately and clearly labelled with the owners name, address, telephone numbers, Sotheby's Client Account Number, (if known) and necessary licences from the country of export. Contact Sotheby's Shipping Department on 020 7293 5357 for further information.

To avoid delay ensure 3 days notice is given along with full consignment details.

Collection

Lots will be released to you or your authorised representative when full and cleared payment has been received by Sotheby's and a release note has been produced by our Cashiers at New Bond Street, who are open Monday to Friday, 9 am to 5.00 pm.

Smaller items can normally be collected from the Packing Room at New Bond Street, however large items may be sent to Sotheby's Kings House Warehouse.

If you are in doubt about the location of your purchases, please contact the Sale Administrator prior to arranging collection or the New Bond Street Packing Room on 020 7293 5358. *Removal, interest, storage and handling charges will be levied on uncollected lots.*

Purchasers wishing to collect lots from Kings House must ensure that their payment has been cleared prior to collection and that a release note has been forwarded to the warehouse by the cashiers at Sotheby's New Bond Street. Buyers who have established credit arrangements with Sotheby's may collect purchases prior to payment, although a release note is still required from the cashiers as above. **Please note that the cashiers department is not open on Saturdays.** Lots will be released only if full payment has been received together with settlement of any removal, interest, handling and storage charges thereon. **Handling and storage charges plus VAT for all purchase lots sent to Sotheby's Kings House will apply two weeks after the sale date at the following rates:**
Handling Charge: £33 plus VAT per lot
Storage Charge: £3.80 plus VAT per lot per day

Payments should be made to Sotheby's at Kings House.

Route Guidance

From Bond Street to Hyde Park Corner take the Knightsbridge Road leading into Brompton Road then the Cromwell Road. Over the Hammersmith Flyover onto the Great West Road. At the Hogarth Roundabout take the Hogarth Road to Chiswick. Follow the A4 route from slip road round the Chiswick Roundabout and take the second turning on the left. Follow the A4 past Capital Interchange on your left and take next left down the ramp signed Sotheby's. Kings House is situated adjacent to the DHL Building.

Kings House Warehouse

Paul Dennis and Salim Hasham
Telephone: 020 8232 5600
Fax: 020 8232 5625

The following paragraphs are intended to give general guidance to buyers on the VAT and certain other potential tax implications of purchasing at Sotheby's book department sales. The information concerns the most usual circumstances (particularly arising from the VAT rules introduced on 1 June 1995) and is not intended to be complete. In all cases the relevant tax legislation takes precedence and the VAT rates in effect on the day of the auction will be the rates charged. It should be noted that, for VAT purposes only, Sotheby's is not usually treated as an agent and most property is sold as if it is the property of Sotheby's.

In the following paragraphs, reference to VAT symbols shall mean those symbols located beside the lot number or the pre-sale estimates in the catalogue (or amending sale room notice).

1. Property with no VAT symbol

Where there is no VAT symbol the property is free from VAT and Sotheby's will not charge VAT on either the hammer price or the buyer's premium.

2. Property with a # symbol

Although these items are not free from VAT, Sotheby's is able to use the Auctioneer's Margin Scheme and VAT will not normally be charged on the hammer price.

Sotheby's must bear VAT on the buyer's premium and hence will charge an amount in lieu of VAT at 17.5% on this premium. This amount will form part of the buyer's premium on our invoice and will not be separately identified.

Please see 'Exports from the European Union' for the conditions to be fulfilled before the amount in lieu of VAT in the buyer's premium may be cancelled or refunded.

(VAT-registered buyers from within the European Union (EU) should note that the amount in lieu of VAT contained within the buyer's premium cannot be cancelled or refunded by Sotheby's or HM Customs & Excise.)

(VAT-registered buyers from within the EU requiring an invoice under the normal VAT rules, instead of a margin scheme invoice, should notify the Cashier's Office or the Client Accounts Department on the day of the auction and an invoice with VAT on the hammer price will be raised. Buyers requiring reinvoicing under the normal VAT rules subsequent to a margin scheme invoice having been raised should contact the Client Accounts Department for assistance.)

3. Property with a † symbol

These items are standard-rated and will be sold under the normal UK VAT rules. Both the hammer price and buyer's premium will be subject to VAT at 17.5%.

Please see 'Exports from the European Union' for the conditions to be fulfilled before the VAT charged on the hammer price may be cancelled or refunded. Sotheby's must always charge VAT on the buyer's premium for these lots and will neither cancel nor refund the VAT charged.

(VAT-registered buyers from other European Union (EU) countries may have the VAT on the hammer price cancelled or refunded if they provide Sotheby's with their VAT registration number and evidence that the property has been removed from the UK within three months of the date of sale. A form is available from the Cashier's Office which will act as such evidence once completed by the buyer or the buyer's agent. If the shipping is undertaken by Sotheby's, no such form will be required.)

(All business buyers from outside the UK should refer to 'VAT Refunds from HM Customs & Excise' for information on how to recover VAT incurred on the buyer's premium.)

4. Property with a α symbol

Items sold to buyers whose address is in the European Union (EU) will be assumed to be remaining in the EU. The property will be invoiced as if it had a # symbol (see 'Property with a # symbol' above). However, if the property is to be exported from the EU, Sotheby's will re-invoice the property under the normal VAT rules (see 'Property sold with a † symbol' above) as requested by the seller.

Items sold to buyers whose address is outside the European Union (EU) will be assumed to be exported from the EU. The property will be invoiced under the normal VAT rules (see 'Property sold with a † symbol' above). Although the hammer price will be subject to VAT this will be cancelled or refunded upon export - see 'Exports from the European Union'. The buyer's premium will always attract VAT. However, buyers who are not intending to export their property from the EU should notify our Client Accounts Department on the day of the sale and the property will be re-invoiced showing no VAT on the hammer price (see 'Property sold with a # symbol' above).

5. Property sold with a ‡ or Ω symbol

These items have been imported from outside the European Union (EU) to be sold at auction under temporary importation. When Sotheby's releases such property to buyers in the UK, the buyer will become the importer and must pay Sotheby's import VAT at the following rates on both the hammer price and buyer's premium:

‡ - 5%
Ω - 17.5%

Buyers intending to take their purchased property out of the EU should see 'Exports from the European Union'.

(VAT-registered buyers from the EU should note that the import VAT charged on property released in the UK cannot be cancelled or refunded by Sotheby's.)

(VAT-registered buyers from the UK should note that the invoice issued by Sotheby's for these items is not suitable evidence for VAT return purposes. You should confirm with the Shipping Department that Sotheby's has a record of your VAT registration number and wait for a certificate C79 to be issued by HM Customs & Excise.)

(VAT-registered buyers from other EU countries may be able to seek repayment of the import VAT paid by applying to HM Customs & Excise with a copy of the C88 import declaration available from the Shipping Department - see 'VAT Refunds from HM Customs & Excise'.)

6. Exports from the European Union

The following types of VAT may be cancelled or refunded by Sotheby's on exports made within three months of the sale date if strict conditions are met:

- the amount in lieu of VAT charged on buyer's premium for property sold under the margin scheme i.e. with a # symbol or a a symbol.

- the VAT on the hammer price for property sold under the normal VAT rules i.e. with a † symbol or a α symbol.

- the import VAT charged on hammer price and buyer's premium for property sold under temporary importation i.e. with a ‡ or a Ω symbol.

In each of the above examples, where the appropriate conditions are satisfied, no VAT will be charged if, at or before the time of invoicing, the buyer instructs Sotheby's to export the property from the EU. If such instruction is received after payment, a refund of the VAT amount will be made. If a buyer later decides not to use Sotheby's shipping services a revised invoice will be raised charging VAT.

Where the buyer carries purchases from the EU personally or uses the services of another shipper, Sotheby's will charge the VAT amount due as a deposit and refund it if the lot has been exported within three months of the date of sale and the following conditions are met:

- for lots sold under the margin scheme (no VAT symbol) or the normal VAT rules († symbol), Sotheby's is provided with appropriate documentary proof of export from the EU. Buyers carrying their own property should obtain hand-carry papers from the Shipping department to facilitate this process.

- for lots sold under temporary importation (‡ or Ω symbols), Sotheby's is provided with a copy of the correct paperwork duly completed and stamped by HM Customs & Excise. It is essential for shippers acting on behalf of buyers to collect copies of the original import papers from our Shipping Department.

- buyers carrying their own property must obtain hand-carry papers from the Shipping Department for which a charge of £20 will be made. The VAT refund will be processed once the appropriate paperwork has been returned to Sotheby's.

- Sotheby's is not able to cancel or refund any VAT charged on sales made to UK or EU private residents unless the lot is subject to temporary importation and the property is exported from the EU within three months of the date of sale.

- any refund of VAT is subject to a minimum of £50 per shipment and a processing charge of £20.

Buyers intending to export lots under temporary importation (‡ or Ω symbols) should notify the Shipping Department **before** collection. Failure to do so may result in the crystallisation of the import VAT charge and Sotheby's will be unable to refund the VAT charged on deposit.

7. VAT Refunds from HM Customs & Excise

Where VAT charged cannot be cancelled or refunded by Sotheby's, it may be possible to seek repayment from HM Customs & Excise. Repayments in this manner are limited to businesses located outside the UK and may be considered for VAT charged on buyer's premium on property sold under the normal VAT rules (i.e. with a † or α symbol) or import VAT charged on the hammer price and buyer's premium for lots sold under temporary importation (i.e. with a ‡ or Ω symbol).

Claim forms are available from:
HM Customs & Excise
Overseas Repayment Section
8th/13th Directive
Customs House
PO Box 34
Londonderry, BT48 7AE
Northern Ireland
Tel: 44 2871 376200
or   44 2871 372727
Fax: 44 2871 372520

8. Sales and Uses Taxes

Buyers from outside the UK should note that local sales taxes or use taxes may become payable upon import of items following purchase (for example, the Use Tax payable on import of purchased items to certain states of the USA). Buyers should obtain their own advice in this regard.

The nature of the relationship between Sotheby's, Sellers and Bidders and the terms on which Sotheby's (as auctioneer) and Sellers contract with Bidders are set out below.

Bidders' attention is specifically drawn to Conditions 3 and 4 below, which require them to investigate lots prior to bidding and which contain specific limitations and exclusions of the legal liability of Sotheby's and Sellers. The limitations and exclusions relating to Sotheby's are consistent with its role as auctioneer of large quantities of goods of a wide variety. Bidders should pay particular attention to these Conditions.

1. Introduction

(a) Sotheby's and Sellers' contractual relationship with prospective Buyers is governed by:
(i) these Conditions of Business;
(ii) the Conditions of Business for Sellers displayed in the saleroom and which are available on request;
(iii) Sotheby's Authenticity Guarantee as printed in the sale catalogue; and
(iv) any additional notices and terms printed in the sale catalogue,
in each case as amended by any saleroom notice or auctioneer's announcement at the auction.

(b) As auctioneer, Sotheby's acts as agent for the Seller. A sale contract is made directly between the Seller and the Buyer. However, Sotheby's may own a lot (and in such circumstances acts in a principal capacity as Seller) and/or may have a legal, beneficial or financial interest in a lot as a secured creditor or otherwise.

2. Common Terms

In these Conditions of Business:
"Bidder" is any person considering, making or attempting to make a bid, by whatever means, and includes Buyers;
"Buyer" is the person who makes the highest bid or offer accepted by the auctioneer, and includes such person's principal when bidding as agent;
"Buyer's Expenses" are any costs or expenses due to Sotheby's from the Buyer, including an amount in respect of applicable VAT thereon;
"Buyer's Premium" is the commission payable by the Buyer on the Hammer Price at the rates set out in the Guide for Prospective Buyers;
"Counterfeit" is as defined in Sotheby's Authenticity Guarantee;
"Hammer Price" is the highest bid accepted by the auctioneer by the fall of the hammer (in the case of wine, as apportioned pro-rata by reference to the number of separately identified items in that lot), or in the case of a post-auction sale, the agreed sale price;
"Purchase Price" is the Hammer Price and applicable Buyer's Premium and VAT;
"Reserve" is the (confidential) minimum Hammer Price at which the Seller has agreed to sell a lot;
"Seller" is the person offering a lot for sale (including their agent (other than Sotheby's), executors or personal representatives);
"Sotheby's" means Sotheby's, the unlimited company which has its registered office at 34-35 New Bond Street, London W1A 2AA;
"Sotheby's Company" is Sotheby's Holdings, Inc. and any of its subsidiaries (within the meaning of Section 736 of the Companies Act 1985) (including Sotheby's);
"VAT" is Value Added Tax at the prevailing rate. Further information is contained in the Guide for Prospective Buyers.

3. Duties of Bidders and of Sotheby's in respect of items for sale

(a) Sotheby's knowledge in relation to each lot is partially dependent on information provided to it by the Seller, and Sotheby's is not able to and does not carry out exhaustive due diligence on each lot. Bidders acknowledge this fact and accept responsibility for carrying out inspections and investigations to satisfy themselves as to the lots in which they may be interested.

(b) Each lot offered for sale at Sotheby's is available for inspection by Bidders prior to the sale. Sotheby's accepts bids on lots solely on the basis that Bidders (and independent experts on their behalf, to the extent appropriate given the nature and value of the lot and the Bidder's own expertise) have fully inspected the lot prior to bidding and have satisfied themselves as to both the condition of the lot and the accuracy of its description.

(c) Bidders acknowledge that many lots are of an age and type which means that they are not in perfect condition. All lots are offered for sale in the condition they are in at the time of the auction (whether or not Bidders are in attendance at the auction). Condition reports may be available to assist when inspecting lots. Catalogue descriptions and condition reports may on occasions make reference to particular imperfections of a lot, but Bidders should note that lots may have other faults not expressly referred to in the catalogue or condition report. Illustrations are for identification purposes only and will not convey full information as to the actual condition of lots.

(d) Information provided to Bidders in respect of any lot, including any estimate, whether written or oral and including information in any catalogue, condition or other report, commentary or valuation, is not a representation of fact but rather is a statement of opinion genuinely held by Sotheby's. Any estimate may not be relied on as a prediction of the selling price or value of the lot and may be revised from time to time in Sotheby's absolute discretion.

(e) No representations or warranties are made by Sotheby's or the Seller as to whether any lot is subject to copyright or whether the Buyer acquires copyright in any lot.

(f) Subject to the matters referred to at 3(a) to 3(e) above and to the specific exclusions contained at Condition 4 below, Sotheby's shall exercise such reasonable care when making express statements in catalogue descriptions or condition reports as is consistent with its role as auctioneer of lots in the sale to which these Conditions relate, and in the light of (i) the information provided to it by the Seller; (ii) scholarship and technical knowledge; and (iii) the generally accepted opinions of relevant experts, in each case at the time any such express statement is made.

4. Exclusions and limitations of liability to Buyers

(a) Sotheby's shall refund the Purchase Price to the Buyer in circumstances where it deems that the lot is a Counterfeit and each of the conditions of the Authenticity Guarantee has been satisfied.

(b) In the light of the matters in Condition 3 above and subject to Conditions 4(a) and 4(e), neither any Sotheby's Company nor the Seller:
(i) is liable for any errors or omissions in information provided to Bidders by Sotheby's (or any Sotheby's Company), whether orally or in writing, whether negligent or otherwise, except as set out in Condition 3(f) above;
(ii) gives any guarantee or warranty to Bidders and any implied warranties and conditions are excluded (save in so far as such obligations cannot be excluded by law) other than the express warranties given by the Seller to the Buyer in Condition 2 of the Sellers' Conditions of Business;
(iii) accepts responsibility to any Bidders in respect of acts or omissions (whether negligent or otherwise) by Sotheby's in connection with the conduct of auctions or for any matter relating to the sale of any lot.

(c) Unless Sotheby's owns a lot offered for sale, it is not responsible for any breach of these conditions by the Seller.

(d) Without prejudice to Condition 4(b), any claim against Sotheby's or the Seller by a Bidder is limited to the Purchase Price with regard to that lot. Neither Sotheby's nor the Seller shall under any circumstances be liable for any consequential losses.

(e) None of this Condition 4 shall exclude or limit Sotheby's liability in respect of any fraudulent misrepresentation made by Sotheby's or the Seller, or in respect of death or personal injury caused by the negligent acts or omissions of Sotheby's or the Seller.

9/02 NBS.CoB.A

5. Bidding at Auction

(a) Sotheby's has absolute discretion to refuse admission to the auction. Bidders must complete a Paddle Registration Form and supply such information and references as required by Sotheby's. Bidders act as principal unless they have Sotheby's prior written consent to bid as agent for another party. Bidders are personally liable for their bid and are jointly and severally liable with their principal if bidding as agent.

(b) Sotheby's advises Bidders to attend the auction but will seek to carry out absentee written bids which are in pounds sterling and, in Sotheby's opinion, clear and received sufficiently in advance of the sale of the lot, endeavouring to ensure that the first received of identical written bids has priority.

(c) Where available, written and telephone bids are offered as an additional service for no extra charge, at the Bidder's risk and are undertaken subject to Sotheby's other commitments at the time of the auction, Sotheby's therefore cannot accept liability for failure to place such bids. Telephone bids may be recorded.

6. Conduct of the Auction

(a) Unless otherwise specified, all lots are offered subject to a Reserve, which shall be no higher than the low presale estimate at the time of the auction.

(b) The auctioneer has discretion at any time to refuse any bid, withdraw any lot, re-offer a lot for sale (including after the fall of the hammer) if he believes there may be error or dispute, and take such other action as he reasonably thinks fit.

(c) The auctioneer will commence and advance the bidding at levels and in increments he considers appropriate and is entitled to place a bid or series of bids on behalf of the Seller up to the Reserve on the lot, without indicating he is doing so and whether or not other bids are placed.

(d) Subject to Condition 6(b), the contract between the Buyer and the Seller is concluded on the striking of the auctioneer's hammer, whereupon the Buyer becomes liable to pay the Purchase Price.

(e) Any post-auction sale of lots offered at auction shall incorporate these Conditions as if sold in the auction.

7. Payment and Collection

(a) Unless otherwise agreed, payment of the Purchase Price for a lot and any Buyer's Expenses are due in pounds sterling immediately on conclusion of the auction (the "Due Date") notwithstanding any requirements for export, import or other permits for such lot.

(b) Title in a purchased lot will not pass until Sotheby's has received the Purchase Price and Buyer's Expenses for that lot in cleared funds. Sotheby's is not obliged to release a lot to the Buyer until title in the lot has passed and appropriate identification has been provided, and any earlier release does not affect the passing of title or the Buyer's unconditional obligation to pay the Purchase Price and Buyer's Expenses.

(c) The Buyer is obliged to arrange collection of purchased lots within five days of the auction. Purchased lots are at the Buyer's risk (and therefore their sole responsibility for insurance) from the earliest of i) collection or ii) five days after the auction. Until risk passes, Sotheby's will compensate the Buyer for any loss or damage to the lot up to a maximum of the Purchase Price paid. Buyers should note that Sotheby's assumption of risk for loss or damage is subject to the exclusions set out in Condition 6 of the Conditions of Business for Sellers.

(d) For all items stored by a third party and not available for collection from Sotheby's premises, the supply of authority to release to the Buyer shall constitute collection by the Buyer.

(e) All packing and handling is at the Buyer's risk. Sotheby's will not be liable for any acts or omissions of third party packers or shippers.

8. Remedies for non-payment

Without prejudice to any rights the Seller may have, if the Buyer without prior agreement fails to make payment for the lot within five days of the auction, Sotheby's may in its sole discretion (having informed the Seller) exercise one or more of the following remedies:

(a) store the lot at its premises or elsewhere at the Buyer's sole risk and expense;

(b) cancel the sale of the lot;

(c) set off any amounts owed to the Buyer by a Sotheby's Company against any amounts owed to Sotheby's by the Buyer in respect of the lot;

(d) reject future bids from the Buyer or render such bids subject to payment of a deposit;

(e) charge interest at 6% per annum above HSBC Bank plc Base Rate from the Due Date to the date the Purchase Price and relevant Buyer's Expenses are received in cleared funds;

(f) exercise a lien over any of the Buyer's property which is in the possession of a Sotheby's Company. Sotheby's shall inform the Buyer of the exercise of any such lien and within 14 days of such notice may arrange the sale of such property and apply the proceeds to the amount owed to Sotheby's;

(g) resell the lot by auction or private sale, with estimates and reserves at Sotheby's discretion. In the event such resale is for less than the Purchase Price and Buyer's Expenses for that lot, the Buyer will remain liable for the shortfall together with all costs incurred in such resale;

(h) commence legal proceedings to recover the Purchase Price and Buyer's Expenses for that lot, together with interest and the costs of such proceedings on a full indemnity basis; or

(i) release the name and address of the Buyer to the Seller to enable the Seller to commence legal proceedings to recover the amounts due and legal costs. Sotheby's will take reasonable steps to notify the Buyer prior to releasing such details to the Seller.

9. Failure to collect purchases

(a) If the Buyer pays the Purchase Price and Buyer's Expenses but fails to collect a purchased lot within fourteen calendar days of the auction, the lot will be stored at the Buyer's expense (and risk) at Sotheby's or with a third party.

(b) If a purchased lot is paid for but not collected within six months of the auction, the Buyer authorises Sotheby's, having given notice to the Buyer, to arrange a resale of the item by auction or private sale, with estimates and reserves at Sotheby's discretion. The proceeds of such sale, less all costs incurred by Sotheby's, will be forfeited unless collected by the Buyer within two years of the original auction.

10. Export

It is the Buyer's sole responsibility to obtain any necessary export, import, firearm, endangered species or other permit for the lot. Without prejudice to Conditions 3 and 4 above, Sotheby's and the Seller make no representations or warranties as to whether any lot is subject to export or import restrictions or any embargoes. The denial of any permit or licence shall not justify cancellation or rescission of the sale contract or any delay in payment.

11. General

(a) All images and other materials produced for the auction are the copyright of Sotheby's, for use at Sotheby's discretion.

(b) Notices to Sotheby's should be in writing and addressed to the department in charge of the sale, quoting the reference number specified at the beginning of the sale catalogue. Notices to Sotheby's clients shall be addressed to the last address formally notified by them to Sotheby's.

(c) Should any provision of these Conditions of Business be held unenforceable for any reason, the remaining provisions shall remain in full force and effect.

(d) These Conditions of Business are not assignable by any Buyer without Sotheby's prior written consent, but are binding on Buyers' successors, assigns and representatives. No act, omission or delay by Sotheby's shall be deemed a waiver or release of any of its rights.

(e) The Contracts (Rights of Third Parties) Act 1999 is excluded by these Conditions of Business and shall not apply to any contract made pursuant to them.

(f) The materials listed in Condition 1(a) above set out the entire agreement and understanding between the parties with respect to the subject matter hereof. It is agreed that, save in respect of liability for fraudulent misrepresentation, no party has entered into any contract pursuant to these terms in reliance on any representation, warranty or undertaking which is not expressly referred to in such materials.

12. Data Protection

Sotheby's will use information provided by its clients or obtained by Sotheby's relating to its clients for the provision of auction and art-related services, real estate, insurance services, marketing and to manage and operate its business, or as required by law.

Sotheby's may wish to record and review video images of you and or telephone conversations for security or legal reasons or as necessary to provide a higher quality of service.

Clients agree that Sotheby's may use any sensitive information that they supply to Sotheby's. Unless permitted by law, Sotheby's will not otherwise process sensitive personal data without express consent.

By agreeing to these Conditions of Business, clients agree to the processing of their personal information and also to the disclosure and transfer of such information to any Sotheby's Company. At times we may also disclose your personal information to third parties in order to fulfil the services you have requested or for the above purposes. These disclosures may be to countries which may not offer equivalent protection of personal information to that offered in the EU. Clients can prevent the use of their personal information for marketing purposes by contacting us at 020 7293 6667.

13. Law and Jurisdiction

Governing Law These Conditions of Business and all aspects of all matters, transactions or disputes to which they relate or apply shall be governed by and interpreted in accordance with English law.

Jurisdiction For the benefit of Sotheby's, all Bidders and Sellers agree that the Courts of England are to have exclusive jurisdiction to settle all disputes arising in connection with all aspects of all matters or transactions to which these Conditions of Business relate or apply. All parties agree that Sotheby's shall retain the right to bring proceedings in any court other than the Courts of England.

Service of Process All Bidders and Sellers irrevocably consent to service of process or any other documents in connection with proceedings in any court by facsimile transmission, personal service, delivery by mail or in any other manner permitted by English law, the law of the place of service or the law of the jurisdiction where proceedings are instituted, at the last address of the Buyer or Seller known to Sotheby's or any other usual address.

CLIENT SERVICES

Catalogue Subscriptions
020 7293 6444

Client Assistance
Enquiries
020 7293 6026

Client Accounts
Michael Hart
020 7293 5890

Communications & Press
Helen Griffith
020 7293 6000

Financial Services
Ann-Marie Casey Jones
020 7293 5273
New York
Shelley Fischer
212 894 1144

Furniture Restoration
London
Roddy McVittie
020 8663 2993

House Sales
James Miller
020 7293 5405
Harry Dalmeny
020 7293 5848
Alexandra Reece
020 7293 5711

Education
Sotheby's Institute of Art - London
Tel: 020 7462 3232
Fax: 020 7580 8160
email: info@sothebysinstitutelondon.com
www.sothebysinstitutelondon.com
New York
J. Thomas Savage
Vice President
212 894 1111

Shipping
Suzanne Swan
020 7293 5353

Restitution
Lucian Simmons
London
020 7293 5257
New York
212 606 7126

Tax & Heritage
Wendy Philips
020 7293 6184

Trusts & Estates
New York
Daisy Edelson
212 894 1115

Valuations
Simon Bishop
020 7293 6422
New York
Daisy Edelson
212 894 1115

SOTHEBYS INTERNATIONAL REALTY
LONDON RESIDENTIAL & COUNTRY HOUSE DEPARTMENT

London & Home Counties
26a Conduit Street
Mayfair London W1S 2XY
020 7495 9580

Sussex & Surrey
Billingshurst
Alistair Morris
01403 833500

Photography
Wayne Williams

Catalogue Designer
Michael Molloy

Colour Editor
Andrew Bishop

Production Controller
David Mountain

Repro/Print
SOT/DIT

SPECIALIST DEPARTMENTS

African & Oceanic Art
New York
Jean G. Fritts
212 894 1312
020 7293 5754
Catherine Elliott, London Liaison
020 7293 5116

Antiquities
New York
Richard M. Keresey
Florent Heintz
212 606 7266
Catherine Elliott, London Liaison
020 7293 5109

Books & Manuscripts
Dr. Stephen Roe
020 7293 5286
Paul Quarrie, FSA
020 7293 5300
Roger Griffiths
020 7293 5292
Dr. Peter Beal, FBA
020 7293 5298
Dr. Susan Wharton
020 7293 5299
Catherine Slowther
020 7293 5291
Peter Selley
020 7293 5295
Paris
Anne Heilbronn
33 1 5305 5318
Thomas Bompard
33 1 5305 5390
Milan
Filippo Lotti
39 2 295 001
Roberta Dell'Acqua
39 2 295 227

**British Paintings & Drawings
1500 - 1850**
David Moore-Gwyn
020 7293 5406
James Miller
020 7293 5405
Lucy Fenwick
020 7293 5408

**British Watercolours
& Miniatures 1500-1900**
Henry Wemyss
020 7293 5409
Lucy Brittain
020 7293 5407

Carpets
Jacqueline Coulter
020 7293 5232

**Chinese Ceramics
& Works of Art**
Alastair Gibson
020 7293 5145
Jonathan Crockett
020 7293 5148

Chinese Export Porcelain
Alastair Gibson
020 7293 5145
Don Victor Franco de Baux
Heraldry Consultant

**Clocks, Barometers & Mechanical
Musical Instruments**
Michael Turner
020 7293 5329
Jonathan Hills
020 7293 5538

Contemporary Art
Cheyenne Westphal
020 7293 5391
Oliver Barker
020 7293 5494
Francis Outred
020 7293 5400
Paris
Grégoire Billault
33 1 5305 5338
Milan
Claudia Dwek
39 02 2950 0250
Amsterdam
Miety Heiden
31 20 550 2254

English Furniture
Fergus Lyons
020 7293 5348
Simon Redburn, Senior Specialist
020 7293 5746

French & Continental Furniture
Mario Tavella
020 7293 5052
Maxine Fox
020 7293 5349
Patrick van der Vorst
020 7293 5733
Amsterdam
Joséphine Baas
31 20 550 2233
Brussels
Chantal de Spot
32 2 627 7181
Frankfurt
Philipp Wurttemberg
49 69 9740 5577
Geneva
Benjamin Lamers
41 22 908 4804
Milan
Francesco Morroni
39 2 295 00203
Munich
Jan Willem van Haaren
49 89 2909 5141
Paris
Brice Foisil
33 1 5305 5301
Pierre-Francois Dayot
020 7293 5304
Patrick Leperlier
33 1 5305 5302
Zurich
Olivier Molina
41 1 226 2241

European Sculpture & Works of Art
Alexander Kader
020 7293 5493
Elisabeth Mitchell
020 7293 5304
Simon Stock
020 7293 5716
Diana Keith Neal, Consultant

Paris
Ulrike Goetz
33 1 5305 5364
Amsterdam
Rosa van der Wielen
31 20 550 2234

Impressionist & Modern Art
Melanie Clore
020 7293 5394
Philip Hook
020 7293 5223
Helena Newman
020 7293 5397
Emmanuel Di-Donna
020 7293 5392
Simon Shaw
020 7293 5723
Geneva
Caroline Lang
41 22 908 4832
Milan
Claudia Dwek
39 2 295 00250
Paris
Andrew Strauss
33 1 5305 5355
Sophie Camu
33 1 5305 5246
Samuel Valette
33 1 5305 5356

Irish Paintings
Grant Ford
020 7293 5497
Frances Christie
020 7293 5575

Islamic & Indian Art
Edward Gibbs
020 7293 5332
Dalya Islam
020 7293 5155

Japanese Works of Art
Sophie Almqvist
Neil Davey
Suzannah Yip
David Macfarlane

Jewellery
Geneva
Brett O'Connor
Douglas Walker
David Bennett
41 22 908 4849
London
Daniela Mascetti
Alexandra Rhodes
Joanna Hardy
Justin Roberts
020 7293 6409
Amsterdam
Pauline Pasmooij
31 20 550 2269
Milan
Stefano Papi
39 2 2950 0219
Paris
Gabriella Mantegani
Stephane Odet
33 1 5305 5305

Judaica
Camilla Previté
020 7293 5334
Tel Aviv
Esta Kilstein
972 3 560 1666

Marine Paintings
Andre Zlattinger
020 7293 5386
Michael Grist
020 7293 6152
Angus Haldane
020 7293 5861

Medieval Manuscripts
Camilla Previté
020 7293 5334
Dr. Christopher de Hamel FSA
Consultant

**20th Century British Paintings
& Sculpture**
James Rawlin
020 7293 5735
Sarah Thomas
020 7293 5381
Freya Mitton
020 7293 6491

Musical Instruments
Tim Ingles
020 7293 5034
Graham Wells
Consultant
020 7293 5342
Paul Hayday
020 7293 5344

Music
Dr. Stephen Roe
020 7293 5286
Dr. J.S.E. Maguire
020 7293 5016

**Nineteenth Century European
Paintings & Drawings**
Adrian Biddell
020 7293 5380
Claude Piening
020 7293 5658
Tessa Kostrzewa
020 7293 5382
Constantine Frangos
020 7293 5704
Amsterdam
Drs. Eveline Van Oirschot
31 20 550 2255
Brussels
Michèle de Kerchove
32 2 627 7189
Madrid
Aurora Zubillaga
34 91 781 2497
Milan
Dominique Reiner
39 2 295001
Paris
Pascale Pavageau
33 1 5305 5310
Zurich
Rebekka Grieshaber
41 1 226 2257

Old Master Paintings & Drawings
Paintings
Alexander Bell
020 7293 5420
George Gordon
020 7293 5414
Richard Charlton-Jones
020 7293 5489
Arabella Chandos
020 7293 5421
Letizia Treves
020 7293 5850
James Macdonald
020 7293 5887
Olympia
Tom Baring
020 7293 5423
Amsterdam
Baukje Coenen
31 20 550 2261
Judith Niessen
31 20 550 2258
Madrid
James Macdonald
34 91 576 5714
Milan
Alberto Chiesa
39 2 2950 0207
Paris
Nicolas Joly
33 1 5305 5341
Drawings
Gregory Rubinstein
020 7293 5417
Cristiana Romalli
020 7293 5419

Oriental Manuscripts
Dalya Islam
020 7293 5155

Photographs
Dr. Juliet Hacking
020 7293 5818

Prints
Jonathan Pratt
020 7293 5212
Susan Harris
020 7293 5211

**Russian Paintings,
Works of Art & Icons**
Joanna Vickery
020 7293 5325
Matthew Stuart-Lyon (Fabergé)
020 7293 5510
Martyn Saunders-Rawlins
Consultant
020 7293 5325

Scientific Instruments
Catherine Southon
Anthony Turner
Consultant
020 7293 5209

Scottish Paintings & Drawings
Andre Zlattinger
020 7293 5386
Simon Toll
020 7293 5731

Southeast Asian Paintings
Mok Kim Chuan
65 732 8239
Amsterdam
Miety Heiden
31 20 550 2254

Swiss Art
Zurich
Urs Lanter
41 1 226 2255

Tapestries
Patrick van der Vorst
020 7293 5733
Stephanie Douglas
020 7293 5469

Travel & Topographical Sales
Richard Fattorini
020 7293 5301
Paintings
Michael Grist
020 7293 6132

**Victorian & Edwardian
Paintings & Drawings**
Grant Ford
020 7293 5497
Simon Toll
020 7293 5731

Watches
Jonathan Darracott
020 7293 5810
Dr. George Daniels, MBE
Consultant
Geneva
Alex Barter
41 22 908 4708

Wine
Serena Sutcliffe, MW
020 7293 5050
Stephen Mould
020 7293 5046
Michael Egan
020 7293 5047
James Reed
020 7293 5014
Damian Tillson
020 7293 5851
Claire Collini
020 7293 5041
Administration
Chloe Craven
020 7293 5829

SOTHEBY'S AT OLYMPIA

Arms, Armour & Militaria
Thomas Del Mar
020 7293 5805
Ian Eaves, Consultant
Nicholas McCullough, Consultant

**Decorative Arts and
Design from 1870**
Jeremy Morrison, MRICS
020 7293 5506
Sarah O'Brien
020 7293 5503
Lydia Cresswell-Jones, Consultant
Paris
Jean-René Delaye
33 1 5305 5333

European Ceramics & Glass
Simon Cottle
020 7293 5133
Sebastian Kuhn
020 7293 5135
Phil Howell, FRICS
020 7293 5505
Joanne Cooper, MRICS
020 7293 5504

**Japanese Ceramics & Works
of Art, Prints & Paintings**
Sophie Almqvist
020 7293 5142
Suzannah Yip
020 7293 5725
Neil Davey
Senior Consultant
020 7293 5141
David Macfarlane, Consultant
020 7293 6411

Furniture & Works of Art
Jonathan Meyer, FRICS
020 7293 5350
Jeremy Smith
020 7293 5072
Edward Rising
020 7293 5507
Lawrence Bright
020 7293 5509
David Macdonald
020 7293 5107
Annabel Findlay
020 7293 5580
Anthony Rogers, Consultant
01403 833555

**Garden Statuary
& Architectural Items**
Rupert van der Werff, MRICS
01403 833561
James Rylands, MRICS
Consultant
01403 833559

**Paintings, Drawings
& Watercolours**
Michael Bing
020 7293 6135
Veronique Scorer
020 7293 5201
Freya Mitton
020 7293 6491
Jennie Rose
020 7293 6134
Michael Grist
020 7293 6132
Frances Christie
020 7293 5575

Bernhard Brandstaetter
020 7293 5561
Tom Baring, Old Masters
020 7293 5423

Silver
Matthew Stuart-Lyon
020 7293 5510
Julia Cook
020 7293 5103
Daniel Packer
020 7293 5102
Harry Charteris
Consultant
Amsterdam
Jacob Roosjen
31 20 550 2266
Munich
Heinrich Graf von Spreti
49 89 291 3151
Paris
Thierry de Lachaise
33 1 5305 5320

Sporting Guns
Gavin Gardiner
01403 833575

Objects of Vertu
Julia Clarke
020 7293 5324

INDEPENDENT SPECIALISTS

**Coins, Medals,
Decorations and Banknotes**
James Morton and Tom Eden
Morton & Eden
45 Maddox Street
London W1S 2PE
020 7493 5344
email: info@mortonandeden.com

Fashion & Textiles
Kerry Taylor
020 8676 4600
Fax: 020 8676 4604
mobile: 07785 734337
email:
fashion.textiles@sothebys.com

Sporting Memorabilia
Graham Budd
020 8366 2525
email: graham.budd@btinternet.com

Stamps
Richard Ashton
01483 771366
mobile: 07932 155287
email: Ashtonstamps@aol.com

Veteran, Vintage & Classic Cars
Peter Arney
Coachbuilt Cars Ltd
6 Buckingham Gate
London SW1 6JP
020 7976 5222
mobile: 07734 106028
email: arney@coachbuiltcars.co.uk

Please note that as independent
specialists in their field, the above
are solely responsible for their
dealings with clients.

KEY
🌳 Sale Rooms

UNITED KINGDOM AND IRELAND

London Bond Street 🌳
34-35 New Bond Street
London W1A 2AA
Telephone: 020 7293 5000
Fax: 020 7293 5989
Henry Wyndham
Chairman
Robin Woodhead
Chief Executive
George Bailey
Managing Director

London Olympia 🌳
Olympia, Hammersmith Road
London W14 8UX
Telephone: 020 7293 5555
Fax: 020 7293 6939
Harry Dalmeny
Chairman
Michael Bing
Managing Director

REGIONAL REPRESENTATIVES

Kent, East & West Sussex & Surrey
William Lucy
Jonathan J. Pratt, FGA
Summers Place
Billingshurst
Sussex RH14 9AD
Telephone: 01403 833500
Fax: 01403 833699

Gloucestershire, Worcestershire, Warwickshire, Oxfordshire and South Wales
John Harvey
18 Imperial Square
Cheltenham
Gloucestershire GL50 1QZ
Telephone: 01242 510500
Fax: 01242 250252

Thomas Lloyd
Freestone Hall
Cresselly, Kilgetty
Pembrokeshire SA68 OSX
Telephone/Fax: 01646 651493

Devon & Cornwall
The Hon. Mrs. d'Erlanger
Hensleigh Cottage
Hensleigh, Tiverton
Devon EX16 5NH
Telephone: 01884 243 663
Fax: 01884 258 692

Elizabeth Fortescue
Lostwithiel, Cornwall
Telephone/Fax: 01208 871133

Dorset, Hampshire, Somerset & Wiltshire
Angus Milner-Brown
Cheviot House
69-73 Castle Street
Salisbury, Wiltshire SP1 3SP
Telephone: 01722 330793
Fax: 01722 330982

Charles Hignett
Bath, Somerset
Telephone: 01225 840101
Fax: 01225 840696

East Anglia
Chantal Cookson
David Asher
The Railway Station
Green Road
Newmarket
Suffolk CB8 9TW
Telephone: 01638 561426
Fax: 01638 560094

The Lord Cranworth
Woodbridge, Suffolk
Telephone: 01473 735581
Fax: 01473 738278

Sara Foster
Fakenham, Norfolk
Telephone: 01328 700032
Fax: 01328 700155

Northamptonshire
Mary Miller
Towcester
Northamptonshire
Telephone: 01327 860020
Fax: 01327 860612

North Wales & the Midlands
Mark Newstead
Knypersley Hall
Marchington Woodlands
Nr Uttoxeter ST14 8RF
Telephone: 01889 560074
Fax: 01889 563828

Lord Ralph Kerr
Melbourne, Derbyshire
Telephone/Fax: 01889 560074

The Marchioness of Linlithgow
Powys, Wales
Telephone: 01691 648646
Fax: 01691 648664

Yorkshire
John Phillips, ARICS
Andrew Parker
8-12 Montpellier Parade
Harrogate
North Yorkshire HG1 2TJ
Telephone: 01423 501466
Fax: 01423 520501

Northern England
Matthew Festing, OBE
The Stable Office
Meldon Village, Morpeth
Northumberland NE61 3TW
Telephone: 01670 775123
Fax: 01670 775246

Henry Bowring
Kirkby Lonsdale, Cumbria
Telephone/Fax: 01524 276464

Judith Heelis
Appleby, Cumbria
Telephone/Fax: 01768 352806

Channel Islands
Clare d'Abo
Telephone: 020 7293 5363
Fax: 020 7293 5907

Scotland & Borders
John Robertson
Georgiana Bruce
112 George Street
Edinburgh EH2 4LH
Telephone: 0131 226 7201
Fax: 0131 226 6866

Anthony Weld Forester
130 Douglas Street
Glasgow G2 4HF
Telephone: 0141 221 4817
Fax: 0141 204 2502

Ireland & Northern Ireland
Arabella Bishop
Anne Dillon
16 Molesworth Street
Dublin 2, Ireland
Telephone: 353 1 671 1786
Fax: 353 1 679 7844

William Montgomery
The Estate Office
Grey Abbey
Newtownards
Co. Down BT22 2QA
Telephone: 028 4278 8668
Fax: 028 4278 8652

EUROPE AND MIDDLE EAST

AUSTRIA

Andrea Jungmann
Palais Wilczek
Herrengasse 5, A-1010 Vienna
Telephone: 43 1 512 4772/3
& 513 3774
Fax: 43 1 513 4867

BELGIUM

Brussels
Count Hubert d'Ursel
Monique Bréhier
32 rue Jacques Jordaens
1000 Brussels
Telephone: 32 2 648 0080
Fax: 32 2 648 0757

CZECH REPUBLIC

Filip Marco
Rytirska 8
110 00 Praha 1
Telephone/Fax: 42 02 24 23 72 98

DENMARK

Nina Wedell-Wedellsborg
Tina Hansen
Vognmagergade 9
1120 Copenhagen K
Telephone: 45 33 13 55 56
Fax: 45 33 93 01 19

FINLAND

Claire Svartström
Bernhardinkatu 5
00 130 Helsinki
Telephone: 358 9 622 1558
Fax: 358 9 680 1208

FRANCE

Paris 🌳
Dr. Philipp Herzog von
Württemberg
P.D.G., France
Princesse de Beauvau Craon
Présidente d'honneur, France
Deputy Chairman, Europe
Jeremy Durack
Managing Director
76 rue du Faubourg St. Honoré
75008 Paris
Telephone: 33 1 53 05 53 05
Fax: 33 1 47 42 22 32

Bordeaux
Alain de Baritault
Telephone/Fax: 33 5 56 58 72 04

Lyon
Albert de Franclieu
Telephone/Fax: 33 4 76 07 15 52

Montpellier
Béatrice Viennet
Telephone: 33 4 67 24 95 72
Fax: 33 4 67 24 93 52

Strasbourg
Marie-France Ludmann
Telephone/Fax: 33 3 88 60 00 61

GERMANY

Frankfurt
Dr. Philipp Herzog von
Württemberg
Managing Director-Germany
Nina Buhne
Mendelssohnstrasse 66
D-60325 Frankfurt-am-Main
Telephone: 49 69 74 07 87
Fax: 49 69 74 69 01

Munich
Heinrich Graf von Spreti
President-Germany
Odeonsplatz 16
D-80539 München
Telephone: 49 89 291 31 51
Fax: 49 89 299 271

Cologne
Ursula Niggemann
Vice President-Germany
St. Apern - Strasse 17-21
D-50667 Köln
Telephone: 49 221 20 7170
Fax: 49 221 257 4359

Hamburg
Dr. Katharina Prinzessin zu
Sayn-Wittgenstein
Tesdorpfstrasse 22
D-20148 Hamburg
Telephone: 49 40 44 40 80
Fax: 49 40 410 70 82

Hannover
Susanne von Lüneburg
Telephone: 49 53 01 13 66
Fax: 49 53 01 12 27

Berlin
Joelle Romba
Telephone: 49 30 49 85 43 85
Fax: 49 30 49 85 43 84

HUNGARY

Countess Dr. Soraya Stubenberg
Telephone: 43 676 566 90 92

ISRAEL

Rivka Saker
46 Rothschild Boulevard
Tel Aviv 66883
Telephone: 972 3 560 1666
Fax: 972 3 560 8111

ITALY

Filippo Lotti
Managing Director

Milan
Filippo Lotti
Managing Director
Claudia Dwek
Deputy Chairman
Maarten ten Holder
Deputy Managing Director
Palazzo Broggi
Via Broggi 19, 20129 Milan
Telephone: 39 0 2 29 5001
Fax: 39 0 2 29 518595

Bologna
Daniela Amati Jovi
Telephone: 39 0 51 331 382

Florence
Clementina Bartolini Salimbeni
Telephone: 39 0 55 247 9021
Fax: 39 0 55 247 9563

Rome
Luisa Lepri
Director
Palazzo Colonna
Piazza SS, Apostoli, 61
00187 Rome
Telephone: 39 0 6 699 41791
Fax: 39 0 6 679 6167

Turin
Laura Russo
Corso Galileo, Ferraris 18B
10121 Turin
Telephone: 39 0 11 544898
Fax: 39 0 11 547675

LUXEMBOURG

Please refer all enquiries to
Count Hubert d'Ursel
in the Brussels Office
Telephone: 32 2 648 0080
Fax: 32 2 648 0757

MONACO

Mark Armstrong
Est-Ouest
24, boulevard Princesse Charlotte
B.P. 45
MC 98001 Monaco Cedex
Telephone: 377 93 30 88 80
Fax: 377 93 25 24 98

NETHERLANDS

Amsterdam
Patrick van Maris
Managing Director
De Boelelaan 30
1083 HJ Amsterdam
Telephone: 31 20 550 22 00
Fax: 31 20 550 22 22

NORWAY

Ingeborg Astrup
Bjørnveien 42, 0774 Oslo
Telephone: 47 22 1472 82
Fax: 47 22 49 38 36

PORTUGAL

Lisbon
Maria do Rosario Horta e Costa
Rua das Amoreiras, 103
1250-022 Lisboa, Portugal
Telephone: 35 1 213 713 310
Fax: 35 1 213 713 319

SPAIN

Madrid
Hélène Marie Montgomery
Managing Director
Alfonso XI, 7 bajo dcha
28014 Madrid
Telephone: 34 91 576 5714
Fax: 34 91 781 2490

SWEDEN

Stockholm
Peder Isacson
Managing Director
Sofia Ström
Arsenalsgatan 2,
111 47 Stockholm
Telephone: 46 8 679 5478
Fax: 46 8 611 4826

Gothenburg
Viviann Kempe
Villa Thalatta
James Keillers Väg 12
S - 429 43 SÄRÖ
Telephone: 46 31 937 150
Fax: 46 31 937 550

South Sweden
Baroness Catharina von
Blixen-Finecke
Näsbyholm Säteri
S - 274 94 SKURUP
Telephone: 46 411 43981
Fax: 46 411 43982

SWITZERLAND

Caroline Lang
Managing Director, Geneva
Dr. Claudia Steinfels
Managing Director, Zurich
Finn Dombernowsky
General Manager & Business Director

Geneva
Caroline Lang
13 Quai du Mont Blanc
CH - 1201 Geneva
Telephone: 41 22 908 4800
Fax: 41 22 908 4801

Zurich
Dr. Claudia Steinfels
Gessnerallee 1
CH - 8021 Zurich
Telephone: 41 1 226 2200
Fax: 41 1 226 2201

Lugano
Iris Fabbri ‡
Riva Caccia 4a
CH - 6900 Lugano
Telephone: 41 91 993 3060
Fax: 41 91 993 3061

AFRICA

SOUTH AFRICA

Johannesburg
Stephan Welz
Managing Director
13 Biermann Avenue
Rosebank
Johannesburg 2196
Telephone: 27 11 880 3125/9
Fax: 27 11 880 2656

Cape Town
PO Box 818
Constantia 7848
Cape Town, South Africa
Telephone: 27 21 794 6461
Fax: 27 21 794 6621

ASIA

CHINA

Wang Jie
Room 510
Dynasty Business Centre
457 Wu Lu Mu Qi Road (N)
Shanghai 200040, PRC
Tel: 86 21 6249 7450
Fax: 86 21 6249 7451

HONG KONG

Hong Kong
Henry Howard-Sneyd
Managing Director, China,
Southeast Asia & Australasia
5/F Standard Chartered Bank
Building
4-4A Des Voeux Road Central
Hong Kong
Telephone: 852 2524 8121
Fax: 852 2810 6238

INDONESIA

Vivi Billion B‡
Telephone: 62 21 571 7016
Fax: 62 21 570 2014

JAPAN

Tetsuji Shibayama
President
Fuerte Kojimachi Bldg. 3F
1-7 Kojimachi
Chiyoda-ku, Tokyo 102
Telephone: 81 3 3230 2755
Fax: 81 3 3230 2754

KOREA

c/o Hong Kong Office
Telephone: 852 2524 8121
Fax: 852 2810 6238

MALAYSIA

Walter Cheah
Managing Director
25 Jalan Pudu Lama
50200 Kuala Lumpur
Telephone: 60 3 2070 0319
Fax: 60 3 2070 6833

PHILIPPINES

Maria Clara Acuña Camacho†
Sotheby's Representative
36/F Tower 1
Enterprise Center
6766 Ayala Avenue
comer Paseo de Roxas
Makati City, 1226, Philippines
Telephone: 632 884 8241
Fax: 632 884 8242

SINGAPORE

Singapore
Esther Seet
Managing Director
1 Cuscaden Road
01- 01 The Regent Singapore
Singapore 249715
Telephone: 65 6732 8239
Fax: 65 6737 0295

TAIWAN, R.O.C.

Winnie Chang
Managing Director
1st Floor, No. 77
Sec. 1, An Ho Road
Taipei, Taiwan, R.O.C.
Telephone: 886 2 2755 2906
Fax: 886 2 2709 3949

THAILAND

Wannida Saetieo
Country Manager
Sukhothai Hotel
13/3 South Sathorn Rd
Bangkok 10120
Thailand
Telephone: 662 286 0788
& 662 286 0789
Fax: 662 286 0787

AUSTRALIA

Justin Miller
Chairman
Mark Fraser
Managing Director

Melbourne
926 High Street, Armadale
Melbourne, Victoria 3143
Telephone: 61 3 9509 2900
Fax: 61 3 9563 5067

Sydney
Queen's Court, Level 1
118-122 Queen Street
Woollahra
New South Wales 2025
Telephone: 61 2 9362 1000
Fax: 61 2 9362 1100

LATIN AMERICA

ARGENTINA

Adela Mackinlay de Casal
Edificio Kavanagh
San Martin 1068
C1005AAQ - Capital Federal
Argentina
Telephone: 5411 5032 8600
Fax: 5411 5032 3330

BRAZIL

Rio de Janeiro
Katia Mindlin Leite Barbosa*
Caixa Postal 62619
Rio de Janeiro
RJ CEP 22250-970
Telephone: 55 21 2553 1946
Fax: 55 21 2553 4594
Heloise Guinle*
Estrada da Gavea 611
Bloco 1, Apt 2503
São Conrado
22610-000 Gavea
Rio de Janeiro
Telephone: 55 21 3322 4500
Fax: 55 21 3322 6397

São Paulo
Pedro Corrêa do Lago*
Rua João Cachoeira 267
São Paulo SP CEP 04535-010
Telephone: 55 11 3167 0066
Fax: 55 11 3168 1559

CHILE

Cecilia Miquel*
Av. Presidente Riesco, 3641
Dpto. 602, Las Condes
Santiago, Chile
Telephone: 562 231 8936
Fax: 562 335 6459

MEXICO

Mexico City
Ana Yturbe de Sepulveda
Campos Eliseos 325-5 Polanco
Mexico 11560 D.F.
Telephone: 5255 5281 2100
5255 5281 2200
Fax: 5255 5280 7136

Luis C. Lopez Morton‡
Internet Consultant
Monte Athos 179
Lomas Virreyes
C.P. 11000
Mexico, D.F.
Telephone: 525 520 5005
525 502 9936
Fax: 525 540 3213

Monterrey
Barbara Perusquia de Lobeira*
Via Triumphalis 127 PTE.
Fuentes Del Valle
Monterrey 66220, Nuevo Leon
Telephone: 528 675 7573 / 74
Fax: 528 129 5081

VENEZUELA

Diana Boccardo*
Edf. Torresamán,
Piso 9, Ofc 91
Avenida Romulo Gallegos con
calle El Carmen
Los Dos Caminos, Caracas 1062
Telephone: 58 212 285 5794
Fax: 58 212 237 3920

HEADQUARTERS

New York
1334 York Avenue
New York, New York 10021
Telephone: 212 606 7000
Fax: 212 606 7107
212 606 7016 (Bids only)

OFFICES AND ASSOCIATES

U.S.A.

Baltimore
Aurelia Bolton*
Elizabeth Schroeder*
P.O. Box 250
Riderwood, Maryland 21139
Telephone: 410 252 4600
Fax: 410 561 9738

Chicago
188 East Walton Place
Chicago, Illinois 60611
Telephone: 312 475 7900
Fax: 312 664 5295
Helyn D. Goldenberg
Chairman, Midwest
Cathy Busch
Director
Cassie Spencer
Trusts & Estates
Eve Reppen Rogers
Jewelry
Gary F. Metzner
Fine Arts
Marjorie S. Susman†

Dallas
The Quadrangle
2800 Routh Street, Suite 140
Dallas, Texas 75201
Telephone: 214 871 1056
Fax: 214 871 1057

Houston
Geraldine Ordway
2001 Kirby Drive, Suite 805
Houston, Texas 77019
Telephone: 713 524 0044
Fax: 713 520 1602

Los Angeles
9665 Wilshire Blvd.
Beverly Hills, California 90212
Telephone: 310 274 0340
Fax: 310 274 0899
Richard S. Wolf
Managing Director, West Coast
Blake Koh
Director, Fine Arts, West Coast
Lisa Hubbard
International Jewelry
Katherine Watkins
Director, Decorative Arts
Andrea L. Van de Kamp*

Miami
Douglas Entrance
800 Douglas Road
Suite 125
Coral Gables, Florida 33134
Telephone: 305 448 7882
Fax: 305 448 7168
Axel Stein
Director
Maria Bonta de la Pezuela
Decorative Arts

Minneapolis/St. Paul
Laura MacLennan*
5108 Newton Avenue South
Minneapolis, Minnesota 55419
Telephone: 612 308 2550

Montana
Kathryn Wilmerding Heminway
Bar 20 Ranch
West Boulder Reserve
McLeod, Montana 59052
Telephone: 406 222 9399
Fax: 406 222 0051

New England
William Cottingham
Director
Patricia Ward*
Rodney Armstrong*
671/2 Chestnut St.
Boston, Massachusetts 02108
Telephone: 617 367 6323
Fax: 617 367 4888

New York City
Barbara Cates*
Lee Copley Thaw†
Telephone: 212 606 7000

Palm Beach
317 Peruvian Avenue
Palm Beach, Florida 33480
Telephone: 561 833 2582
Fax: 561 655 4583
David G. Ober
Chairman, Southeast
Hope P. Kent*
Louis J. Gartner*

Philadelphia
Angela Hudson
Director
Wendy Foulke*
18 Haverford Station Road
Haverford, Pennsylvania 19041
Telephone: 610 649 2600
Fax: 610 649 7995

Richmond
Virginia Guest Valentine†
Telephone: 804 353 1579
Fax: 804 353 0575

San Francisco
Jennifer Foley Biederbeck
Mrs. Prentis Cobb Hale*
Mrs. John N. Rosekrans†
214 Grant Avenue, Suite 350
San Francisco, California 94108
Telephone: 415 772 9028
Fax: 415 772 9031

Santa Barbara
Carolyn Amory*
PO Box 5736
Montecito, California 93150
Telephone: 805 695 8344
Fax: 805 969 6811

BERMUDA

William S. Cottingham
c/o Margot Cooper
PO Box 99
Warwick WK BX Bermuda
Telephone: 441 234 6900
441 236 7026

CANADA

David P. Silcox
President
9 Hazelton Avenue
Toronto, Ontario M5R 2E1
Telephone: 416 926 1774
Fax: 416 926 9179

Canadian Art Sales in Association
with Ritchie's Auctioneers
Ira R. Hopmeyer
Chairman & CEO
288 King Street East
Toronto, Ontario M5A 1K4
Telephone: 416 364 1864
Fax: 416 364 0704

---

* Associate of Sotheby's
† International Representative
‡ Consultant

SOTHEBY'S

ABSENTEE WRITTEN BID FORM

SEE IMPORTANT INFORMATION REGARDING ABSENTEE BIDDING AND INSTRUCTIONS ON HOW TO COMPLETE THIS FORM.
PLEASE ALSO COMPLETE THE SHIPPING INSTRUCTIONS ON FACING PAGE.

PLEASE BID ON MY BEHALF FOR THE FOLLOWING LOT(S)

up to the hammer price(s) written below, to be executed as cheaply as is permitted by other bids or reserves. I agree to be bound by the Conditions of Business applicable to this sale and agree to pay a buyer's premium on the hammer price(s) at the rate stated in the Guide for Prospective Buyers section in the catalogue for the sale and any VAT or amounts in lieu of VAT, which may be due on the buyer's premium and hammer price(s). (Please see facing page for further information).

PLEASE WRITE CLEARLY AND SUBMIT YOUR BIDS AS EARLY AS POSSIBLE

SALE NUMBER	SALE TITLE	SALE DATE
L05402	THE LIBRARY OF THE EARLS OF MACCLESFIELD REMOVED FROM SHIRBURN CASTLE PART 5: SCIENCE I-O	14 APRIL 2005

LOT NUMBER	LOT DESCRIPTION	MAXIMUM STERLING PRICE (EXCLUDING PREMIUM AND VAT)
		£
		£
		£
		£
		£
		£
		£
		£
		£
		£
		£

PLEASE PLACE YOUR BIDS AS EARLY AS POSSIBLE, AS IN THE EVENT OF IDENTICAL BIDS, THE EARLIEST WILL TAKE PRECEDENCE. BIDS SHOULD BE SUBMITTED AT LEAST 24 HOURS BEFORE THE AUCTION.

Please mail or fax to:

BID DEPARTMENT
SOTHEBY'S
34-35 NEW BOND STREET
LONDON W1A 2AA

For Bids only telephone 020 7293 5283 or fax to 020 7293 6255

I consent to the use of this information and any other information obtained by Sotheby's in accordance with the Guide for Absentee Bidders. If you would like further information on Sotheby's policies on personal data, or to make corrections to your information, please contact us on 020 7293 6667.

Signed _____ Dated _____

10/04 Bidslip Main

TITLE (EG. MR, MRS, DR) _____ NAME _____

SOTHEBY'S CLIENT ACCOUNT NO. (IF KNOWN) _____

ADDRESS _____

POSTCODE _____

TELEPHONE (HOME) _____ (BUSINESS) _____

EMAIL* _____ FAX _____

IF YOU ARE SUCCESSFUL AND WOULD LIKE YOUR INVOICE SENT TO THE ABOVE EMAIL OR FAX, PLEASE TICK BOX ☐ A COPY WILL FOLLOW BY POST.

I AM/AM NOT VAT REGISTERED (DELETE AS APPROPRIATE)   VAT NO. _____

IF YOU WOULD PREFER NOT TO RECEIVE DETAILS OF FUTURE EVENTS BY EMAIL OR POST, PLEASE TICK HERE ☐
*WE WOULD LIKE TO SEND YOU MARKETING MATERIALS AND NEWS CONCERNING SOTHEBY'S, OR ON OCCASION, THIRD PARTIES. IF YOU PROVIDE YOUR E-MAIL ADDRESS, WE WILL CONTACT YOU FOR THIS PURPOSE.

PAYMENT IS DUE IMMEDIATELY AFTER THE SALE IN POUNDS STERLING. FULL DETAILS ON HOW TO PAY ARE INCLUDED IN THE GUIDE FOR BUYERS. **OR:** PLEASE CHARGE MY CREDIT / DEBIT CARD FOR MY PURCHASES IN THIS SALE. WE ACCEPT VISA, MASTERCARD (SUBJECT TO 1.5% SERVICE CHARGE) AND DELTA, SWITCH AND CONNECT, BUT NOT AMERICAN EXPRESS OR DINERS CLUB. NB. PAYMENTS EXCEEDING £20,000 CAN ONLY BE MADE BY THE CARDHOLDER IN PERSON.

NAME ON CARD _____ TYPE OF CARD _____

CARD NUMBER ☐☐☐☐ ☐☐☐☐ ☐☐☐☐ ☐☐☐☐   EXPIRY DATE ☐☐

ISSUE NUMBER ☐ SWITCH ONLY

FOR YOUR PURCHASES

SHIPPING INSTRUCTIONS

PLEASE COMPLETE THIS PART OF THE FORM TO ARRANGE FOR THE DESPATCH OF YOUR PURCHASES THROUGH ONE OF OUR NOMINATED FINE ART SHIPPING AGENTS, AT YOUR EXPENSE.

PLEASE INDICATE BELOW YOUR PREFERRED METHOD OF SHIPMENT :-

SOTHEBY'S TO SELECT ☐   COURIER ☐   AIR FREIGHT ☐   ROAD ☐   SEA FREIGHT ☐

PLEASE PURCHASE TRANSIT INSURANCE ☐ YES ☐ NO   PLEASE SEND A QUOTATION ☐ YES ☐ NO
(UNLESS INDICATED ALL LOTS WILL BE INSURED)   BEFORE SHIPPING

DELIVERY ADDRESS (IF DIFFERENT FROM ABOVE)

_____ POSTCODE _____

TELEPHONE _____

EMAIL _____ FAX _____

LICENCES   SHOULD ANY OF YOUR PURCHASES REQUIRE A LICENCE PRIOR TO THE EXPORT, SOTHEBY'S WILL SUBMIT THE APPLICATION PRIOR TO DESPATCH. (SEE OPPOSITE FOR ADDITIONAL INFORMATION)

NAME ON CARD _____ TYPE OF CARD _____

CARD NUMBER ☐☐☐☐ ☐☐☐☐ ☐☐☐☐ ☐☐☐☐   EXPIRY DATE ☐☐

ISSUE NUMBER ☐ SWITCH ONLY

FOR SHIPMENT ONLY

IF YOU DO NOT GIVE CARD DETAILS, YOUR SHIPMENT WILL NOT BE PROCESSED UNTIL YOUR PAYMENT HAS BEEN RECEIVED BY THE NOMINATED SHIPPER

SIGNED _____ DATED _____

GUIDE FOR ABSENTEE BIDDERS

If you are unable to attend an auction in person, you may give Sotheby's Bid Department instructions to bid on your behalf by completing the form overleaf.

This service is free and confidential.

Please record accurately the lot numbers, descriptions and the top hammer price you are willing to pay for each lot.

We will try to purchase the lot(s) of your choice for the lowest price possible and never for more than the top amount you indicate.

"Buy" or unlimited bids will not be accepted.

Alternative bids can be placed by using the word "OR" between lot numbers.

Bids must be placed in the same order as in the catalogue.

This form should be used for one sale only - please indicate the sale number, title and date on the form.

Please place your bids as early as possible, as in the event of identical bids the earliest received will take precedence. Wherever possible bids should be submitted at least twenty-four hours before the auction.

Where appropriate, your bids will be rounded down to the nearest amount consistent with the auctioneer's bidding increments.

Absentee bids, when placed by telephone, are accepted only at the caller's risk and must be confirmed by letter or fax to the Bid Department on 020 7293 6255.

Please note that the execution of written bids is offered as an additional service for no extra charge at the bidder's risk and is undertaken subject to Sotheby's other commitments at the time of the auction; Sotheby's therefore cannot accept liability for failure to place such bids, whether through negligence or otherwise.

Successful bidders will receive an invoice detailing their purchases and giving instructions for payment and clearance of goods. Unsuccessful bidders will be advised.

Successful buyers of large objects are earnestly requested to arrange early collection of their goods as they will incur storage charges after 14 days.

Bidders on large objects are recommended to check on the afternoon of the auction whether they have been successful.

All bids are subject to the conditions of business applicable to the sale, a copy of which is available from Sotheby's offices or by telephoning 020 7293 6152. Conditions of Business particularly relevant to buyers are also set out in the sale catalogue.

It is against Sotheby's general policy to accept single or multiple related payments in the form of cash or cash equivalents in excess of the local currency equivalent of US$10,000.

It is Sotheby's policy to request any new clients or purchasers preferring to make a cash payment to provide: verification of identity (by providing some form of government issued identification containing a photograph, such as a passport, identity card or driver's licence), confirmation of permanent address and identification of the source of the funds.

Sotheby's will use information provided by its clients or which Sotheby's otherwise obtains relating to its clients for the provision of auction and other art-related services, real estate and insurance services, client administation, marketing and otherwise to manage and operate its business, or as required by law. Some gathering of information about Sotheby's clients may take place using technical means to indentify their preferences and provide a higher quality of service to them, and Sotheby's may gather information about its clients through video images or through the use of monitoring devices used to record telephone conversations. Sotheby's will generally seek clients' express consent before gathering any sensitive data, unless otherwise permitted by law. You agree that Sotheby's may use any sensitive information that you supply to Sotheby's. By signing this Absentee Bid Form, you agree to the processing of your personal information and also to the disclosure and transfer of such information to any Sotheby's associated company and to third parties anywhere in the world for the above purposes, including to countries which may not offer equivalent protection of personal information to that offered in the UK.